# St. Mary's

## Bramber

### A Sussex House and its Gardens

Peter Thorogood

The Bramber Press

*To all those who give so generously of their time and energies to help in keeping St. Mary's open for visitors.*

Especial thanks are due to Tony Ketteman, archivist of St. Mary's, for his valuable assistance in the research and compilation of this guide book.

I am also extremely grateful to Roger Linton, Curator of St. Mary's, for expert advice on both the structure of the building and the house collections described in the text.

The Bramber Press

©1998 Peter Thorogood
All rights reserved

Published by The Bramber Press
St. Mary's House
Bramber, West Sussex. BN44 3WE
Tel/Fax: 01903 816205

ISBN   0 9526786 4 0

Cover design, typesetting and computer graphics
by Tony Ketteman
Photographs selected from the St. Mary's archives by
Peter Thorogood and Roger Linton
Pen–and–ink drawings of St. Mary's by Harry Ford FRIBA AMTPI

**S**t. **Mary's Bramber** is a house of mystery and legend. Tales of tunnels beneath the garden and a chapel under the hall are among a number of secrets that past residents have taken with them to the grave. An exact history of this magnificent old house will never be fully established but, through the persistence of local historians and the memories of those who are still alive to reveal some of the hidden past, it has been possible to piece together a fascinating story.

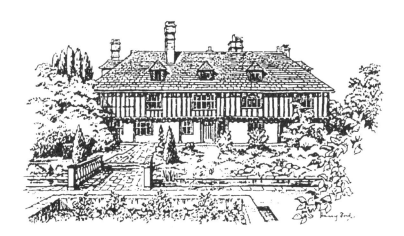

# History of St. Mary's

 **he Origins of Bramber**

The valley of the River Adur as we know it today was formerly a broad tidal estuary which, at low water, was reduced to a pattern of mud-flats intersected by channels, some of which were navigable as far as the port of Steyning. Travellers following the ancient east-west route along the South Downs must have crossed the estuary by ferry or ford. A Roman road certainly crossed the river south of Henfield and possibly another route near the present Lancing College. The first indication of the existence of a bridge was at Bramber during the years of the Norman conquest when Sussex was divided into six divisions or 'rapes', each with its own castle. A defensive hill overlooking the estuary was the natural choice for William de Braose when he came to build a castle for the Rape of Bramber. He then set about establishing his new borough of Bramber as a port and built the first bridge for which we have any evidence, together with a causeway made to connect Bramber Castle with the port of Bramber. By 1086, de Braose was levying tolls at his bridge on ships passing to and from the port of Steyning.

 **he Templars**

Philip de Braose, William de Braose's son, entered Jerusalem in 1099 to open up the Holy Places to pilgrims. This First Crusade led to the foundation of the Order of Knights of the Temple of Jerusalem and it was therefore fitting that, on Philip's death in 1125, his widow, the Lady Aanor, gave five acres (two hectares) of land at Bramber to the Knights Templar. The land was beside the new causeway, on a reclaimed promontory, which, according to one account, was an extension of the manor of Bidlington, and here a Templar 'Chapter House' was built. Nearly nine hundred years later, in 1990, during the renewal of the floor in one of the ground floor rooms of the present building, an old hearth – possibly Templar – was discovered, with a primitive plinth made of vertically-placed clay tiles. The Knights stayed in Bramber until 1154, after which time they removed to Sompting. About 1190, the old timber bridge across the western channel was replaced by a splendid four-arched stone bridge

Conjectural drawing of the Great Bridge of Bramber
(adapted from an original sketch by J.G. Garratt)

with a chapel, dedicated to St. Mary the Virgin, on the central pier. This bridge was eventually given to the Benedictine Priory of Sele by John de Braose in 1230. Fragments of the earlier wooden bridge (carbon-dated to approximately 1070) are still to be seen in the house today.

# he Chapel House

After the departure of the Templars, the Chapter House, or 'Chapel House' as it came to be called, passed to the direction of the monks of Sele, four of whom served as Wardens of the Bridge and looked after the running of the House as an 'inn'. By now, many of the travellers availing themselves of the route from west to east were pilgrims. Following the period of the Crusades, a renewed interest in journeying on foot to Holy places increased, the best known routes converging on such centres as Santiago de Compostela and Canterbury. Yet, by 1320, the Chapel House had become so impoverished as to be excused paying taxes, the bridge and its chapel had fallen into decay, and, owing to mismanagement by the monks, the future of the house seemed precarious. By 1459, the link between the Priory of Sele and its parent Abbey at Saumur had been dissolved and the Priory, together with its lands, came under the jurisdiction of the Bishop of Winchester, William of Waynflete, first Provost of Eton, Lord High Chancellor of England and illustrious and learned founder of Magdalen College, Oxford. About 1470, Waynflete embarked upon the work of restoring the bridge, the chapel and the chapel house with the help of his cathedral mason, John Cowper, and a new and flourishing phase followed in which the newly-built monastic inn welcomed through its doors countless pilgrims, who would have entered the courtyard under an impressive entrance archway. A fragment of this arch, carved with the Plantagenet rose, bishop's mitre and other religious details, is displayed in the North Hall.

# onastic Inn to Private House

St. Mary's, prior to the dissolution of the monasteries, had ceased to be a monastic building, having passed into the hands of Magdalen College, the beneficiary of William of Waynflete's estate. The nearby manor of Wiston, which had remained in the de Braose family since Domesday, had now passed from John de Braose (who had no heir) to his great-nephew, Sir Ralph Shirley, whose grandson, Francis Shirley, was granted a lease on the 'Chappil House and

6

Seller' on the south side of Bramber Bridge, by authority of Magdalen College, Oxford. In 1555, he was member of parliament for Shoreham and was appointed Sheriff of Surrey and Sussex in 1574. Francis Shirley died at his Sussex home, West Grinstead Park, on 24th March 1578.

Gradually over the years, as the chapel fell from use, the name 'St. Mary's' began to be applied to the house itself, a fine two-storeyed building framed in massive oak, with a central galleried courtyard, fine carved oak entrance arches on the north and south sides and jettied first floor dorters (dormitories) in six constructional bays. The monks had not provided many creature comforts for their travellers. Panelling and chimneys had to he introduced by later occupants to make the rooms more habitable. Marquetry panels provided a rich element of decoration, together with carved balustrades and elaborately gilded and painted wall-leather. The galleries were covered in with a cat-slide roof and an internal staircase was built, replacing the courtyard access to the first floor. Now the house began to take on a grander appearance.

William of Waynflete
Bishop of Winchester

St. Mary's about 1470 – how the Monastic Inn may have looked from The Street

7

How the central courtyard may have looked

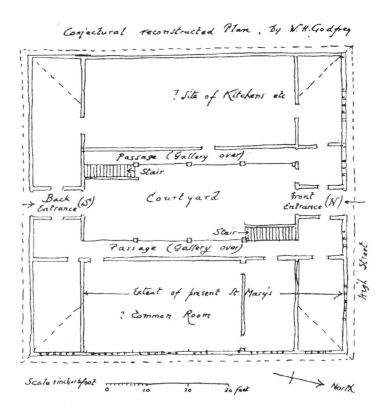

Original drawings by W Godfrey in the St. Mary's Archive

8

# House Fit for a Queen?

 Through the mists of time, we begin to hear murmurings about the impending visit of Queen Elizabeth I to western Sussex on one of her 'Progresses'. Since her Treasurer-at-War, Sir Thomas Sherley (sic), resided at Wiston, it seemed that his house would be a likely contender for her favours, had the Queen not disliked him and perhaps preferred hospitality at St. Mary's. Itinerant painter-stainers, so the story goes, were brought in to decorate an upper chamber with *trompe l'oeil* panels depicting scenes of a sea-battle with galleons at sail, believed to be the fleet of King Henry VIII in battle with the French in 1545. We may never know for sure that Elizabeth's visit actually took place, though some later occupants allowed themselves to be convinced of its truth, however fanciful it may have been. A fascinating stereoscopic photograph of St. Mary's was taken by the Brighton photographer, William Cornish, in 1860. The legend reads: "The house at Bramber at which Queen Elizabeth put up during her Summer Tour through the South of England."

During the 17th century the threat of the Civil War came all too close to the doors of St. Mary's. It has been suggested that the ancient building suffered considerable damage in the 'Bramber Skirmish' when Royalist troops tried to rush the bridge. The whole of the western wing seems about this time to have disappeared, exposing the ancient courtyard to full view from the street, and the southern bay of the east wing had also to be demolished. Of course, there may have been some major conflagration, similar to the disastrous fire of 1286, when the earlier 'Chapel House' was the only building in Bramber left standing (possibly because it was situated on the south side of the street). Whilst the 'fire' theory appears to be reasonably acceptable, the 'war damage' theory was completely refuted when a sketch by a local artist, John Dunstall, drawn for the engraver, Hollar, was discovered. This sketch, a representation of Bramber village, dated 1635, now in the Courtauld Institute Witt Library, shows St. Mary's already without its west wing before the Civil War began.

The mystery may be compounded by the possibility that the residents of the late 16th century (or even Magdalen College itself) may have allowed the building to decay through neglect, deciding to demolish the offending part and save the best of whatever remained. The south wall was rebuilt in flint, with mullion windows of stone. The 'Common Room' was divided up to give an 'Inner Hall' and an 'Outer Hall' flanking a newly proportioned room (embellished with fielded panels of oak, centred with ebony veneer, and a fine intarsia overmantel with a decorated canopy supported by black ebonised columns). The installation of two huge chimneys had allowed the introduction of further decorative marquetry overmantels and an inglenook fireplace in the room once used by the Wardens of the Great Bridge. The existence of the 'Painted Room', with all its intriguing historical associations, may well have been a further reason for preserving this eastern wing.

## he Flight of Charles II

One of the most romantic stories in English history is the account of the flight of Charles II after losing the battle of Worcester (1651). Having taken the road from Boscobel to Lyme Regis, frustrated at every turn in his desperate search for a ship to take him to France, he was forced to descend the Downs into Bramber. The bridge had been captured by Parliamentary troops, who were coming away into the village to find food, jostling Charles, Lord Wilmot and Colonel Gounter as they passed by in the direction of St. Mary's. The several accounts of the escape agree in principle but differ in some of the detail. The account much favoured by scholars is that of Captain Gounter. The King also recounted his story to Samuel Pepys – disappointingly uninformative! No matter which account may be preferred, exactly where Charles rested in Bramber or Beeding still eludes us. The 'King's Room' at St. Mary's has been known as such for well over a century. Sons of a 19th–century owner, Richard Hudson, who were born in the King's Room, were all given the middle name, Charles. Another story, straight from the horse's mouth (though not the King's horse alas!) comes from Dr McConnel's grand-children (resident in the

1920's), now grand-parents themselves, who, with their schoolfriends, played a game known as 'The King's Escape' in which they scrambled through a secret door (still *in situ),* down into the chapel beneath the hall and along a tunnel to the Monks' Gate. It seems that generations of owners and occupiers at St Mary's, especially their children, believed this escape route to be the true one.

## ard Times

St. Mary's connections with Parliament began in 1690, when the then occupant, Dr Nicholas Barbon, became the Member for Bramber. His father, Praise–God Barebones, had opposed the restoration of Charles II and was imprisoned in the Tower of London for his pains. Nicholas's uncles are memorable for their elaborate Puritan names:*Christ-came-into-the-world-to-save Barebones* and *If Christ-had-not-died-thou-hadst-been-damned Barebones* (commonly known as 'Damned Barebones'). Prior to the Reform Act of 1832, voting was by burgage, or tenure by rent, a right which belonged to those persons who inhabited ancient houses or those houses built on ancient foundations. This kind of property qualification was helpful to any landlord intending to secure a seat in parliament. It would be a foolish tenant who did not vote for his own landlord! In 1788, Sir Henry (Harry) Gough inherited the Elvetham estate, in Hampshire, from his uncle, Sir Henry Calthorpe, and assumed by Royal Licence the additional surname, Calthorpe. Sir Henry, one of the Gough family who owned St. Mary's after 1713, sat as Member of Parliament for Bramber in 1774, 1780 and 1784, and was created Baron Calthorpe of Calthorpe (Norfolk) in 1796. It seems that during Sir Henry Gough's ownership, St. Mary's came to be divided into two tenements in the 1770's. A tenant of Lord Calthorpe's in 1837, Richard Charles Ambrose, appears to have used the upper rooms as store-rooms and kept the cattle at one end of the ground floor. The Calthorpes had little or no interest in the house after a time and gave their attention to their Elvetham estate and also their estate at Edgbaston in Warwickshire. Sketches of the interiors of St. Mary's by

H G Hines in 1841 show the house to have fallen into a derelict state: the treads of the stairs have collapsed and the panelling is broken and neglected, a well-worn besom leans against a pile of wood, and a rickety upper staircase appears where no staircase exists today. The decline and fall of the old 'Chapel House' seemed all but complete.

## ew Beginnings

It is so often the case that life has a way of renewing itself in the direst of circumstances. Richard Hudson, one of Bramber's 'worthies', a God-fearing, hard-working farmer, had acquired St. Mary's with a modest two acres (0.8 hectares) of land from Lord Calthorpe in 1860 and cultivated a further 80 acres (32 hectares), which served him well and brought him to prosperity. As a former

Harriet and Richard Hudson

tenant of Lord Calthorpe at St. Mary's, he and his large family (the eleven children all had biblical names – Isaac, Matilda, Esau, Rebekah, Isaiah, Abel, Seth, Ruth, Noah, Naomi and Meshak) worked their two acres of land and gathered the fruit from their plum trees for market. St. Mary's in those days had none of its former distinguished external appearance, being rendered and white-washed, its timber-framing hidden from view. A number of windows had been blocked up and those that remained were shuttered. By the corner of the house was a five-bar gate and a stile for the use of villagers making their way over the fields to St. Botolph's Church across the valley. The sale of Richard's effects on 14 November 1879 shows that he had become a man of some substance. He was for 32 years Clerk to the Parish of Bramber. He had a well-stocked pantry, a well-equipped kitchen, a number of fine mahogany and rosewood tables and chairs in the parlour, and a splendid tent-bed with dimity hangings. Then there were his clocks: a handsome eight-day rosewood clock inlaid with mother of pearl, and, not least, his magnificent grandfather clock (his pride and joy) which he installed in his temporary retirement home at Little St. Mary's only by digging a hole in the floor to set it in, for the ceilings were so low. Today Richard and Harriet, together with some of their offspring, lie at rest in a quiet corner of Bramber churchyard.

 ## ising Fortunes

The next step up the ladder of fortune for St. Mary's was the arrival of Captain Anderson James Ashmore of the 87th Regiment, the Royal Irish Fusiliers. The Captain had forsaken his regiment for life in an Episcopalian community at Decorah, Iowa, USA, and by 1868 had built himself a farmhouse and barn. After a few years, wheat crop failures forced him to sell up and return to England, where he settled at St. Mary's. He died there, aged only 41, on 19 November 1883 and was buried in Beeding churchyard. His principal interest lay in his advanced ideas on what might now be called 'organic' farming. The Department of Bio-Diversity in the University of Iowa has undertaken the restoration of his splendid Gothic-style barn in Decorah.

Towards the end of the century, we find a confusing set of circumstances since essential documents have been made inaccessible to us. All we can glean from other sources is that Baron Burton (of Bass Brewery fame) signed a reconveyance to Henry Padwick of Horsham, who in turn leased all or part of St. Mary's to the Hon. Algernon Bourke. Before this, Henry Francis Dickins, of Dickins and Jones, the famous London store, resided at St. Mary's as did the distinguished Bishop of Peterborough, Dr Carr Glyn; but let us leave these interesting intruders into our story and concentrate on the Bourke era.

# High Society

The Hon. Algernon Bourke was the second son of the Earl of Mayo, Viceroy of India. His family history is intriguing, for amongst his close relatives we find such fascinating figures as the poets, Wilfred Blunt and the sensational *enfant terrible,* Lord Alfred Douglas, who, with his outrageous father, the Marquis of Queensberry, helped to bring about the downfall of Oscar Wilde. It was Bourke who wrote to Sybil Queensberry, his cousin, warning of her husband's intention to cause a scandal at the theatre on the opening night of *The Importance of Being Earnest.* The play had been written in Worthing and it is

Gwendolen and Algernon Bourke

of interest to note here that Algernon and his beautiful wife, Gwendolen, were the originals for two of the principal characters. There are also many references in the play to cucumber sandwiches and muffins which have some relevance when we learn that Algernon was a society caterer, proprietor of

White's Club in St James's and Chairman of the Grand Hotel, Monte Carlo. He was debonair, witty, a brilliant *raconteur* and conversationalist, and very much in demand at parties. His grand-daughter tells us that the Bourkes had houses in London, Venice and County Mayo. His uncle, George Wingfield Bourke, was Rector of Pulborough, some twelve miles (19 km) from Bramber.

In the 1890's, Bourke had extravagant designs drawn up with a view to converting St. Mary's into an elegant country seat. To achieve this, he set about a complete refurbishment of the interiors as part of a grander scheme, as well as adding a whole new wing to the west, providing a kitchen, servants' hall, butler's pantry, still room and nursery. He extended and landscaped the gardens with lime avenues, rose walks, a circular orchard, sunken tennis court, croquet lawn and woodland glades. He created a fine music room (with excellent acoustics), the setting for many glittering soirées and other splendid social occasions. Unfortunately, he threatened to remove the ancient stile giving access to a right of way through the garden and across the fields to St. Botolph's Church, an action which met with some opposition from the villagers of Bramber. After some years, he

The 'Spy' Cartoon
of the
Hon. Algernon Bourke

decided to move to Taplow, where he could be nearer to his London Club and to his cousin, Lady Queensberry, at Bracknell.

# The New Century

The next resident, Alfred Musgrave, soon after his arrival in Bramber, managed to placate the villagers by building a new bridge and moving the right–of–way some distance from the house – to everyone's satisfaction. Musgrave had the advantage of all Algernon Bourke's 'improvements' and more spacious accommodation. It is likely that he negotiated to take on some, or all, of Bourke's possessions, including a Florentine urn and two Roman sarcophagi in the garden. Musgrave appears to have been immensely wealthy. The thirty or so rooms at St. Mary's were filled with furniture fit for a palace. The sale catalogue of 1913 includes several antique four-poster beds, Florentine mirrors, early Flemish tapestries, and an astonishing collection of genuine Louis XV and Louis XVI carved gilt furniture. Never had such an array of exquisite porcelain, silver, embroideries, lace, damasks and countless *objets d'art* been seen before or since at St. Mary's. Yet, for all that, Musgrave, the man, still eludes us. We know that he was distinguished enough to have been invited to open the Beeding and Bramber Regatta celebrating the Coronation of Edward VII in 1902. His name appeared above that of the Duke of Norfolk and his donation to the funds was more than double that of the Duke.

# Fun and Frolics

The years between the wars continued comfortably and happily with the McConnel family, of whom we know through first-hand accounts given by their grand-daughters. With homes in Norfolk, Dorset and Malta, the McConnels often allowed St. Mary's to be occupied in their absence as an exclusive 'finishing school' for wealthy young American girls. Tales are told of young men flying over from Shoreham Airport and dropping love-notes into the gardens. Young subalterns drove down from Sandhurst to take the girls swimming, play tennis and croquet, and dance to 'Pennies from Heaven' in the drawing-room. The house, we are told, was constantly filled with laughter. In 1938, the family moved to

Bramber Castle as it might have looked in Norman times
*(from an original sketch by J. G. Garratt)*

Bramber village in 1907 during the time of Alfred Musgrave

West view of St. Mary's c.1860 in Farmer Hudson's time

Three generations of Hudsons in the orchard at apple picking time

Bramber floods in 1904, showing the two large elms in front of St. Mary's

The Rose Tea Gardens (now the Castle Hotel)
showing St. Mary's Cottages on the right

Sketch of the main staircase
in 1841 by H. G. Hine
showing its ruinous condition

Canadian
troops
billeted at
St. Mary's
in 1944

The Music Room
added by the Bourkes
to display their
collection of early
Flemish tapestries

# "St. Mary's," Bramber, Sussex

Five minutes' walk from Bramber Station (L.B. & S.C.R.), and only ten miles from Brighton,
with a good service of trains.

## CATALOGUE OF

### THE VERY VALUABLE

# Antique & Modern Furniture

COSTLY APPOINTMENTS AND EFFECTS, comprising Brass and Iron French Bedsteads,
a large quantity of good quality Linen and Blankets,

## JACOBEAN ANTIQUE OAK FOUR-POST BEDSTEAD,

Antique Chippendale Four-post Bedstead,

### Antique Persian, Khiva Bokhara and Turkey Carpets

And Rugs, Wilton and Axminster Carpets, Antique Tall-boy Chests and Two William and Mary Hautbois,

## VERY VALUABLE OLD SPANISH CABINET OF DRAWERS

Satinwood, Mahogany and Tulipwood Cabinets and Tables,

### Carved Gilt Louis XV. and Louis XVI. Chairs and Settees, Genuine Old Louis XVI. Chaise Longue,

And an Empire Settee,

## ÆOLIAN GRAND ORCHESTRELLE

### BOUDOIR GRAND PIANOFORTE, in Satinwood case,

Florentine and Venetian Mirrors,

### Six Very Valuable Early Flemish Tapestry Panels,

A Pair of Louis XV. Tulipwood Encoigneurs, Two Louis XVI. Inlaid Upright Escritoires, Crown Derby,
Chelsea and Worcester Ornaments, Early English Services and Cut Glass, Cartel and Bracket Clocks,

### Two Antique Magnificently-sculptured Marble Sarcophagi

A beautiful old Well Head, and other Garden Ornaments,

### ANTIQUE AND MODERN SILVER AND PLATE,

Oil Paintings and Engravings, and the usual Appointments of a Household.

# Messrs. HARRODS, Ltd.

Have been favoured with instructions to Sell by Auction,

### At this Historical Old Residence,

## On MONDAY, the 1st day of DECEMBER, 1913

AND THREE FOLLOWING DAYS, at ONE o'clock precisely each day.

On View, by Card only, on Thursday, 27th November, and Publicly on Friday and Saturday prior to Sale.
Catalogues (price 1s. each) may be obtained of the Auctioneers, Messrs. HARRODS, Ltd.,

**BROMPTON ROAD, LONDON, S.W,**

"Estates Gazette," Ltd., 34-35, Kirby Street, E.C,

Haven St. Mary's (now Valerie Manor) in Upper Beeding and the jollities and frivolities came to an end.

## he House at War

At the outbreak of the Second World War, the empty old house was requisitioned by the Ministry of Defence as a billet for troops stationed in the area. Bramber once more became, as it had not been since Norman times, of great strategic importance. In 1941, the 578th Company the Royal Engineers moved in and subsequently St. Mary's was used as the Battery HQ for a number of other regiments, in particular several Divisions of the Royal Canadian Artillery. In July 1944, the house became the HQ for the 97th Anti-Tank Regiment, 15th Scottish Division. Through all this time, the interior of the house suffered damage from vandalism almost beyond repair. The young Canadians, snatched from the prairies, found themselves billeted in an empty medieval monastic inn older than anything of the kind they had ever known. It is a sober thought that few were to survive the first Normandy landings. One or two 'lucky' ones have returned with their families in recent years on a sentimental journey.

## Lady to the Rescue

Once more St. Mary's was saved by an extraordinary coincidence. A lady recalled how in 1944 she went to have her hair done in London and was given a magazine in which there was an advertisement for the sale of St. Mary's. After reading the account of its history, this lady, Miss Dorothy Ellis, decided, against the advice of her friends, to attend the auction at the Old Ship Hotel in Brighton. To her dismay, she found that a local builder was bidding against her with the hope of demolishing the building for its timbers. Fortunately, she was able to save the house from the very jaws of fate. "It was dismally dark," she wrote, "the permanent blackouts were still up as it was wartime. The panels in the Painted Room were scratched, dirty and covered with tin-tacks and drawing pins. Ivy was growing inside the music room; much of the wall-covering lay on the floor; the rest showed evidence of the food which had been fed to 120 soldiers. The treads of the staircase showed the wear caused by their boots, and water from broken pipes ran down the staircase. The electric cables had split under the weight of military boots. The beautiful 300 year-old leather was torn and so dark that the pattern was obscured ... the panelling in various rooms was green with mildew. On the walls of the hall in 12–inch high words was 'Home Sweet Home' in red paint....."

Dorothy Ellis and her mother in 1944

Of the thirty rooms, Dorothy Ellis set about furnishing twelve with the intention of opening them to visitors. Gradually, she acquired other furniture, pictures and ornaments to add to her family pieces. Her attempt to save St. Mary's is an amazing story of courage and determination against all odds and cannot be elaborated on here. Suffice to say that, in an age when grants were so impossibly conditional, she attempted a number of business ventures to raise money for the house, selling off precious land and turning Bourke's Victorian annexe into flats. Over thirty–five years of her life were spent in protecting St. Mary's from speculators and at the same time preserving it for posterity. In 1979, now advanced in years, she was forced to sell St. Mary's, but her remarkable achievement cannot be underestimated.

For a brief three years the family of the lepidopterist and author, Paul Smart, lived at St. Mary's, which they continued to open to the public as an historic house, together with their extensive butterfly collection. Sad as it was, economic pressures meant that, in 1983, the contents had to be sold and St. Mary's remained largely empty for over a year.

# n Safe Hands

In November 1984, the Thorogood and Linton families, on hearing that the house was about to be purchased by a national commercial organisation (and would therefore be closed to public view) bravely joined forces to save this lovely old building once more in its hour of need. Spurred on by family links with the McConnels going back to 1915, and having known the house for so many years, Peter Thorogood and Roger Linton, together with other family members, set about a programme of restoration.

The Thorogood family originated in Essex, farming for generations the very land that had once been part of the estate of Bishop Waynflete's Patten ancestors when they were Lords of Dakenham (Dagenham). Samuel Thorowgood (sic), a great-great uncle of Peter and Mary Thorogood, had gone into partnership with Thomas Deeble Dutton in the 1840's and had founded the well-known firm of shoe-makers, Dutton and Thorowgood, by appointment Royal shoe-makers to Queen Victoria and King Edward VII. By the 1880's, the firm was associated in business with Edwin Hearsey, great-great uncle of Roger Linton, and had branches in London, Brighton and Worthing. A further 17th century family connection came through the marriage of Thomas Thorogood and Anne Wyndham, an ancestor of Algernon Bourke.

eter Thorogood is an author and composer whose early writings grew out of his love for the East Anglian countryside of his childhood. He was educated at Brentwood School, Essex, and studied piano and composition at the Guildhall School of Music. After a year at the London School of Economics under Harold Laski, he went on to read Modern Languages at Trinity College, Dublin, at the same time continuing his musical studies at the

Royal Irish Academy of Music under the distinguished Swiss pianist and musicologist, Francis Engel. It was through the inspiring teaching of his French and Italian professors, notably Sir Robert Tate and Count Tomacelli, that Peter decided to go to Florence and Venice to further his studies. It was there that he developed a great interest in Italian life and culture. Following his graduation from Dublin, Peter Thorogood was appointed to the British School of Milan, eventually becoming its Vice-Principal. He also managed to make time for his music, studying piano and composition with the well-known concert pianist, Giuliana Brengola. Peter's professional life led him to travel extensively throughout Europe and the Middle East. He was one of the first lecturers to go to Bulgaria towards the end of the Cold War to re-establish quasi-diplomatic educational links. Through the succeeding years, Peter was Visiting Lecturer with the British Council and taught in Germany, Israel, Poland and Greece.

On his return to England, whilst still with the British Council, he continued to give his popular *History of English Literature* course and gave many recitals of music and poetry, including his own compositions, in and around London. Among his other activities, Peter was Radio Talks Critic for the BBC magazine, *The Listener*, compiled a series on *English Humorous Writing* for the BBC World Service, published three collections of his own poetry and delivered a number of scholarly papers on his researches into the life and work of Thomas Hood, at King's College and University College, London. From 1984, following his early retirement, he devoted his energies to the restoration of St. Mary's, where the Music Room has proved to be the perfect setting for his successful series of concerts and recitals. These have included distinguished performances by Paul Scofield, Gwyneth Powell, Donald Swann, Glyndebourne tenor Neil Jenkins, and dancers from the Royal Ballet. Apart from his literary and musical pursuits, Peter is actively involved in promoting English culture and heritage. He has for many years been a Fellow of the Royal Society of Arts, and has served as a member of the Executive Council of the Historic Houses Association and Key Keeper of Bramber Castle on behalf of English Heritage.

 **oger Linton's** Sussex links go back to at least 1668, to Nicholas Hearsey, whose descendant, Edwin, was connected, as we have seen, with the Sussex branch of the Thorowgood family. Edwin's mother, Esther Woolgar (Roger's great-great-grandmother), married Henry Hearsey in Bramber in 1839. Earlier Woolgar ancestors are buried in the churchyard of St. Nicholas, Bramber, next to the Hudson family, the former owners of St. Mary's. Countless visitors will remember Renée Linton (Esther's great-grand-daughter and Roger's mother), who with her husband, Lawrence, contributed so much to the life of the house.

Renée's grandfather was a talented painter and musician, and her father, Paulus Everard Letchford, was a member of the Guild of Cordwainers and a Freeman of the City of London. Renée had an exceptional contralto voice and made her first recordings in 1934. Lawrence, after training for the Ministry, was posted to India, where he and Renée were married in 1936. Their official residence at Meerut had once been the refuge of the British women and children during the Indian Mutiny. Here Roger spent his first formative years. Returning to England in 1946, Lawrence took a chaplaincy in the Worthing circuit (which included Steyning) and the family settled in nearby Shoreham. During this happy time, Roger and his school-friends enjoyed cycling round the Adur valley – free-wheeling down the steep Beeding bostal! One of Roger's earliest visits to Bramber was to see the quaint Museum of Curiosities, founded by the famous Victorian taxidermist, Walter Potter. It would be many years before Roger was to pay his first memorable visit to St. Mary's to meet its valiant owner, Dorothy Ellis, in 1965.

Educated at John Wesley's Kingswood School at Bath, Roger Linton proceeded to Leicester College of Art and later gained a place at the Royal College of Art in London, where he trained as a designer, specialising in ceramics under the tutelage of Professor Lord Queensberry. Whilst studying at the Staatliche Porzellan Manufaktur in Berlin, he produced his prototype

'Lotus' design tea–service. After working for some years as a designer in the Potteries, Roger went on to teach art and design at Thanet Technical College and later at Brighton College of Technology, at the same time developing his talents as painter and sculptor and following his keen interest in antique china restoration. An exhibition of his portrait sculptures with the Guild of Sussex Craftsmen at Michelham Priory created considerable interest. In 1981, he designed and made a complete panelled library for Peter Thorogood's home in Kensington to house the unique Thomas Hood Collection, now at St. Mary's. His abiding interest in architecture and art history was put to good use in his restoration of the Linton family home – a 15th century timber-framed hall-house in Suffolk – providing him with invaluable expertise in the considered conservation of an English vernacular building such as St. Mary's.

## nto the Future

The condition of the house in 1984 was reminiscent of the situation found by Dorothy Ellis forty years before: rotting floors and panelling, plaster work and ceilings loosened by traffic vibration, broken windows with ivy growing through, dangerous electrical wiring, and rain damage through ceilings and walls, resulting in mildew. A dankness pervaded the sad, empty rooms. Restoration work, including the sensitive revival of the magnificent panelled rooms, had to proceed despite the lack of any grant aid. Personal funds began to run uncomfortably low and it was timely, therefore, when Peter Thorogood's aunt, Irene Swann, the last surviving pupil of the composer, Gustav Holst, and mother of the world-famous entertainer, Donald Swann, gave funds for the restoration of Bourke's Victorian Music Room, in which she had played the viola to her friends, the McConnels, some 75 years earlier. Her brother, Colonel Eric Swithin Bonnett, and later his son, Peter's cousin, John Bonnett, contributed further funding for the improvement of the gardens, to Roger Linton's designs, including the planting of many shrubs and trees together with more topiary, and the creation of knot gardens, fountains and waterfalls.

It was fortuitous that St. Mary's came into the care of the Thorogood and Linton families. Despite the daunting task of works to be undertaken in the house and gardens, a growing sense of fulfilment has made the herculean effort seem all the more worthwhile. Encouragement has come from every quarter, not least from the notable contribution of the volunteer team of friends who, over the years, continue to give unstintingly of their time and energies to help keep St. Mary's open to the public. In April 1991, the *Friends of St. Mary's* was formed with the purpose of raising funds through events and subscriptions and is today a thriving and enthusiastic group, dedicated to helping St. Mary's in a variety of ways. Further substantial funding is vital if St. Mary's is to survive into a more secure long-term future and, with this in mind, Peter Thorogood and Roger Linton founded the *Waynflete Heritage Trust* in 1996, thus enabling St. Mary's, in its wider context of historic Bramber, to invite financial support through bequests, covenants, donations and grants. St. Mary's has been willed to the Trust, by Peter Thorogood, Roger Linton and Mary Thorogood, together with its family furniture, archives, special collections and historic memorabilia, for the benefit of future generations. No account of this fascinating house can convey its atmosphere and charm. Today we see St. Mary's once more resplendent – rediscovering its ancient role in welcoming visitors from all parts of the world.

*Photo: Beckett Newspapers, 1991*

Peter Thorogood and Roger Linton with their team of voluntary helpers
on receiving the South East England Tourist Board's 'Warmest Welcome' Commendation

Samuel Thorowgood
c.1865, a founder of
Dutton & Thorowgood,
Shoemakers,
By Appointment to Queen Victoria

Irene Swann
(née Bonnett)
in 1915

Mary Thorogood

Peter and Mary Thorogood
in 1929. Their Teddy Bears
are on display in the house!

Thomas Hood
by William Hilton R.A., c.1833
*(by kind permission of the
National Portrait Gallery)*

Peter Thorogood at the launch of
one of his books on Thomas Hood
*(Photo: Evening Argus)*

Renée Linton and Peter Thorogood in the Library with one of the
volumes of Camden's History of England originally presented
to Peter and Mary's grandfather Samuel Thorogood in 1871
*(Photo: West Sussex County Times)*

Lawrence and Renée Linton outside her parents' home in Worthing in 1934.
Roger's grandfather, Paulus, in background

Roger Linton aged eleven,
at Shoreham by Sea.
His father was Methodist
minister at Steyning
and Chaplain to the
Grammar School

Roger with his mother Renée,
by the Shell Fountain, 1989

St Mary's
today

A corner of
the Topiary Garden

Dancers from the
Royal Ballet, 1990 –
one of the many events
held during each season

The Music Room
is a popular venue
for Corporate Hospitality
and Wedding Receptions

# A Brief Guide to the Rooms
# and Gardens

W e owe much of our knowledge of the present building to valuable research undertaken in the 1940's by the distinguished founder and Director of the National Buildings Record, Walter Godfrey:

"St. Mary's is a building of great interest and charm .... It consists of a long two-storeyed (now three) range, framed in massive oak, running north and south, with the upper storey overhanging on the north and east sides. This framework dates from the 15th century .... We can see on the first floor sufficient evidence to satisfy us that it was divided into five rooms ....this series of five apartments was formerly open to the roof, the kingpost trusses four of which stood over the intervening partitions. This arrangement would necessitate some form of gallery for access to the five doors and we are led to the conclusion that the building must have been planned in the manner of the galleried inns and that what we have here is in all likelihood the eastern side of a spacious courtyard...."

Since Professor Godfrey's ingenious analysis of these structural features was published in the Sussex Archaeological Society's journal, further researches have revealed important facts and clues on both the building itself and its occupants. Tantalising 'missing' pieces of the jig–saw still await discovery.

**The Wardens' Room**

The Priory of Sele provided four monks to serve as wardens of the Great
Bridge of Bramber and its chapel dedicated to St. Mary. Appropriately, it is
in this room in which the wardens may have had their cells, that visitors are
introduced to the story of St. Mary's. A large timber pier from the earlier
wooden bridge can be seen, together with fragments of the ancient causeway.
The foundations of the later bridge, discovered in 1839 beneath what is now
the topiary garden, were of Sussex marble or 'winklestone', (a grey mottled
stone incorporating the shells of *paludina* freshwater snails). Pieces of
winklestone are displayed in the Wardens' Room with other items found during
the recent restoration of the house and gardens. A notable feature of the room
is the massive 'dragon' beam ('dragon' being a corruption of 'diagonal'), with
strengtheners in a herring-bone design, which carries the weight of the 'jetties'

The Wardens' Room

26

on two adjacent sides at first-floor level. The large inglenook fireplace, installed in Elizabethan times, was used for cooking after the loss of the great kitchen on the far side of the courtyard. Among the principal features of the inglenook are the decorative 17th century fire-back displaying the royal coat of arms and the original pot crane (still in working order). In this part of the room the beams are more elaborately carved, which suggests a more public use. The Wardens' Room, which, in more recent times, was used as the Morning Room, is embellished with some of the earliest oak panelling in the house, dating from the 16th century.

The Entrance Hall

## The Entrance Hall

Adjacent to the Wardens' Room, occupying the rest of the eastern wing of the inn, was a long 'Common Room' for the use of travellers. The present Hall, Drawing Room and South Hall now occupy this area. The Elizabethan chimney stack is adorned with a fine parquetry overmantel, composed of hundreds of pieces of holly and oak set in a variety of geometrical patterns. How this remarkable piece of decoration came to the house is not known. (It was common practice to dispose of the more precious furnishings of a house being altered or demolished, as was the case with Henry VIII's Nonsuch Palace at Ewell in Surrey.) The present front door forms one half of the original arched double doorway. In the 1920's and 1930's, the Entrance Hall was used as an additional sitting room. A door in the panelling once led directly down a steep staircase to the cellars (now flooded). A number of visitors in recent years have testified to the existence of a mysterious chapel in the cellars and have recorded tales of tunnels beneath the garden and a stream running under the house. Researches made by the present owners of St. Mary's have revealed that the house may have provided Sir Arthur Conan Doyle with the setting for his story, *The Musgrave Ritual*, in which Sherlock Holmes comes to an ancient house in western Sussex and finds the butler dead in the cellar, clutching the treasure left behind for safe-keeping by Charles II on his flight to France over Bramber Bridge.

**The South Hall**

Ancient houses invariably engender tales of mystery and imagination. During some Canadian Army revels at St. Mary's in the Second World War, a 'mysterious monk' was seen wandering about in the Monks' Walk (where else?) and landgirls are said to have witnessed 'manifestations'! A small child in Elizabethan doublet and hose has been glimpsed on the upper landing, a musky perfume has been noticed from time to time in the 'Painted Room', and Mrs McConnel had several encounters with a 'lady in grey' on the main staircase. If these extraordinary emanations ever made themselves known in the past, they certainly never come to us now. We do sometimes smell incense in the South Hall – or is that merely the smell of soot fallen from the chimney? Of more tangible beauty in the South Hall is the rare, painted wall-leather, charmingly decorated with flowers, fruit and birds. Once thought to have been part of the dowry of Catherine of Aragon, it is now believed by experts to belong to the 17th century, and probably English in origin.

Close by the Garden Door can be seen some decorative stone corbels, thought to be part of the earlier Templar building. During the 1980's a way-through had to be made to give access from the South Hall to the present kitchen, which had once been the Victorian conservatory. This work proved to be more of a problem than had been anticipated as the stone wall was found to be 2 ft (60 cm) thick. From this it seems clear that Waynflete's builders chose to incorporate parts of the previous structure in the new monastic inn.

**The Drawing Room**

Visitors passing through the Entrance Hall and South Hall into the Drawing Room still find themselves in a part of the ancient monastic Common Room for, as we have explained, it was divided up to suit the needs of the first of the Elizabethan occupants. It is immediately noticeable that there is no dragon beam to match that of the Wardens' Room, due to the fore-shortening of this end of the house in the early 17th century, at which time a new flint wall was erected, incorporating a stone mullioned window. The principal feature of the Drawing Room is the splendid Jacobean panelling reminiscent of the Dutch style – raised fielded panels inset with ebony veneer. The impressive fireplace is embellished with a fine 17th century marquetry overmantel in a variety of woods including oak, box, and burr walnut, representing flint-lock guns, bayonets, cannon-balls, kegs of gunpowder and military musical instruments. The central crest represents a bull with a pig's snout (known in heraldry as a 'porcine bull') adorned with ermine denoting a royal connection. The whole canopy is supported by magnificent ebonised columns in the traditional style of the time.

**The Main Staircase**

The finely-proportioned bifurcated staircase was constructed in the early 17th century in the space which formerly occupied part of the medieval open gallery. The earlier balustrade was re–utilised and two carved lions rampant, with flat crowns to serve as rests for portable candlesticks, were subsequently added to the newel-posts.

Over the staircase can be seen a massive oak beam with the ancient adze marks. High above the doorway leading to the Music Room is a medieval 'shutting' window, with fine decorative panels carved in 1912 by Edwin Briar Woodford. The window was generously given to St. Mary's by his descendant, Joseph Howard, and installed in 1997. The staircase to the right leads up to the level of the gallery which overlooked the courtyard. On the left can be seen an earlier survival of a 'shutting' window which, until the recent installation of the 'Howard' window, was the only known example to survive *in situ* in an English house. Usually, windows were primitive openings, frequently barred or covered with sacking or oiled skins, but the invention of the triple hinge made possible a comparatively draught-proof protection from the elements. Though this type of shuttered window was still in use in the 17th century, glazed replacements were more often favoured as the price of window-glass dropped.

### The Gallery

Six doors once gave access to dorters on this eastern range of the inn. Today, three of these doorways can still be seen; one of them appears to be suspended in space owing to the insertion of the staircase. A further improvement to the building in the late 17th century was the addition of an attic floor reached by a staircase, embellished with a richly-carved balustrade. Clerestory windows were inserted to give extra light to the Gallery.

### The Painted Room

In this unique room can be seen one of the earliest examples of *trompe l'oeil* three-dimensional painting in England. This in particular is known to have been adopted in Tudor times as a means of creating an illusion of space, thus lending an element of grandeur to the appearance of a room. There is good reason to suppose that the magnificent Painted Room at St. Mary's was created by itinerant 'painter-stainers' for an illustrious visitor. Through a series of small windows can be seen landscapes and seascapes some of which are thought to be local scenes depicting a windmill and a saltcote a simple turf-roofed hut used by salt workers). The most important of these seascapes depicts a dramatic naval battle, a mirror image of the more elaborate painting on the overmantel opposite, which is said to represent the engagement of the French with Henry VIII's fleet in 1545. This famous battle is associated today with the loss of its flagship, the *Mary Rose*. The panels are thought to have been restored in the 17th century, which accounts for some contemporary over-painting. In 1947 the former curator of the Duke of Gloucester's collection, Dr Gilbey Ellis, undertook a complete restoration of the panels. Basically, they were intact but had suffered damage during wartime when soldiers were billeted at St. Mary's and 'time, grime and smoke' had obscured the original splendour of the paintings. Today, after much care and attention by the present curator, the panels provide a central experience for visitors. Only one other

The Painted Room

English house is known to have painted panels of this kind. Walter Godfrey has drawn a parallel with the *trompe l'oeil* Elizabethan mural decorations at Eastbury Manor in Barking, Essex, which co-incidentally had once been the home of Peter Thorogood's grandparents.

## The King's Room

The panelling beyond the foot of the attic stairs on the Gallery conceals a space behind the chimney. Could it have been a hiding place or was it used for smoking food? As we have seen, Hudson and McConnel family tradition for over a century has linked the King's Room with the flight of Charles II after the Battle of Worcester. This room is of particular interest in that it has no panelling to hide the basic medieval structure and we are thus afforded a glimpse of how the rooms appeared in earlier times. The timber-framing of medieval buildings was infilled with woven hazel strips (the wattle) covered with a mixture of lime, straw, horse hair and dung (the daub). A section of the wattle and daub has been left on view. Centuries of over-painting concealed the original medieval wall-surface and it was not until 1986, when Peter Thorogood and Roger Linton were restoring the room, that evidence of mural decoration was revealed. Furthermore, the installation of the 17th century ceiling had hidden some rare medieval stencil painting in the form of five-petalled flowers painted on the beams.

## The Library

The visitor enters the Library by a door which incorporates an ancient confessional linen-fold screen, complete with its folding door, found in the cellars and thought to have come from the chapel of St. Mary on the Great Bridge of Bramber. Originally known as the North Bedchamber, the Library contains the world's largest collection in private hands of the works of the celebrated 19th century poet and caricaturist, Thomas Hood, on whose life and work Peter Thorogood is the leading authority. Hood's *I Remember, I Remember/ The house where I was born* and the celebrated poem of social conscience, *The Song of the Shirt*, are among the best known poems in the English language. Apart from his extensive poetical output, Hood, one of the most popular comic poets of his day, also distinguished himself as the designer and engraver of more than 900 comic woodcuts. Oak panels, with 38 classical pilasters, line the Library walls and complement the elegance of the 18th century ceramic fire–surround. Above the fire–place is an intricate Georgian marquetry panel, in the centre of which is the Sabine family crest with the scallop shell, a symbol of medieval pilgrimage. Between the fireplace and the window is a portrait of Charles Dickens by W P Frith, the well-known painter of *Derby Day*. Parian figures of Milton, Burns and Sir Walter Scott complement a large plaster bust of Shakespeare, one of the principal influences on the early poetry of Thomas Hood. One special feature of the Library is the Armada Door, one of two brought from County Mayo by Algernon Bourke at the time of his restoration of St. Mary's. The doors incorporate Spanish strap-work panels which are said to have come from one of the 24 Armada ships caught in the severe storm off the coast of Mayo.

The Library

**The Octagon and Music Room**

Leaving behind Waynflete's 15th century building, we enter the glittering world of Victorian high society, with its elegant musical soirées and weekend house-parties. In the early 1890's, the Hon. Algernon Bourke acquired St. Mary's, a property in which he could create a country house setting for family and London society friends. Bramber was conveniently close to his Wyndham cousins at Petworth House; his uncle, the Rev. George Wingfield Bourke, lived at Pulborough, and a cousin, Wilfred Blunt, the poet and political agitator, was close by at Horsham. Bourke's plans could not be fully realised without extending the older building; work began on extra family accommodation to provide nursery, kitchen, servants' hall, still room, butler's pantry and a library. (Unhappily, this wing had to be sold by Dorothy Ellis in the 1960's to raise funds for the maintenance of the ancient part of the house.) Bourke had married the beautiful society debutante, Gwendolen Sloane-Stanley, a descendant of the distinguished scholar, physician and founder of the Chelsea Botanic Gardens, Sir Hans Sloane. Gwendolen's musical talents inspired her husband to provide her with a fine music room, which would be the scene of many splendid social occasions.

The octagonal dining room, created and decorated in Pre-Raphaelite style by Roger Linton to serve as an entrance to the Music Room, has a ribbed ceiling rising to an open 'lantern' giving a suggestion of sunlight. A series of shields bearing the coats of arms of the families linked with the history of the house over the centuries, embellish the elaborate gothic cornice. Portraits from the Bourke family album showing Algernon and Gwendolen at the time of their engagement in 1887 include one of Gwendolen in Court dress. A 'Spy' cartoon, published in *Vanity Fair* in 1895, portrays Algernon as the portly owner of White's Club in St. James's and as an elegant society caterer. Algernon's wit and Gwendolen's beauty assured them entry to the brilliant salons of the day, inspiring Oscar Wilde to re-create them as two of the principal characters in his world-famous play *The Importance of Being Earnest.* The play was written in nearby Worthing at the time of the Bourke's residence at St. Mary's. In the play, Algernon causes much amusement by eating Lady Bracknell's cucumber sandwiches, an example of how Wilde drew upon family connections – Bourke's cousin, the Marchioness of Queensberry, mother of Lord Alfred Douglas, lived at Bracknell.

Passing beneath a fine Sir Gilbert Scott altar piece, beautifully restored by Roger Linton, we enter the spacious Music Room with its high vaulted ceiling decorated with Victorian anaglypta panels and elegant gothic plaster cornice. The two gothic carved stone fireplaces were formerly part of a 14th century chantry tomb and it is thought that the two fluted Ionic columns were installed at the time when Bourke was also engaged in the re-designing of the billiard-room at White's. The sprung floor allowed for dancing and even in the 1990's some older visitors could remember the halcyon days of the 1920's when they put on their evening gowns to attend a ball at St. Mary's. With changing social and economic circumstances,

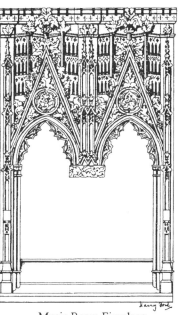

Music Room Fireplace

dancing gave way to more practical uses: from ballroom to drawing room, wartime officers' mess, antique showroom, and butterfly museum. Since the late 1980's, Peter Thorogood, as author, pianist and composer, has re-created the atmosphere of earlier times by presenting concerts, recitals, drama and poetry readings.

**The Topiary Garden**
A large topiary snail guards the entrance to the car-park. Visitors approach the house along a pleached lime-walk and pass through a wicket-gate set in a zig-zag hedge of yew, which suggests the old idea of a maze. Here can be seen a

variety of box and yew shrubs trimmed into the shapes of amusing animals and birds. To the right of the knot-garden is a shell fountain, half-hidden by spring-flowering magnolias. Crossing the stone bridge between the moat-pools, past a fountain depicting the legendary 'Green Man', visitors are challenged by a spirited topiary bull with flying tail. This impressive animal is attended by a crested bird and a heron. Beside the York stone path is a bob-tailed hare of box and a bulbous-eyed yew frog resting on a lily-pad. Other topiary subjects include a chess piece, a green submarine, a 'sugar' cube, a crested quail and a wren. In Maytime, two resplendent red chestnut trees are ablaze with blossom, complementing the equally colourful *rosa plena* hawthorns bordering the village street. In keeping with the age-old tradition of the English garden, a host of hollyhocks grow, in all their summer profusion, against the fine medieval timber-framed frontage of the house.

## The Terrace Garden

Hidden behind a high 'rampart' hedge of yew is the Terrace Garden, which can be glimpsed through a wide stone arch. This private part of the garden, traditionally used by members of the family, is usually approached through the house. On the left, the romantic ivy-clad pergola known as 'The Monks' Walk' can be entered through a tunnel of yew. Part of the flint wall is inset with ornamental stone fragments from the medieval chapel on the bridge, discovered during excavations in the gardens in the late 19th century. The lawn terrace was laid out in the late 1890's by the Hon. Algernon Bourke. Steps lead down to the lower lawn, formerly the old croquet lawn, where, from 1915 onwards, Peter and Mary Thorogood's cousin, Irene Bonnett, had first learnt to play the game she still enjoyed well into her nineties. Following hurricane damage in 1987, this part of the garden was re-landscaped by Roger Linton with architectural hedges of yew on the plan of a church, with 'apse' and 'transepts', which, with the adjoining Monks' Walk 'Cloister', serve as a tribute to the founder of St. Mary's, Bishop Waynflete. Among other notable features of the Terrace Garden is an exceptional example of the 'Living Fossil' tree, the prehistoric *Ginkgo biloba*, the oldest species of tree in the world, once thought to be extinct. On the Terrace, by the corner of the house, stands one

View from the South Garden

of the tallest examples of *Magnolia grandiflora* which, in late summer, bears large, exotic lemon-scented blooms. The garden, being on two levels, makes an attractive, natural theatre, which provides a perfect setting for open-air performances of Shakespeare's plays in the summer and serves as a romantic venue for receptions, fêtes and other events.

**The Lost Gardens**
To the west of the house, Bourke laid out pleasure grounds and kitchen gardens. When the house was put up for sale in 1913, the Harrods' sale catalogue emphasised the beauty of the gardens, going so far as to say that they rendered 'description exceedingly difficult, if not impossible':

> *There are Spacious Lawns for Tennis and Croquet, Smaller Lawns with flagged walks, long stone-flagged Pergola, charming Rose Garden with Pergola and Summer-house, fan-shaped Lavender Bed, delightful Grass Avenues, affording vistas of the South Downs, beautifully kept Hedges, Flower*

*Borders and Shrubberies, all of which combine to make the*
*Gardens as fine as any in the County.*

*THE KITCHEN GARDENS, sub-divided by other fine*
*hedges, are fully stocked and in splendid order, while the*
*ORCHARD, encircled by a fine yew hedge, includes trees of*
*the best kinds. There is a good range of Glass-houses, several*
*smaller Glass-houses, a range of Pits (all heated), and a long*
*Fruit Wall, behind which are large Tool House, Store Room,*
*Potting Shed, Workshops &c.*

*The area of the Property, which is well timbered with a*
*large variety of Trees and Conifers, including the Paddocks,*
*amounts to between nine and ten acres.*

Fortunately, the lawns and flagged walks to the south and east of the house remain to this day. The hedges, grass walks, flower borders and shrubberies have been reinstated since 1985, continuing to give pleasure to visitors. However, owing to serious financial constraints, Miss Dorothy Ellis had decided to sell the pleasure and kitchen gardens in the 1940's and it was feared that they were lost for ever. In 1997 an opportunity arose to regain these 'lost gardens' which had been part of the old Knights Templar land. The gardens had become a picture of dereliction and neglect, having remained asleep for over fifty years, and were overgrown with an impenetrable jungle of brambles, nettles and saplings. At least one of the three glass-houses remained intact as did the magnificent 140 foot (43m) Victorian brick fruit wall, the rare circular orchard, the heated pits with their stove-house, and the Boulton and Paul potting shed with its apple store. The universal excitement at the discovery of these 'secret' gardens can hardly be imagined! Loans had to be quickly raised and a 'Lost Gardens Appeal' set up. Thus, the gardens were re-purchased for St. Mary's. This important acquisition once more restored the full legacy bequeathed by successive owners from Templars to Waynflete and Magdalen College, from Calthorpe to Hudson and Bourke, from Dorothy Ellis to Thorogood and Linton. Today, St. Mary's Bramber remains one of the most enchanting and atmospheric houses in England.

# TEACHING
# MOVEMENT EDUCATION

## FOUNDATIONS FOR
## ACTIVE LIFESTYLES

Karen Weiller Abels

Jennifer M. Bridges

**Human Kinetics**

## Library of Congress Cataloging-in-Publication Data

Abels, Karen Weiller.
 Teaching movement education : foundations for active lifestyles / Karen Weiller Abels and
Jennifer M. Bridges.
    p. cm.
 Includes bibliographical references and index.
 ISBN-13: 978-0-7360-7456-8 (soft cover)
 ISBN-10: 0-7360-7456-2 (soft cover)
 1.  Movement education--Study and teaching. 2.  Movement education--Curricula. I. Bridges,
Jennifer M. II. Title.
 GV452.A32 2010
 372.86'8--dc22
                                           2009049492

ISBN-10: 0-7360-7456-2 (print)
ISBN-13: 978-0-7360-7456-8 (print)

The Web addresses cited in this text were current as of December 2009, unless otherwise noted.

**Acquisitions Editor:** Scott Wikgren; **Developmental Editors:** Amy Stahl and Ragen E. Sanner; **Assistant Editor:** Anne Rumery; **Copyeditor:** Patsy Fortney; **Indexer:** Andrea Hepner; **Permission Manager:** Dalene Reeder; **Graphic Designer:** Joe Buck; **Graphic Artists:** Tara Welsch and Dawn Sills; **Cover Designer:** Bob Reuther; **Photographer (interior):** Photos courtesy of Jennifer Bridges, unless otherwise noted.; **Art Manager:** Kelly Hendren; **Associate Art Manager:** Alan L. Wilborn; **Illustrator (cover):** Dan Clayton; **Illustrator (interior):** KinetiKidz © Karen Weiller Abels and Jennifer Bridges.; **Printer:** Sheridan Books

Printed in the United States of America        10  9  8  7  6  5  4  3  2  1

The paper in this book is certified under a sustainable forestry program.

**Human Kinetics**
Web site: www.HumanKinetics.com

*United States:* Human Kinetics
P.O. Box 5076
Champaign, IL 61825-5076
800-747-4457
e-mail: humank@hkusa.com

*Canada:* Human Kinetics
475 Devonshire Road Unit 100
Windsor, ON N8Y 2L5
800-465-7301 (in Canada only)
e-mail: info@hkcanada.com

*Europe:* Human Kinetics
107 Bradford Road
Stanningley
Leeds LS28 6AT, United Kingdom
+44 (0) 113 255 5665
e-mail: hk@hkeurope.com

Australia: Human Kinetics
57A Price Avenue
Lower Mitcham, South Australia 5062
08 8372 0999
e-mail: info@hkaustralia.com

*New Zealand:* Human Kinetics
P.O. Box 80
Torrens Park, South Australia 5062
0800 222 062
e-mail: info@hknewzealand.com

E4469

Robert S. Bridges
1957-2009

# CONTENTS

# ACTIVITY AND LESSON FINDER

## Chapter 7 Body Activities

# Chapter 8 Space Activities

# Chapter 9 Effort Activities

# Chapter 10 Relationships Activities

# Chapter 11 Teaching Educational Games

# Chapter 12 Teaching Educational Gymnastics

# Chapter 13 Teaching Educational Dance

# PREFACE

In the past, active lifestyles were assumed to be almost hardwired into childhood. It wasn't necessary to program physical activity for children; they just played naturally. Unfortunately, though, we have seen the sedentary habits of some adults become the norm for many children. Sitting in front of televisions and computers as well as consuming high-calorie food and beverages have resulted in an epidemic of childhood obesity. While fitness and activity are critical to changing this trend, we believe that an approach focused only on fitness will not solve the problem. We believe that a broader base of knowledge and movement is necessary for creating the motivation, ability, and atmosphere that can lead to a lifetime of physical activity, which is more likely to address the childhood obesity epidemic. Built on the movement education frameworks of the past as well as today's national standards, our Flip-n-Fold movement education framework (MEF) lays out the broader base of knowledge and movement in a success-oriented, problem-solving approach that teachers need and from which children benefit. This book makes the foundational information for physical education easy to understand, meaningful, and practical to implement.

## Practical and Professional

Although this text draws on experience and documents the research of others, it is not a summary of research. The cumbersome aspects of movement education of the 1960s to the 1980s are addressed with the desire to make it more useful today. Not only physical education specialists but also classroom teachers who are involved in the physical education of elementary-level children need to be able to have a clear and manageable system that will allow them to implement a practical movement education curriculum.

It is also our wish that today's preservice physical education candidates, practicing physical educators, and classroom educators will focus on the use of the MEF in all three learning domains (motor, cognitive, and affective). We hope that

the Flip-n-Fold, presented in detail in chapter 2, inspires a focal point on agreement, practicality, and support of intellectual variety. In chapter 3 we share how to implement the developmental perspective of teaching physical education through the application of both motor development and motor learning theories to the movement education framework. The holistic view of fitness and movement education is explained in detail in chapter 4.

## Answering Your Questions

Today's teachers and parents need to be responsible for ensuring that children get enough physical activity for health-related fitness. We answer questions teachers ask themselves, such as these:

- In my everyday teaching, how can I use the movement elements described in this text?
- Do I have to choose between getting my students fit and teaching movement education?
- I have only 10 minutes in my classroom to do some physical activity. How can I fit this in?
- Can I teach movement education in the hallway, classroom, or outdoors if I have to?

These kinds of questions are answered throughout the book with an innovative examination of teaching the MEF (see chapter 5 for new ways and new technologies to use for teaching movement education and chapter 6 for a method of analyzing any activity and modifying it to achieve your movement goals). Activities that address the four movement concepts (body, space, effort, and relationships) are in chapters 7 through 10. Units and lessons in the three core content areas (educational games, educational gymnastics, and educational dance) are in chapters 11 through 13. A glossary of movement language (in both English and Spanish) appears in the back of the book to help you keep track of all the new terms and definitions that appear throughout the text. Look for words shown in **bold** indicating that a definition is available in the glossary.

## Summary

Teaching and learning should be enjoyable, and there should be a natural approach to blending content standards into activities, lessons, and units in both the classroom and the gym. The first section of the book gives you the theory and background of our MEF approach so that you can implement the ideas in your own classroom. The second section of the book contains the practical activities and lessons that you can use or modify as your own. Meeting national and local standards for physical education and literacy education can sometimes seem like an impossible job. But in this book, we present teaching and learning as enjoyable experiences.

# ACKNOWLEDGMENTS

First and foremost, we want to thank our families, Robin, Ethan, Emmie, Kris, and Riley for their incredible patience, support, and love throughout this amazing experience. The writing of this book has been a journey for us and we appreciate the love of our families over the many, many hours we have spent.

Second, we would like to thank developmental editors Amy Stahl for beginning our editing journey and Ragen Sanner for jumping in and taking over for Amy who delivered a healthy baby girl. We thank Ragen for her incredible patience with us and her detailed work in making our book the best it could be! Many thanks also to assistant editor Anne Rumery for her support in working with Ragen and particularly to acquisitions editor Scott Wikgren for providing us with this opportunity to share our work. We also want to extend thanks to Pratyush Lal at Sportime for his flexibility and willingness to work in a coordinated way with us and the folks at Human Kinetics.

A special thank you goes to Dan Clayton, graphic illustrator, who we fondly call KinetiDan, the father of the KinetiKidz. We appreciate Dan's creativity in developing the basic plan for the cover design of the book. We also extend thanks to Carla Lents for her graphic design of the Flip 'n' Fold and Lisa Losasso for her support and insight into the development of the personality of our Kidz.

We are so pleased to have had so much support in bringing the movement glossary to our readers in both English and Spanish. We were blessed to have the help of the following people: Ricardo Deleon Talavas, David Rodriguez, Sylvia Mora, Espie Dennis, Jackie Traub, Samantha Weimer, and Jesse Jabe.

We would also like to thank the many individuals who helped us with their specialized aspects of content development throughout the book: Glenna deJong, Cathy Ennis, Bonnie Gilliom, Arlene Ignico, Rae Pica, Gregory Payne, De Raynes, Debbie Rhea, Judith Rink, Mary Ann Roberton, and Craig Wrisberg.

Thanks also go to the teachers and schools who provided opportunities for us: Jane Koval, Karen Myers, and M. Lynn Vande Sande, Madison Metropolitan School District; Paulette Layfield, Kelli Folsom, and Kim Crane, Denton ISD; Charlita Smith-Kratz, Fort Worth ISD; Deb Lane, Keller ISD; and Georgi Roberts, Fort Worth ISD. Each afforded us opportunities to share our movement education framework with the teachers and students in their respective districts.

Students and faculty at each of our universities have helped us develop our ideas and insights and test out our methods; their participation has been instrumental and we truly thank them. During the past two years, students provided feedback and support during the many editions of our Flip 'n' Fold. We want them to know how much their feedback was appreciated. Of particular note are the University of North Texas students who worked with us in our movement education pedometer pilot study and provided much feedback with respect to the Flip 'n' Fold, movement activities, and the Kidz: Stephanie Calhoun, Frank Arthurs, Crystal Perez, and Emilie Schmid.

Faculty of special note are Gladys Keeton, Texas Woman's University, who allowed us to film her and provided her creative expertise in the educational dance chapter, and Jim Morrow, University of North Texas, who was instrumental in the development of the pedometer pilot study.

I would like to give a special and wonderful thank you to Jenni. I cannot imagine a better writing and working partner. We have endured many, many hours of agreeing, disagreeing, and learning from each other as we have grown in this process. Thank you, Karen, for always putting our friendship first—a priority that keeps a project like this fun and meaningful!

# Introduction to Movement Education

# History and Philosophy of Movement Education

This first chapter provides a brief, but intense, look at critical moments in the history of, and the intent of, movement education. When did movement education originate? Why was it popular in the 1960s, 1970s, and even into the 1980s? Who should know the movement education framework (MEF)? Why did its popularity fade, and where are we today? Who were the contributors to the beginnings of movement education? Because we offer only a brief historical overview of movement education, we mention only some key people connected with the formulation of this approach.

A critical event in the history of physical education was the implementation of national content standards. In addition to the development of movement education as a delivery method for physical education content, a critical historical event for physical education was the implementation of national content standards. These standards can be linked directly to movement education. The success of any movement education program is rooted in the ability of those who teach it to embody the essence of the movement education philosophy. How a teacher delivers a program based on a movement education philosophy is vital to students' learning. This issue is addressed at the end of this chapter.

## Creators of a New Idea: Movement Education in the 1800s to Early 1900s

The early pioneers of movement education were influenced by the idea of the body being an expression of movement. Three of the most historically influential individuals were Francois Delsarte, Liselott Diem, and Rudolf von Laban.

### Delsarte

One of the first people to articulate ideas of movement was Francois Delsarte, a Frenchman who lived in the 19th century. This era was influenced by Romanticism, which emphasized the notion of expression of thought and emotion. Delsarte developed what he termed applied aesthetics (Brown & Sommer, 1969) and focused his work in the arts, where he contributed critical ideas of connections among the mind, body, and spirit. He also saw movement as a union of time, space, and motion. Delsarte suggested that the combination of movements toward and away from the center of the body was critical to all other movements.

Delsarte believed that expressive movement should relate to the emotion that inspired that

movement. In addition, he introduced the idea of parallelism in movement—the simultaneous motion of two body parts in the same direction and in succession. His nine laws of motion referred to altitude, force, motion, sequence, direction, form, velocity, reaction, and extension. These ideas gave rise to much of what was to come in the field of movement education.

## Liselott Diem

In the mid- to late 1930s, Professor Liselott Diem and her husband, Carl, founded an internationally known college in Germany, Deutsche Sporthochschule Köln, to train teachers in sport and physical education. The college taught a "natural approach to teaching children to move effectively in all kinds of situations" (Brown and Sommer, 1969, p. 62 ). Children were encouraged to explore movement freely in their own way and according to their unique stages of development. The teacher's role was to provide an environment that supported and fostered this focus. The teacher would use simple equipment such as balls, wands, ropes, boxes, and benches to allow children to develop a wide variety of movement responses individually, with partners, or within small groups.

Diem's approach centered on learning to build movement skills and balance. Teachers were encouraged to challenge children by asking questions such as "Who can do this?" and "How can this be done differently?" They would then guide the children toward improving their quality of movement. Diem's focus for older children was more on developing an awareness and analysis of muscular force as well as how to move in time and space.

## Rudolf von Laban

Rudolf von Laban (1879-1958) is considered by most as the true pioneer of movement education. A critical contribution was his theory of movement, focusing specifically on the concept of effort. Laban believed that the body was an instrument of expression and made a distinction between

this expressive movement and movements that serve a purpose in everyday life (functional movement). Expressive movement communicates ideas in dance or other forms of artistic expression. Functional movement has a purpose in addition to helping with the tasks of everyday life, such as sports and games. The four factors of movement that Laban identified (weight, space, time, and flow) became the bedrock of what became known as movement education.

## Development of a Curricular Approach: 1960s, 1970s, and 1980s

Whereas Laban and his colleagues were concerned with the inner attitude of the mover and the function of each movement (Stanley, 1977), those who came after them provided a way of regarding movement and applying this perspective to the teaching of physical education. The intent of those working at this time was to provide a framework that teachers could use to apply these movement concepts broadly in the following three learning domains:

- Cognitive
- Psychomotor
- Affective

The 1960s and 1970s witnessed a growth in the field of movement education. Gilliom (1970), Kirchner (1977), Logsdon and colleagues (1977, 1984), Maulden and Layson (1965), Maulden and Redfern (1969), Russell (1975), Stanley (1977), and many others brought movement education to the forefront of elementary physical education.

## Movement Concepts

Stanley (1977) and Logsdon and colleagues (1984) identified the four major movement concepts as body (representing the instrument of the action), space (where the body is moving), effort (the quality with which the movement is executed), and relationships (the connections that occur as the body moves—with objects, people, and the environment). Logsdon and colleagues (1984) suggested that how much children gain from their physical education learning experience is related to how well the teacher is able to understand, interpret, and implement the movement content. They suggested that the teacher's goal should be to develop enough knowledge about movement to help learners become skilled in executing all aspects of the movement content.

## Fitness Overshadows Movement Education

The fitness boom of the 1970s resulted in a base of research that contributed a solid scientific basis to the study of movement. Movement education was not getting this kind of support and therefore was not met with the same level of enthusiasm in this era. As other curriculum models were introduced that were easier to understand and appealed to the fitness and activity focus of the time, movement education faded from popularity.

## Movement Education: At the Heart of Physical Education

The MEF is clearly not a new idea. As ideas developed, the framework for movement education became more and more complex. Professionals began to disagree about the use or exact meaning of terms. As a result, the concepts of human movement and early presentations of the MEF sometimes became intimidating and difficult to use in practical settings. This may have been one of the reasons movement education lost momentum and was by and large replaced by other curricular frameworks over the years. Critics might say that movement education, which was popular in the 1960s, 1970s, and even into the 1980s, is now passé. One of our objectives is to revive this most basic approach to teaching physical education because we believe that it provides not only the basic framework for physical education, but also the basics all educators—both physical education and classroom teachers—are searching for to provide the foundation for teaching physical education. The framework used in this book is a distillation of former versions of the MEF and a combination of the previous works of many, including but not limited to, the authors cited in this chapter (e.g., Laban, Stanley, Logsdon, Roberton, Gilliom, Maulden).

One of the primary goals of this text is to present a revised MEF that is easy to follow, easy to use, and meaningful for physical educators, classroom educators, and most important, children. We do this by focusing on the movement concepts, movement categories, and particularly, the movement elements, and their application to what we are calling the core content areas:

educational games, educational gymnastics, and educational dance.

It is important for readers of this text to understand how the MEF is tied to current national standards.

Some of the classic outcomes of a movement education program are described in the first two National Association for Sport and Physical Education (NASPE, a subspecialty group of the American Alliance for Health, Physical Education, Recreation and Dance [AAHPERD]) standards (2004):

- Standard 1. Demonstrates competency in motor skills and movement patterns needed to perform a variety of physical activities.
- Standard 2. Demonstrates understanding of movement concepts, principles, strategies, and tactics as they apply to the learning and performance of physical activities.

From NASPE, 2004, *Moving into the future: National standards for physical education*, 2nd ed. (Reston, VA: National Association for Sport and Pysical Education) 11.

## The Philosophy That Makes Movement Education Different

All physical educators want to provide lessons that foster success. The MEF, however, focuses on not only fostering motor success, but also developing cognitive knowledge about movement. Movement education is about developing a very wide base so that students develop skill in executing many types of movement. To establish this wide base, the movement education approach uses a specific framework for classifying movement and encourages learners to build a movement vocabulary that they can apply to all subsequent movement content.

The MEF is adaptable to students of all ages and developmental stages. It serves as a thread that runs through all movement in all situations. As Logsdon and Barrett (1984) noted, "Movement is the content of physical education" (Logsdon et al., p. 141). Teachers can continually incorporate vocabulary from the framework into lesson introductions, feedback during a lesson, and

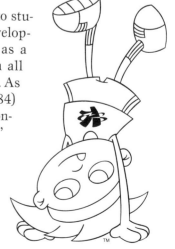

lesson closures. Similarly, children can communicate with the teacher and with other children about their movement, thus creating a wonderful learning environment for all.

## Student Problem Solving in Movement Education

Success for all, activity for all, and contributions by all are all key values in a movement education program. Specific approaches in presenting content are critical. Using methodology based on the process of discovery and techniques of problem solving (Gilliom, 1970) allows children to discover their own methods and ways of solving movement problems. Creative thinking is required, and individual solutions, which may be unique to the problem solver, are not only allowed but also encouraged because we all experience new and often more complex movement challenges throughout life. Children in movement education programs do much more than merely learn skills; they learn to apply movement elements and create solutions to both simple and complex movement problems.

## Guided Problem Solving in Movement Education

We address some guided discovery methods in the core content chapters of this book (11-13). According to Mosston and Ashworth (1986), the guided discovery approach involves students solving teacher-created problems with guidance from the teacher. In addition to guided discovery, teachers also provide students with learning cues. Chapter 3 provides examples of the teacher-directed cues for learning locomotor skills such as skipping, hopping, and jumping, as well as manipulative skills such as throwing and catching.

Problem-solving techniques were expounded upon by Gillion (1970). An example of putting teaching cues and problem solving together might sound like this: "Today, we are going to learn about the springlike actions of leaping, hopping, skipping, jumping, and galloping." You might then present the learning cues via pocket chart cards (movement element definitions) for each of these skills. After formally presenting the definition of hopping, you can then informally remind the students that when we hop, we travel from one foot to the same foot, whereas jumping involves several

different types of movement patterns. With these cues in mind, students may then be encouraged to demonstrate the various springlike actions by creating a traveling sequence using those actions. This task emphasizes a pure problem-solving approach.

## Providing Choices Enhances Learning

The way you present the movement challenge or task can foster success by respecting students' individuality. One way to present a challenge is to provide extensions, making the task either easier or harder as needed. Following is an example of how you might use extensions with movement education.

A more traditional approach to presenting a movement problem related to rocking and rolling might be to ask all children to do a forward roll. However, using extensions, you might say, "Some of you may wish to try this next task, whereas others may choose to continue working on log rolls. For those who would like to try, think about rolling in a forward direction, keeping your chin tucked to your chest and pushing with your hands to help you transfer your weight onto the back of your shoulders as you complete rolling in a forward direction." Other ways to offer extensions could be, "If you are ready, you can try . . ." or,

"For those of you who would like to try a more difficult task . . . ." Giving students options in all situations helps them decide their comfort level in task completion (Logsdon et al., 1984; Rink, 2006).

## Summary

The earliest inklings of movement education occurred in the late 1800s in the field of dance. The concept really didn't gain popularity and become known as movement education until the 1960s, 1970s, and into the 1980s. The fitness boom and other curriculum models replaced movement education, possibly as a result of its complexity and the difficulty teachers had making it relevant to middle and high school physical education curricula. In the late 1990s and early 2000s, the development of national content standards for physical education brought back the essence of movement education by emphasizing that children should know basic movement concepts and be able to perform basic movement patterns.

# Movement Education Framework Content

Every academic content area has fundamentals on which most concepts are built. Reading and writing begin with learning the alphabet. Mathematics begins with learning numbers. Most people, however, would probably have a hard time identifying the fundamentals of physical education content. So, where do we begin to identify the fundamentals of physical education, and why is it important for children to become competent with these fundamentals? The intent of this book is to make this foundational content information in physical education easy to understand, meaningful, and practical to implement. We begin by identifying the four basic movement concepts and their associated movement elements, which form the type of foundation in physical education that the ABCs do in literacy and the "1, 2, 3s" do in mathematics.

Addressing all movement terms and all of the possible movement forms in the movement education framework (MEF) would be exhaustive and impractical. Thus, we include movement terms that are regularly used in physical education. Movement terms that broaden the understanding of movement and allow users of the framework to eventually advance to higher levels of movement analysis (e.g., biomechanics, motor development, and exercise physiology) have been taken into consideration in developing the framework presented here.

## Roots of Movement Education

We use the roots of a tree in this section as an analogy for the most basic concepts in movement education. Figure 2.1 is a visually appealing aid that will help you use this analogy to explain the movement education framework. The tree is also a simple visual aid to which young children can relate.

The movement concept tree is easy to understand. It helps to classify the movement elements and answer the following questions on basic movement concepts:

- What do we move?
- Where do we move?
- How do we move?
- What are the connections with whom or what we move?

To move, we need something to move—our bodies. We need a place to move—space. We need energy to move—effort. And we often move in connection with other people, things, and ideas—that is, in relationships. These four concepts (body, space, effort, and relationships) are the essence of the movement education framework and are represented in figure 2.1 by four roots that serve as the basis from which all other functioning parts of the tree are formed.

Basically, the movement concepts begin with the body, which is the tool of movement. To move, we must have a means of moving. The body, its parts, and its most basic, or fundamental, movements are the foundation of this framework: it is the center taproot of the tree, which is the most important. So, now that there is something to move with, the body needs to go somewhere, or be able to use the space for movement. How one moves in this space is the movement concept of effort. The space and effort roots surround the center taproot, creating more stability for the tree to grow taller and begin to expand in breadth. This analogy helps children broaden their body concept knowledge and experience as they grow taller—just like a tree. From the addition of space and effort children can perform many more variations of the fundamental movements.

The most complex of the movement concepts is relationships, and so it is presented as the top tree root, closest to the surface. For a tree, this layer is a very broad and complex network that provides nourishment, increased stability, and hydration; it is critical to the tree's long-term survival and expansion. In the same way, movement relationships provide the best opportunity to build long-term movement capabilities that can affect our physical, emotional, and cognitive health (i.e., long-term survival).

Similar to the wandering of the root system in the ground, the progression of the movement concepts is not purely linear. The various layers of the root systems are actually developing at the same time, with each system depending on the development of others. The movement concepts develop best when presented simultaneously; however, using a logical progression that is rooted in motor development optimizes the process. Plenty of overlap occurs as you review movement concepts and create challenges at higher levels of complexity. However, the basic idea of the tree roots creating a foundation is simple and easy to remember, making it a good introduction to the organization of movement concepts.

## Organizing the Movement Education Framework

In the past, teachers have had difficulty understanding the movement education framework. The complexity of previous presentations was overwhelming. To avoid this, we simplify the information, create logical associations, provide clear examples, and build a practical understanding. We use a consistent set of terms for each of the four movement concepts, which are also coded by letter and number to help you stay organized. In addition to providing descriptions and examples of the movement education terms in this chapter, we include definitions in both Spanish and English

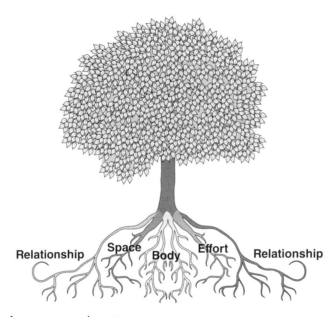

**Figure 2.1**  The roots of movement education.

in the glossary at the end of this book (indicated by words in bold).

Our organizational structure helps you mentally organize the material, communicate it orally, and visually present it. New to this presentation and organization of the movement education frame-work are three basic terms, which are presented in table 2.1: movement concept, movement category, and movement element. Although these terms do not match exactly the previous descriptions of the movement education framework, they link nicely with the terms NASPE uses in its national

**Table 2.1**  Movement Education Framework

| Concepts | Categories and subcategories | | Movement elements |
|---|---|---|---|
| Body | Body parts | | Head, neck, ears, eyes, nose, mouth, shoulders, elbows, wrists, hands, fingers, belly, chest, spine, back, bottom, hips, knees, ankles, feet, and toes |
| | Body shapes | | Narrow, wide, round, twisted*, symmetrical, and asymmetrical |
| | Actions of body parts | | Weight bearing, receive force or weight, apply force, lead the action, and weight transfer |
| | Actions of the whole body | Nonlocomotor | Stretch, curl, twist*, turn, spin, swing, push, pull, rise, sink, gesture, dodge, balance, counterbalance, and countertension |
| | | Locomotor | Walk, cartwheel, crawl, bear walk, crab walk, run, leap, hop, skip, jump, gallop, slide, rock, and roll** |
| | | Manipulative | Throw, roll**, strike, kick, volley, catch, trap, dribble, and carry |
| Space | Location | | Self-space and general space |
| | Direction | | Forward, backward, sideways, up, down, clockwise, and counterclockwise |
| | Level | | Low, medium, high |
| | Pathway | | Straight, curved, and zigzag |
| | Plane | | Sagittal, frontal, and transverse |
| | Extension | | Small and large |
| Effort | Time | | Fast, slow, and acceleration |
| | Force | | Hard and soft |
| | Flow | | Bound and free |
| | Focus | | Direct and indirect |
| Relationship | People | | Solo, alone in a mass, partners, even groups, uneven groups, individual to group, group to group, triangle, circle, square, scattered, spokes of a wheel, and X |
| | Position | | Above/below, over/under, inverted, mount/dismount, in front of/behind, beside, alongside, through, surround, around, support/supported, lift/lifted, meet/part, and near to/far from |
| | Timing | Simultaneous | Mirror, match, contrast, and unison |
| | | Alternate | Take turns |
| | | Successive | Movement sequence, canon, question/answer, act/react, and lead/follow |
| | Goal | | Cooperative, collaborative, and competitive |
| | Environment | | Static and dynamic |

*Twist(ed) appears correctly twice; as a nonlocomotor primary body movement (B15) and then again as a body shape (B5).
**Roll appears correctly twice; as a manipulative sending an object away (B43) and as a locomotor roll-like action (B41).

standards and help to add a consistent and more detailed structure to the movement language.

## Movement Concepts

It is important to recognize how the language of movement education ties into the national standards for physical education. The word *concept* is the primary term used by NASPE (2004) in standard 2. The movement education framework speaks directly to standard 2 because it addresses the movement concepts. The term *movement concept* is the most general of the organizational terms used in this book and in NASPE standard 2. In this case, they refer to body, space, effort, and relationships. *Movement concept* collectively refers to all of the movement elements.

## Movement Categories

The term *category* is used within a concept to create smaller groupings of similar terms (e.g., actions of the whole body). When needed, the categories are organized into smaller groups called subcategories (e.g., locomotor) and, even smaller, subdivisions (e.g., springlike actions).

## Movement Elements

Our intention is to show how the NASPE standards relate to the movement education framework. The movement elements in the category actions of the whole body (nonlocomotor, locomotor, and manipulative) are what NASPE describes as motor skills in standard 1. Movement patterns, also a main part of NASPE standard 1, are easily identified as the subdivisions within actions of the whole body (e.g., send away). NASPE standard 2 encompasses all 121 movement elements (e.g., run forward, bound, mirror, and so on) via the phrase "demonstrates understanding of movement concepts."

## Movement Education Framework: The Body Concept

Learning about the body may be the most basic and important of all the movement concepts. The body is the instrument of movement that gives meaning to the other concepts (e.g., space, effort, and relationships). The **body concept** (B) focuses on the entire body or its parts. It has four categories: body parts, body shapes, actions of body parts, and actions of the whole body.

## Body Parts

In the coding system for the MEF, and for the sake of simplicity, the entire category of **body parts** (B1) is numbered instead of each body part. The body parts category include common body segments and joints including the head, neck, ears, eyes, nose, mouth, shoulders, elbows, wrists, hands, fingers, belly, chest, spine, back, bottom, hips, knees, ankles, feet, and toes.

## Body Shapes

The second category is body shapes, which form silhouettes, or outlines, of the body in space. There are six body shapes: **narrow** (pin; B2), **wide** (wall; B3), **round** (ball; B4), **twisted** (screw; B5), **symmetrical** (same; B6), and **asymmetrical** (different; B7). The words inside the parentheses following the names of the shapes offer other descriptors that some children might understand more readily.

## Actions of Body Parts

Actions of body parts is the third category and includes the kinds of roles a body segment can play in a movement. The movement elements of **weight bearing** (B8), **receive force** (or weight) (B9), **apply force** (B10), **lead the action** (B11), and **weight transfer** (B12) complete the actions of body parts category.

Although the action of the entire body is considered in the next category, the intent of the actions of body parts category is more specific. For example, the base of support for weight bearing could be two feet (typical standing), two hands (handstand), one hand and two feet (offensive lineman position), the head (headstand), or even the buttocks (V-sit).

The hands receive force when a ball is caught in them or when a barbell is lifted. The back of the shoulders may receive force from someone using a hand to tag them (e.g., when playing Tag). A foot applies force to a starting block or to the ground when walking.

The hands are the point of force application when swinging a bat. The hands might lead the action when stretching them toward the water during a dive into a swimming pool. The feet might lead the action while coming down into the pool from a dive. The head might lead the action when turning first for a dancer or ice skater performing a spinning action.

Weight transfer involves moving the focus of weight from one body part to another body part or shifting weight from one foot to the other foot while walking. Changing from a crab walk to a cross-legged sit would move the weight from both hands and both feet to the legs and buttocks.

## Actions of the Whole Body

The final category for the body concept is actions of the whole body, which are movements or activities performed by the entire person. Actions of the whole body is a very complex category, having three subcategories: nonlocomotor, locomotor, and manipulative skills. These three subcategories form the fundamental movements ("movement skills and movement patterns" in NASPE standard 1, 2004) that are critical to motor development.

### Nonlocomotor Skills

The nonlocomotor skills are executed on a fixed base of support, and include 15 movement elements. The first three elements (stretch, curl, and twist) are the primary body movements from which all of other movements can be made.

- A **stretch** (B13) extends or lengthens the body. A swimmer stretches to touch the wall at the end of a race.
- A **curl** (B14) involves some type of flexion or bending at the joints. Bringing the hand in to scratch the nose requires the person to bend the elbow.
- A **twist** (B15) is not the same as a turn or spin. In a twisting action, one end of the body is fixed or turns in the opposite direction of the other part of the body. The dance called

the Twist, done to a Chubby Checker song, is a great example of this nonlocomotor skill. Sitting at a school desk and reaching to take a piece of paper from the person at the desk behind is another example of a twist.

Some more common nonlocomotor elements are as follows.

- A **turn** (B16) can be clearly identified when the base of support for the person shifts to face a new direction (in a twist, the base of support is stationary). For example, the feet may face the north wall, and after turning, they may now be facing the east wall, along with the torso.
- In a **spin** (B17) the entire person moves like a toy top around a central axis. Consider an ice figure skater rotating on one foot.
- A **swing** (B18) also has rotation, but the rotation occurs only at one end of the body, which is fixed. The other end moves freely. A gymnast on the high bar with the hands fixed at one end but the extended body moving freely around the bar is performing a maneuver called a giant swing. A more common example is the arms swinging back and forth along the sides (fixed at the shoulder and free at the hand).
- A **push** (B19) and a **pull** (B20) are opposites; a push involves exerting force away from the body, whereas a pull works to bring the resistance toward the body. The body, at the hands, is technically pushing the floor away in a push-up, and the hands are attempting to pull the stationary pull-up bar closer to the body.
- **Rise** (B21) and **sink** (B22) are also opposites: elevating the body, or moving up toward the ceiling (rise) versus lowering the body, or moving down toward the floor (sink).
- **Gesture** (B23) can refer to a feeling or mood expression using movement as well as to a movement made when attempting to maintain balance. A thumbs-up is usually thought of as a gesture to indicate something positive, but this hand movement is not the intent of the word *gesture* in the movement framework. Rather, flailing the arms while trying to maintain balance on a narrow surface is a better description of gesturing.

- A **dodge** (B24), when viewed as a nonlocomotor movement, refers to the shifting of the body to avoid something, such as avoiding an approaching ball. Alternatively, if the focus is on the foot movement needed for moving the body, a dodge might be considered a locomotor skill (e.g., avoiding being tackled while on the run).
- **Balance** (B25) is being able to keep all forces affecting the body equal (maintaining equilibrium). In a practical way, this often means keeping the center of gravity or body weight within the base of support. Having a strong core and maintaining strong muscle tension assists with creating and holding a balanced position. Remaining in a headstand position or remaining still while standing in a moving bus illustrates balance. Maintaining body balance is very important and often a prerequisite to developing skill with the limbs (e.g., legs for locomotor skills and arms for manipulative skills).
- **Counterbalance** (B26) is a specific aspect of balance that requires all of the elements to be actively participating in the creation of a stable condition (e.g., two people placing palms together and leaning into each other).
- **Countertension** (B27) is simply reversing the direction of the force application (e.g., two people holding hands and leaning away from each other).

## Locomotor Skills

The locomotor movements are those that move the body from one place to another. This subcategory has additional subdivisions (Logsdon et al., 1984). Steplike actions is the first subdivision, and these movements do not have flight; in other words, one body part is always in contact with the supporting surface. Commonly taught elements include:

- the **walk** (B28), an alternate stepping action with arm–leg opposition in the sagittal plane;
- the **cartwheel** (B29), the alternation of hand-hand and foot-foot in the frontal plane;
- the **crawl** (or climb; B30), alternating right- and left-side ipsilateral arm–leg movements;
- the **bear walk** (B31), walking on hands and feet with the belly facing the ground; and
- the **crab walk** (B32), walking on hands and feet with buttocks facing the ground.

Springlike actions include the aspect of flight (a momentary time in which there is no contact with the supporting surface). Commonly taught elements include:

- a **run** (B33), steps (alternating right, left, right, left, and so on) with arm–leg opposition at a fast pace;
- a **leap** (B34), an elongated run (longer flight time);
- a **hop** (B35), involves a one-foot takeoff and a landing on the same foot;
- a **skip** (B36), alternates step–hop combinations;
- a **jump** (B37), involves a two-foot takeoff and two-foot landing, a two-foot takeoff and a one-foot landing, or a one-foot takeoff and a one-foot landing;
- a **gallop** (B38), moving forward using a continuous pattern of stepping with the lead foot followed by bringing the rear foot up next to the lead foot; and
- a **slide** (B39), moving sideways using a continuous pattern of bringing the rear foot up beside the lead foot.

Greater technical detail of these springlike skills is presented in the chapter on motor development, chapter 3.

**Roll-like actions** are similar to steplike actions in that the body maintains its contact with the supporting surface; however, these actions involve a sequential pattern of adjacent body parts coming in contact with the surface such as in a **rock** (B40) and a **roll** (B41). Because the transfer of weight in rocking is back and forth and doesn't result in much change in location, some do not consider it a locomotor skill, but rather, a nonlocomotor skill. The roll involves various adjacent body parts coming into contact with the supporting surface (e.g., hands, head, shoulders, back, and feet in a forward roll) and does move the person to a different place. The use of the body (not an object) along the supporting surface defines the use of the term *roll* in this subdivision, in contrast to rolling an object (e.g., a ball) in the manipulative subcategory.

## Manipulative Skills

Manipulative skills, also known as object control skills, are actions that involve controlling an object or piece of equipment such as a ball, bat, or racket. The following skills are in the subdivision of sending objects away.

- A **throw** (B42) is the use of the hand to release an object, sending it into the air.
- A **roll** (e.g., a bowling ball; B43) is different from throwing in that the object is made to move across the supporting surface rather than through the air. The term *rolling* in the manipulative category indicates that an object, other than the body, is being used. For example, a child may roll a ball toward a pin or set of pins to knock them down. In the locomotor category, the person uses the body to roll across the surface instead of directing something such as a ball to roll across a surface.
- A **strike** (B44) involves forceful contact, often a collision between an implement and a ball.
- Although a **kick** (B45) can also be a strike, we classify it as a kick because it is done with the foot. Similar to a throw, a kick uses the foot to make an object fly through the air.
- The **volley** (B46) involves making contact with an airborne object where the intent is to direct the object with accuracy and a light touch. For example, a tennis volley at the net needs a soft touch and accurate placing. The setter in volleyball needs to have a soft touch to redirect the ball accurately so that the hitter can get an effective spike.

The following skills are in the subdivision of gaining control of an object.

- A **catch** (B47) involves a grasp of one object, whereas collecting involves gaining control of an object moving along the ground to redirect it. (Collecting is not on the Flip 'n' Fold, but because some people use it, we include it here as additional information.) Both catching and collecting suggest reducing the speed of the object by bringing it in toward the body (Logsdon et al., 1984, p. 130). For example, gaining control of a soccer ball to redirect its path would be an example of collecting.
- A **trap** (B48) is similar to a catch except that it involves holding the ball between two things (one inanimate), such as trapping a soccer ball between the knee and the ground.

The last subdivision is propelling an object, or keeping an object under control while traveling with it, which includes the following skills.

- A **dribble** (B49) occurs when traveling with an object that is repeatedly contacted by hands or feet. For example, dribbling a basketball with the hand or dribbling a soccer ball with the feet.
- A **carry** (B50) occurs when traveling with an object held in the hands. When rugby or American football players hold the ball against the body with an arm while running toward the goal, they are said to be carrying.

# Movement Education Framework: The Space Concept

Learning about space will help children become efficient movers. For example, learning to dribble at a low level is important to successful performance as a basketball guard. The space concept focuses on where the body moves. It has six categories: location, direction, level, pathway, plane, and extension.

## Location

Generally, the location (or area) of where the movement occurs is described as either **self-space** (S1) or **general space** (S2). Self-space—also called personal space or, Laban's coined term, the kinesphere—is defined by the three planes and refers to the personal bubble that surrounds and moves with the performer. In contrast, general space is all of the area available for movement such as the gymnasium, the boundaries of a court or field, or the dance floor. Self-space is located within general space.

## Direction

Common directional movement elements include **forward** (S3), or moving toward the direction one is facing, and **backward** (S4), or moving in the direction the back of the body is facing. Sliding to the right or left, as in stepping to the side to receive a volleyball serve, are also general space examples of **sideways** (S5) movements of the whole body. Moving toward the ceiling or sky is **up** (S6) and moving toward the floor or ground is **down** (S7).

Finally, one can move in a **clockwise** (S8) or **counterclockwise** (S9) circle as a member of a group participating in parachute activities within the general space.

## Level

Levels are a description of how high or low the movement occurs. Near the floor or below the knees is typical of a **low** movement (S10), whereas a **high** movement (S12) takes the performer into the air or includes movements above the shoulders. **Medium**-level movements (S11) are those that are generally between the low and high levels or at the height of the trunk. Doing a bear walk is a low-level movement, doing a defensive slide across the floor is a medium-level movement, and jumping high into the air or stretching high are examples of high-level movements.

## Pathway and Extension

Pathway is typically an invisible pattern or tracing of the movement of the body through space that can occur in either the air or water or on a solid surface (e.g., a floor). The following are basic pathway elements.

- A **straight** (S13) pathway means to move in a direct line. For example, a 50-meter sprint occurs in a straight pathway if the runners or swimmers are in lanes on a track (solid surface) or in a pool (in the water). An arrow flies through the air in a straight line toward the target.
- A **curved** (S14) pathway moves in an arch or semicircle. An arrow can also fly through the air in a curved pathway if it is shot upward and must arc down toward the target. A cross country runner often follows a curvy pathway on the ground if the pathway has been set up on a golf course.
- A **zigzag** (S15) pathway moves in a crisscross manner. A zigzag path is sometimes used as part of an offense plan for an American football receiver running on the football field. Dodging, as in a tag type of activity, also uses zigzag pathways.

## Planes

As children become more skilled and the teacher is able to provide more challenges to the students, the application and progresion of planes knowledge should be included in the lessons. The inclusion of planes in chapters 11, 12, and 13 will provide examples of how and why planes might be used in a lesson or unit.

In the lower stages of development (see chapter 3), the use of planes is applied during the presentation of movement concepts. Teaching children the ideas and language of planes will help them learn how to analyze movements, how to communicate with others in a technically correct manner about movement, and how to better receive instructions, feedback, and information regarding movement which generally increases the speed and accuracy of learning and doing movement. All of this may lead to increased movement competency, identified by Stodden and colleagues (2009) as a critical factor in motivating adults to have an active lifestyle.

At the higher levels of core content learning, children need to be able to combine a variety of movement elements in order to be successful. For example, in educational gymnastics, children need to begin to understand why and when moving in a certain plane will enhance balance on a balance board. In educational dance, knowing that a dance movement (e.g., spinning) can be done faster if performed more purely in the transverse plane helps the dancer make a better choice of how to do the spin. Finally, in educational games, a hockey player might improve their defense by using an intercepting posture that occurs in the frontal plane.

An understanding of self-space is the prerequisite for understanding planes. The ideas of spatial planes are too complex for children operating at the initial developmental skill level (see chapter 3) where self-space should be introduced instead. However, it is very useful to begin teaching the planes concept as children are beginning to develop their fundamental motor skills and an understanding of these skills. If the child can understand phrases like "pump with your arms," "swing level," and "explode with your legs," then phrases like "keep your arms in the sagittal plane," "swing your bat in the transverse plane," or "jump straight up in the frontal plane" will provide meaningful feedback to the child. The time to begin teaching about the planes should be about the same time that a child starts to perform locomotor and manipulative skills with some consistency at the elementary level (explained in chapter 3). Children can then incorporate this kind of verbal feedback into their understanding and performance of the fundamental motor skills.

The name of the plane (e.g., sagittal) and the term *plane* have different meanings. While *sagittal* describes the actual area of the space, *plane* is a geometry term meaning a flat or level surface. This flat surface is what is used to divide the area of the self-space. Some visualize the plane as a rectangular piece of glass that slices through the body, separating it into two sections. Others view it like a hard square of cheese sandwiched between two slices of bread, separating the two pieces of bread. The three plane names (sagittal, frontal, and transverse) are used to help people communicate about areas of self-space. The idea of planes is also helpful in describing more specifically where or how a person is moving within self-space, such as joint movements (flexion).

Because many teachers of elementary physical education do not have a clear understanding of the three planes, we provide the following definitions and examples. A helpful three-dimensional model, cleverly called Plane Jane, makes for a good learning tool. This model shows each of the planes dividing the body as well as upper limb movements in each of the planes (see appendix C for information on how to obtain this model from www.denoyer.com).

- Sagittal
- Frontal (also known as coronal)
- Transverse (also known as horizontal)

## Sagittal Plane

The **sagittal plane** (S16) divides the body into right and left sides with the plane sandwiched between them. All sagittal plane movements occur in one or both of these two sides of the body with the movement being parallel to the pane of glass that is sandwiched in the middle. For example, someone pretending to saw a piece of wood that is in front of him using a handsaw or swinging his arms forward and backward in opposition to his legs when running is moving in the sagittal plane. When the elbow extends during a basketball free throw shot, the forearm is moving parallel to the piece of glass that is sandwiched between the right and left sides, or through the sagittal plane.

A less technical and more familiar term, *wheel*, might good to use to introduce the sagittal plane to children. Most children can visualize a wheel turning around its axis and make the connection of how a wheel rolling across the ground is similar to them doing a forward roll across the ground (both the right and left halves of the body are moving through the plane).

The front and back movements in the sagittal plane are called flexion (bend) and extension (stretch). Table 2.2 on page 18 provides additional practical examples for each of the core physical education content areas to assist you in giving students helpful verbal cues. More detail on anatomical planes can be found in the beginning of almost any basic biomechanics textbook.

## Frontal Plane

The **frontal plane** (also known as the coronal plane; S17) divides the body into front and back sections with the plane being sandwiched between them. As presented in table 2.2, a person doing a cartwheel or a jumping jack moves her limbs parallel to the piece of glass that is sandwiched between the front and back of the body. These sideways movements are called abduction (out, or away from the middle) and adduction (in, or toward the middle). A more familiar term that might be used to make this idea less abstract is *door*. To illustrate this plane, have a child stand inside a door jamb and tell him that he cannot move any part of his body in front of or behind the door jamb. Students will soon discover the frontal plane movements and have a phrase that they can relate to easily to describe them: door plane movements.

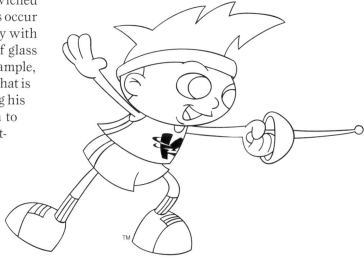

**Table 2.2** Examples of Movements in the Planes for Core Content Areas

| Plane | Core content area: Educational | | | | | |
| --- | --- | --- | --- | --- | --- | --- |
| | Games | | Dance | | Gymnastics | |
| | Skill | Teaching cue | Skill | Teaching cue | Skill | Teaching cue |
| Sagittal—Forward and backward movements | Shooting a free throw | "Parallel to the plane is the name of the game" | Bow to your partner | "Simple sagittal style" | Forward roll | "Sagittal roll like a car wheel (in the 'wheel' plane)" |
| Frontal—Sideways movements | Defensive slide | "Glide to the side" | Slide step | "Squeeze mouselike past people seated in a movie theater" | Cartwheel | "Pretend you are doing a cartwheel within a door jamb (in the 'door' plane)" |
| Transverse—Turning and twisting movements | Swing of a baseball bat | "Hit the ball off the top of the table (in the 'table' plane)" | Spin on the ball of the foot | "Be a turntable (in the 'table' plane)" | Log roll | "Keep in tight for twisting right" |

## Transverse Plane

The **transverse plane** (also known as the horizontal plane; S18) divides the body into top and bottom sections with the plane being sandwiched between them. In a coffee-grinder stunt, the leg that circles under the body moves parallel to the pane of glass sandwiched between the top and bottom sections of the person, or in the transverse plane. Movements in the transverse plane are called inward and outward rotation (clockwise or counterclockwise). Additional movements in this plane are beyond the scope of this book, but are described in any biomechanics text.

A discussion of a magic show in which the magician puts someone in a box and separates the box (top and bottom half) may be a fun way to help children understand this plane. You may also call it the table plane and have a child stand in front of a table so she can clearly see that part of her body is above the table and part is below the table. You can then ask her to move her body or body parts across the top of the table. Movements such as trunk twisting and shaking the head to

indicate *no* are simple examples that illustrate the table, or transverse, plane.

## Extensions

The extensions category describes the range or size of the movements in space relative to the body: **small** (near the body; S19) or **large** (far from the body; S20). Stretching an arm away from the body is a large (far) extension, whereas using the hand near or on the hip is a small, or near, extension. Extensions are often discussed when teaching racket sports and activities.

## Movement Education Framework: The Effort Concept

While utilizing space concepts provides more efficient movement, appropriate effort application yields more effective movement. For example, a child who uses the correct amount of tension (hard-soft) will be more likely to hit their target rather than under- or overthrowing it. The effort concept describes the quality of movement. It has four categories, time, force, flow, and focus.

## Time

The time category addresses how fast the movement is, or its rate. **Fast** (sudden; E1), **slow** (sustained; E2), and **acceleration** (change of pace; E3) are the time elements. Running is a fast movement, whereas walking is slow in comparison. Changing from a walk to a run involves acceleration, and similarly, changing from a run to a walk is also acceleration. *Deceleration* is a lay term that is sometimes used in place of the more accurate term, *negative acceleration* (i.e., a decrease in speed).

## Force

The force category addresses how much tension there is in the movement: **hard** (strong; E4) and **soft** (light; E5). Striking a balloon lightly uses very little force, whereas striking a balloon really hard might make it pop!

## Flow

The flow category addresses how continuous or fluid the movement is. **Bound** (stoppable; E6) and **free** (ongoing; E7) are the two elements of flow. A child running all over the playground without a specific objective shows freely flowing activity. Moving like an elephant (strong, powerful movements that are choppy and heavy) is an example of a bound movement.

## Focus

The category of how effort is used in space has been called space (Laban & Ullmann, 1971; Logsdon et al., 1977; Stanley, 1977). However, because using the word *space* as both a category term and a movement concept term could be confusing, we use *focus* as the category term in the effort concept. There are two focus category movement elements: direct and indirect.

**Direct** (E8) force is energy that is very focused and penetrating. A sprinter in a race and children learning how to run a track event are examples of direct force because the energy is channeled to a single point. Indirect force is not very focused. Force that is directed in a line is more focused than force that moves in a wavy or flexible manner (indirect).

Another way to describe the two elements of focus is to describe movement that comes together to a point versus movement that spreads out, or expands. Dancers often exhibit indirect focus (or energy) as they travel in curved or wavy pathways. Children running out onto the playground at recess often have an **indirect** (E9) focus as they scatter to all parts of the area; when they run back toward the building to find a single place in line at the end of recess, they are moving more directly. A clean dive into a pool causing little splash exhibits direct energy; whereas a belly flop exhibits indirect energy.

# Movement Education Framework: The Relationships Concept

The focus of the relationships movement concept should be on the types of connections that can occur when moving. Thus, the "who" or "what" of a movement is secondary to the connections between and among the movers or objects in this concept. Common things that have these connections are body parts, individuals, groups, rules of how to move or play, objects, boundaries, equipment, and aspects of the various arts (e.g., writing, music, pictures, lighting, and nature). The following five categories of the relationships concept provide cohesion of the material presented in this concept:

- People
- Position
- Timing
- Goal
- Environment

These categories describe and emphasize the types of connections between and among the "who" and the "what" of movement.

## People

People is the first relationships category and describes a variety of ways students can be organized to relate (or not relate) to one another. The following are the most basic categories of people.

- **Solo** (R1) refers to a child working by himself in a demonstration or performance capacity. Children in an elementary physical education setting might work solo when they are demonstrating a skill or performing a creative dance sequence.

- **Alone in a mass** (R2) refers to a child moving independently in her own personal space among other children who are often also working independently.
- **Partners** (R3), **even groups** (R4), and **uneven groups** (R5) are important organizational tools. It is critical at the beginning of the academic year for children to learn how to find and work with a partner or one other child. The activity or task dictates whether even or uneven groups are necessary. Rather than pairing children by having them count off "1" and "2," you can ask them to find partners with whom they think they can work well. There are many other creative ways to form groups that are quick and encourage inclusion and the expansion of social skills. At least 40 examples can be found at mrgspepage.tripod.com. The same type of phrase can be used for forming small even or uneven groups. You should give children a limited amount of time in which to find partners or create small groups.
- **Individual to group** (R6) is an arrangement in which one person relates to a group of others. In a game of Tag, one person works toward a goal that is the opposite of that of the group (e.g., trying to make someone else "It"). **Group to group** (R7) is what we commonly think of as team sport (e.g., one basketball team playing against another).

Formations are used within the people category to implement a wide variety of activities in physical education. The following are common geometric shapes that are used to quickly assemble people in helpful arrangements.

- Sport skills are practiced using **triangle** (R8) formations such as a fungo hitter sending fly balls to fielders who throw the ball back to a catcher who underhand tosses the ball back to the hitter to repeat the sequence.
- Students might form a **circle** (R9) when working on directions, levels, and force with a parachute activity.
- A **square** (R10) is often used in square dancing.

- Little children **scatter** (R11) throughout the general space to work in their personal bubbles when volleying a balloon for the first time (working individually).
- **Spokes of a wheel** (R12), or children forming lines radiating out from a center point, is a formation used in dance and synchronized swimming.
- Finally, an **X** formation (R13) is two lines that cross in the middle instead of being parallel to each other. This is used in doing some sport skill drills such lay-ups, in which one line shoots and the other rebounds and they cross over at the hoop.

## Position

A variety of positional relationships are often in opposite pairs. Some of these relationship terms are very similar, differing only in whether people are moving or stationary. The following elements come from the category of position.

- **Above/below** (still; R14) refers to being on top or beneath. A child may put his hand above the head of another child or place his hand below another child. He might sit below a piece of playground equipment or climb above where other children are sitting.
- **Over/under** (moving; R15) also suggests on top of or beneath, but the person is not stationary. Students working on passing an object from one person to another might pass the object over their heads or between (under) their legs.
- **Inverted** (R16) is upside down or having the head below other body parts. This can be demonstrated when working on gymnastics tasks by asking children to think of how they can place their heads below other body parts such as their hips. A tripod as well as a lead-up to a tripod (knee to elbow) is an example of inverted.
- **Mount/dismount** (R17) suggests getting onto or off of an object such as a bench or beam. Children can problem solve how to mount a bench. Which body part would they like to use? In dismounting, do they want to dismount with a jump, a step, or a turn?
- The elements **in front of/behind** (R18) are very important, particularly in educa-

tional games. For example, understanding the positional relationships of sending an object ahead of a team member (in front of) to achieve a successful pass is beneficial for scoring in a game.

- **Beside** (R19) and **alongside** (R20) are very similar elements. Beside is generally near the side of another person (e.g., classmates spread out across the gym floor doing aerobic dance). Alongside would be very close to, or right next to, a partner as in a dance that requires them to hold hands. Using these elements correctly will help children understand the intent as well as the meaning of each element.

- **Through** (R21) suggests moving from one side of a barrier or plane to the other side, such as moving through a hula hoop that a partner is holding. You may ask students, "How many ways can you think of to move through the hoop?" Asking children at the mature or transitional stage to identify the plane within which they are working while teaching the movement element *through* would be beneficial.

- Children who are having fun with a parachute would be asked to **surround** (R22) the parachute and then place their hands in an overhand grip as they prepare to lift the parachute to various levels.

- As children are moving in a clockwise or counterclockwise motion with the parachute, they are moving **around** (R23) in a circular motion (which is different from surround).

- **Support** (R24) is a term that describes the person or object that is holding something up, whereas **supported** (still) is the one who is being held. For example, when doing a cheerleading pyramid, the bottom row of cheerleaders provide the support to those in the top row (who are supported). Any other kind of human pyramid done in an educational gymnastics unit is a good demonstration of the nonmoving aspects of support versus supported.

- **Lift** and **lifted** (R25) are very similar to support/supported; however, lift indicates the action of moving the person or object up. Therefore, lifting a dumbbell or lifting one's own arm is a dynamic movement element. Lifted describes the person or object that is being moved: the arm or the dumbbell is lifted.

- **Meet** (R26) describes two square dancers coming forward to bow to each other, and **part** describes the two dancers moving backward to their original positions.

- **Near to** and **far from** (R27) describe the distance between objects or people in general space. The defensive player may be right near the offensive player, or the offensive player may evade the defensive player and be far away at the other end of the field.

## Timing

The category of timing in the relationships concept has three subcategories: simultaneous, alternate, and successive. Actions in the timing category relate to the starting and stopping of movements. Actions that are simultaneous are done at the same time (e.g., mirroring). Actions that are alternating are done one after the other. In order to be alternating actions, one person must complete the action before the other person begins (e.g., taking turns). In successive movements, while they are not done at the same time, there is only a bit of a lag between when the first person completes the action (or the first action as in a movement sequence), and the second person begins the action (or second action as in a movement sequence).

Simultaneous movements are those where the performers are moving together at the same time. They begin together at the same time and they end together at the same time. The following elements come from the simultaneous subcategory.

- When **mirroring** (R28) another person's movement, the person is often facing the other person. When one person moves her right arm, the other person moves her left arm exactly the same way, as if the first person were looking in the mirror.

- **Matching** (R29) is very similar to mirroring, except that the two people are facing in the same direction so that when the first person moves his right arm, the other person also moves his right arm (i.e., they are the same, or they match).

- A **contrasting** (R30) movement is one that is the opposite of, or different from, another; when one moves up, the other moves down.

- **Unison** (R31) refers to movement at the same time, like synchronized swimmers who are perfectly in unison. However, the movements do not have to be identical to be in unison. It is that they are occurring together rather than at different times that makes them in unison. For example, it is considered unison when a teacher says "Everyone, ready, go!" and the children do unique movements at the same time.

Alternate is the second subcategory of timing; it describes the frequent need in the movement environment to **take turns** (R32). Examples are batters in softball and kickers in kickball. In gymnastics, performers take turns making attempts such as jumping over the vaulting horse. During the Virginia Reel, dancers take turns traveling down the middle of the lines formed by people clapping to the music.

Successive is the last subcategory of the timing category and describes situations in which one movement is followed by another, often as a logical response to the first movement. Successive timing of movements is a little more complex than simultaneous or alternate timing of movements. The beginning and ending process in successive timing is more staggered than the very clearly identified start and stop in the previous timing subcategories. For example, in a successive relationship, one might start to move slightly after the first person begins moving and they might end at the same time or at different times. The following elements come from the successive subcategory.

- A **movement sequence** (R33) is a really critical element because most skills are formed by combining several parts in a specific order, such as swinging a bat or throwing a ball. A movement sequence must have a clear beginning and a definite ending. Here is a typical gymnastics routine that serves as a good example of a movement sequence: step-up mount (beginning), walk across the beam, squat turn, leap, and tuck-jump dismount (end). An offensive play in a team sport can also represent a highly complicated movement sequence that involves many people logically timing their movements to be successful.
- **Canon** (R34) is a really fun movement element to practice. The canon is successive in that one person begins a movement and another person initiates movement that is

begun prior to the ending of the first person's movement. Like movement sequence, it is a series of movements, but it is the timing of the dynamics that sets this movement element apart. Like the exploding of fireworks in the night sky, canon movements use the emphasis of the expression of effort to distinguish the timing of the movements. Each series of explosions has unique pauses between the sounds that make up the unique dynamics. For example, conga line dancing and stadium waves are silly ways to teach the idea of canon. Movements are done one right after the other with the same dynamics (effort) as the person who originally performed the movement.

**Question/answer** (R35) is an interesting relationship of timing. The timing relationship for question and answer is captured in the understanding that there is a conversation occurring. Instead of using words, the conversation is being done with movements. The first movement is presented as some kind of question or challenge. A movement is then used to respond to the query. In terms of timing, there may be an immediate response or there may be a delay. The amount of time is determined by the respondent's answer. This is often the case in a dance when the lead dancer presents an open hand to their partner, asking the question, Will you join me? The partner then responds, Yes, by taking the leader's hand. Another question/answer scenario common to a game is exemplified when one player sends a lob shot over a net to their opponent. The question is, Can you hit this? The opponent's answer is likely to be a smash in movement language or, in English, a resounding Yes, and take that!

- In **act/react** (R36) the main idea is that one movement causes another. Act/react is a proportional timing issue. If there is a slow action, then the reaction is slow; if the action is fast, then the reaction is fast. Bouncing on a fully inflated balloon would result in its popping loudly. Act (or cause) = bounce; React = pop!
- In **lead/follow** (R37) the second movement is a form of copying the first movement. Lead/follow timing is about the followers attempting to keep up with the leader. One person (the leader) begins the movement and the others (the followers) begin to move as soon

as they recognize the movement and can copy it. The followers do not wait for the leader to complete the movement prior to beginning their movement. The classic game of Follow the Leader is a great example of this timing. Exercisers in an aerobic dance class are also demonstrating the lead/follow timing aspect intended here. The more familiar the followers are with the leader's movements, the more identical their timing is with the leader. The more unfamiliar the followers are with the leader's movements, the more delayed their movements are from the leaders. Simon Says is a game in which one person does a movement (e.g., takes three steps forward) and the rest of the players must do exactly the same movement (but only to the phrase *Simon Says*). Lead = three steps forward; Follow = three steps forward.

## Goal

The goal of the movement is the next category in the relationships movement concept and describes how people connect to one another. There are three basic situations, each with a different goal: cooperative, collaborative, and competitive. **Cooperative** (R38) situations are those in which people are helping each other reach a common goal, such as assisting a partner in a drill or in a game. The ultimate cooperative relationship is the functioning of a team in which each player has a specialized role.

Collaborative and competitive goals are similar in that they refer to a desire to be better than someone else. **Collaborative** (R39) involves outwitting an opponent by cooperating with another (possibly an opponent) to create a winning strategy, whereas in **competitive** (R40) the goal is simply trying to win. For example, in a game of Tag, the person who is "It" may try to tag another person to win by not being "It" anymore; this is competitive. If we add the element of several players collaborating, or working together, to create a strategy to physically shield themselves from the "It" player, we now have a more complex and very interesting collaborative relationship.

## Environment

In this final category, the environment can be either static or dynamic. In a **static** (R41) environment, the object, implement, or apparatus is fixed, or stationary. For example, a target on the wall toward which students are throwing balls is static, or stationary. A bench, box, or beam on which students are balancing does not move. In a **dynamic** (R42) environment, the object, implement, or apparatus is in motion. A small group of players throwing and catching while traveling is an example. Both the players and the object are in motion.

## Definitions of Movement Education Terms

Because the movement elements describe the movements to be performed, they are really the most important content in the movement education framework. Teaching the movement elements is the priority over teaching any of the other content or terms (i.e., movement concepts or movement categories). The use of these elements in activities and tasks forms the basis for all movement endeavors. The more successful and broader a child's movement competency, the more likely that child is to continue to participate in movement opportunities throughout the life span.

Definitions of the movement elements appear in both Spanish and English in the glossary at the end of this book. We hope this glossary of movement education terms and the examples in the activities chapters (7, 8, 9, and 10) as well as in the core content area lessons (chapters 11, 12, and 13) provide a better and more consistent understanding of these terms in both the physical education profession and the general population and culture.

## Utilizing the Movement Education Framework

The framework may sound complicated, but it is actually quite easy to remember and use in your own classes. You can see table 2.1 for a quick reference and you can see the glossary for complete descriptions. For easy reference when you don't want to hold your book, you can use the Flip 'n' Fold shown in appendix A.

Appendix A is a presentation of the entire movement education framework. After completing the two paper folds, the booklet size of the Flip 'n' Fold makes it easy to store in a pocket or on a clip board when teaching and makes a handy tool for teachers or even students, depending on their reading level.

The sections of the Flip 'n' Fold document (its name refers to the two folding procedures used to make an 8.5- by 11-inch piece of paper read like a book) are presented in figure 2.2*a* (body), figure 2.2*b* (space), figure 2.2*c* (effort), and figure 2.2*d* (relationships). There are four sections to the Flip 'n' Fold; each section represents one of the movement concepts. The concept is listed at the top of the section followed by numbered category terms (in figure 2.2*a,* the body category terms are numbered 1 to 4). The subcategory and subdivisions are in bold under the actions of the whole body category. There are six space category terms and four effort categories. There are five category terms for the relationships concept, with three subcategories in the timing category.

The movement elements in each section are the actual movements that children need to learn to do. The terms listed within a category are what we are calling the movement elements. For example, in figure 2.2*a* (body concept) under the body shapes category (number 2) are the movement elements narrow, wide, round, twisted, symmetrical, and asymmetrical. An alphanumeric code helps identify each term. For example, the letter B is used to identify all of the terms associated with the body concept, the letter S identifies the space concept movement elements, the letter E represents the effort concepts, and finally, the letter R signifies relationships concepts. In addition, each movement element is numbered with the first term for each movement concept beginning with 1. The alphanumeric code is used on the Flip 'n' Fold, in the glossary at the end of this book, as well as on the pocket chart teaching cards available from Sportime (see appendix C for information on how to obtain the pocket chart cards) and any other related products.

An additional element that you will see in the Flip 'n' Fold, in this book, on the related pocket chart cards by Sportime, and on a poster set by Sportime, is a set of characters called the KinetiKidz. The job of the KinetiKidz characters is to help children everywhere to move more, feel good and think better. The KinetiKidz characters demonstrate technically correct form for each of the 121 movement elements (50 body elements, 20 space elements, 9 effort elements, and 42 relationships elements).

One KinetiKid character is on each page of the Flip 'n' Fold demonstrating one example of the movement elements for that movement concept.

The characters also appear on a set of pocket chart cards and a set of 18 posters (to be used as word walls) available from Sportime at www.sportime.com. The card set has both a written definition of each term and a line drawing of a KinetiKidz demonstrating the movement element. The KinetiKidz characters help to teach nonreaders and visual learners.

The Flip 'n' Fold is simply a means to provide a structure to the ideas of movement education. We have attempted to create the most authentic representation we could from the movement education literature, recognizing that compromises and interpretations may have limited how true we could be to history. Movement education experts have a variety of opinions and viewpoints regarding classification and definition of terms. Thus, we acknowledge that what we are calling the movement elements can be arranged, described, and defined in a variety of equally valid ways. We do not present the Flip 'n' Fold as the correct or only organization of movement education terminology and ideas. What we hope to provide is a presentation of the movement education terminology that is practical, easy to remember, and meaningful to both teachers and children, and that provides a current and clear vision of the NASPE national physical education standards 1 and 2.

# Extending the Basics for Children

Critical to any child's movement success is the way the movement challenge is presented. Central to the movement education framework approach are the following general objectives:

- Success for all
- Activity for all
- Contribution by all

Children are encouraged to problem solve and thus take control of their own movement choices. Teachers guide children toward these challenges and present movement problems in such a way that children are encouraged to apply their movement knowledge toward success.

Learning occurs in three domains: cognitive, motor, and affective. Movement education facilitates movement content learning both cognitively and physically (motor). When children learn the

## BODY
CONCEPT: WHO?

**B**

Teach Body Concepts with **Sportime Pocket Chart Cards B1–B50**

1. **Body Parts**  **B1**
Head, Neck, Ears, Eyes, Nose, Mouth, Shoulders, Elbows, Wrists, Hands, Fingers, Belly, Chest, Spine, Back, Bottom, Hips, Knees, Ankles, Feet, Toes

2. **Body Shapes**  **B2–B7**
Narrow, Wide, Round, Twisted, Symmetrical, Asymmetrical

3. **Actions of Body Parts**  **B8–B12**
Weight bearing, Receiving force or weight, Apply force, Lead the action, Weight transfer

4. **Actions of the Whole Body**
**Nonlocomotor**  **B13–B27**
Stretch, Curl, Twist, Turn, Spin, Swing, Push, Pull, Rise, Sink, Gesture, Dodge, Balance, Counterbalance, Counter-tension
**Locomotor**  **B28–B41**
Step-like actions:  Walk, Cartwheel, Crawl (climb), Bear walk, Crab walk
Spring-like actions: Run, Leap, Hop, Skip, Jump, Gallop, Slide
Roll-like actions:  Rock, (Body) roll
**Manipulative**  **B42–B50**
Send away:  Throw, Roll, Strike, Kick, Volley
Gain control:  Catch, Trap
Propel:  Dribble, Carry

© 2009 Bridges & Weiller-Abels

*a*

## SPACE
CONCEPT: WHERE?

**S**

Teach Space Concepts with **Sportime Pocket Chart Cards S1–S20**

1. **Location**
Self-space, General space  **S1–S2**

2. **Direction**  **S3–S9**
Forward, Backward
Sideward (right, left)
Up, Down
Clockwise, Counterclockwise

3. **Level**  **S10–S12**
Low, Medium, High

4. **Pathway**  **S13–S15**
Straight, Curved, Zigzag

5. **Plane**  **S16–S18**
Sagittal (divides into sides; wheel)
Frontal (divides front/back; door)
Transverse (divides top/bottom; table)

6. **Extension**  **S19–S20**
Small (near), Large (far)

© 2009 Bridges & Weiller-Abels

*b*

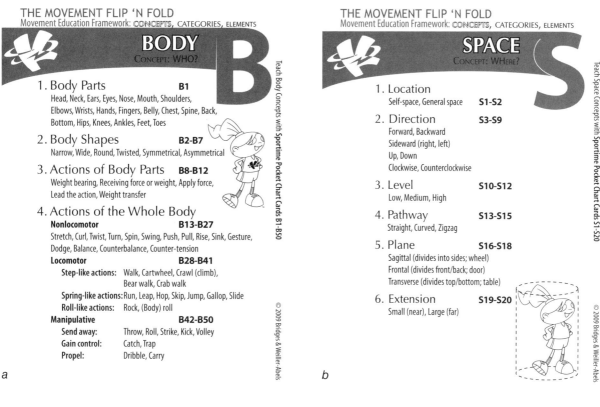

## EFFORT
CONCEPT: HOW?

**E**

Teach Effort Concepts with **Sportime Pocket Chart Cards E1–E9**

1. **Time** *(rate)*  **E1–E3**
Fast (sudden)
Slow (sustained)
Acceleration (Change)

2. **Force** *(tension)*  **E4–E5**
Hard (strong)
Soft (light)

3. **Flow** *(fluidity)*  **E6–E7**
Bound (stoppable)
Free (ongoing)

4. **Focus** *(effort in space)*  **E8–E9**
Direct (pointed or in a line)
Indirect (expanded or flexible)

© 2009 Bridges & Weiller-Abels

*c*

## RELATIONSHIPS
CONCEPT: CONNECTIONS WITH WHO? OR WHAT?*

**R**

Teach Relationship Concepts with **Sportime Pocket Chart Cards R1–R42**

1. **People** *(organization of)*  **R1–R13**
Solo, Alone in a mass, Partners, Even group(s),
Uneven group(s)
Individual to group, Group to group
Triangle, Circle, Square, Scattered, Spokes of a wheel, "X"

2. **Position** *(spatial relationship)*  **R14–R27**
Above/below (still), Over/under (moving), Inverted,
Mount/dismount, In front of/behind, Beside, Alongside,
Through, Surround, Around, Support/supported (still),
Lift/lifted (moving), Meet/part, Near to/far from

3. **Timing**  **R28–R37**
Simultaneous: Mirror, Match, Contrast, Unison
Alternate:  Taking turns
Successive:  Movement sequence, Canon, Question/answer,
Act/react, Lead/follow

4. **Goal** *(of the activity)*  **R38–R40**
Cooperative (help), Collaborative (outwit), Competitive (win)

5. **Environment** *(nature of the)*  **R41–R42**
Static, Dynamic

\* The Who or What can be...
Body parts, Individuals, Groups
Rules, Objects, Boundaries, Equipment
Wrting, Music, Pictures, Lighting, Nature (Arts)

© 2009 Bridges & Weiller-Abels

*d*

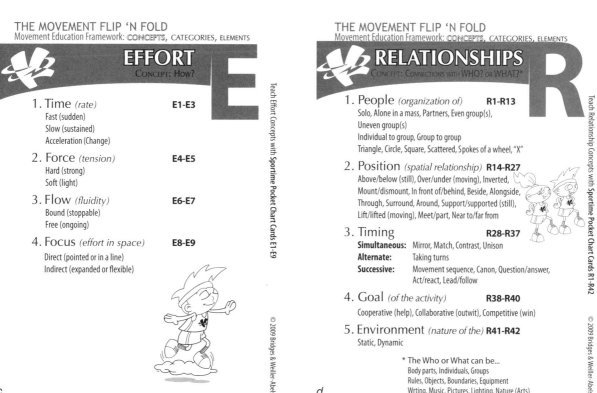

**Figure 2.2**  Flip 'n' Fold sections *(a)* the body concept, *(b)* the space concept, *(c)* the effort concept, and *(d)* the relationships concept. For a reproducible version of the Flip 'n' Fold, see appendix A on page 243.

© Karen Weiller Abels and Jennifer Bridges.

entire framework, they have a strong basic movement (motor) foundation. This foundation not only consists of movement knowledge (cognitive), but also extends to a movement vocabulary that aids in movement acquisition (motor), and finally to valuing physical activity for a lifetime (affective, which encompasses NASPE standard 6). The KinetiKidz motto of "move more, feel good, and think better" thus addresses all three learning domains (motor, affective, and cognitive).

## The Big Picture: Movement Education Tree

Figure 2.1, which showed the roots of movement education, illustrates the general idea of progression in movement education. Figure 2.3 is a more complete picture of the movement education tree showing how the movement concepts fit into a curriculum and lifelong movement framework.

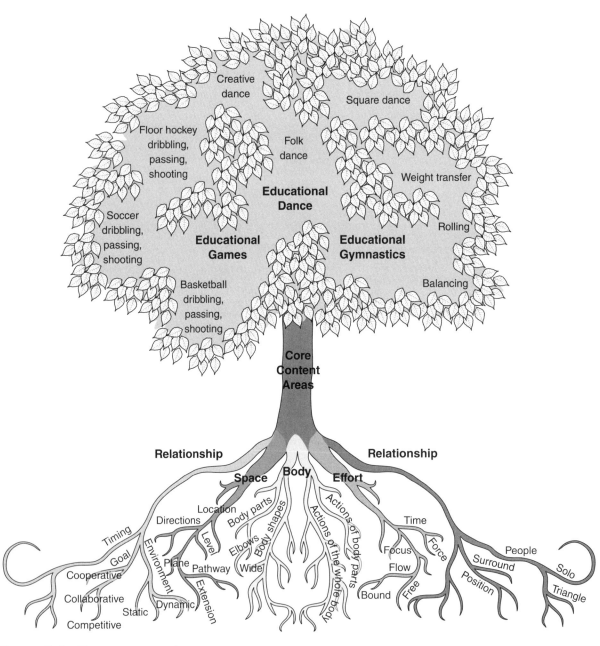

**Figure 2.3** The movement education tree.

The roots of complex movement lie in the development of the movement elements that are organized into the four movement concepts: body, space, effort, and relationships. Thus, the tree roots in figure 2.3 represent this basic beginning point (presented earlier in figure 2.1), which serves as a basis for movement language and content that can be applied in the primary grades or later in middle and high school. A more detailed discussion of the tree root analogy was presented along with figure 2.1. Because young children can readily acquire a movement foundation, movement concepts should first be introduced in early childhood. Continued refinement and broader experiences should follow preschool into elementary school so that children become more skilled and move to higher developmental stages.

The basic root movement concepts are combined in various ways into three general areas at the center, or core, of the tree. Typically, the core of the tree (the trunk), representing the core content areas of movement, is the focus in later elementary grades and in middle school. In middle school and high school the curriculum branches out to provide more specialized and complex movement challenges in each of the three core content areas. The main branches that divide off at the top of the tree represent the three specific core content areas (educational games, educational dance, and educational gymnastics). The leaves of the tree represent specific activities within each of the three core content areas. For example, floor hockey is a game; creative, folk, or square are dance forms; and rolling or weight transfer skills are examples of gymnastic tasks that are all frequently used at the elementary level.

Educational games, educational dance, and educational gymnastics are the three core content areas of movement education. The MEF organization allows movement education content to be structured and communicated in a way that students can best understand and utilize. We provide brief descriptions of the core content areas here to provide a complete picture of the application of the movement education framework.

## Educational Games

Educational games essentially address manipulative skills (e.g., striking, throwing, catching) that help children learn to become skillful games players. These manipulative skills are combined with nonlocomotor skills and locomotor skills as well as many of the other movement elements within the space, effort, and relationships concepts. All combine to develop children who are skilled at playing games.

The games used in this content area include activities as simple as standing in self-space and throwing to a spot on a wall. Children may work on throwing objects such as beanbags or balls at various levels and with varying amounts of force. The game aspect may involve having children collect the object and seeing how many times they can send it to the desired target. Children can be challenged to move to different starting places and use different amounts of force depending on where they are standing.

Another game example is One Step. Working with partners, children throw and catch an object. When they are successful, they take one step back and continue. Games at the elementary stage of development can have as few or as many rules as you deem necessary. As your students progress to a mature or transitional stage of development (see chapter 3), you can add additional rules and skills.

## Educational Gymnastics

The focus of educational gymnastics is for the individual child to be successful; it allows for the "unique style in which each [child] moves, learns, and develops" (Logsdon et al., 1984, p. 241). This approach encourages children to feel movements, to learn how their bodies move, and to develop variety in their movement. There are no stunts that all children need to perform; rather, they are offered choices and options to explore as they are ready. The problem-solving approach is most critical in educational gymnastics. This is highlighted in chapter 12.

An educational gymnastics activity at the elementary school level might involve having children choose a balanced shape and try to hold that shape for at least three seconds. They can then change their shape. Children can also be asked to create a gymnastics routine that consists of striking a balanced pose, followed by traveling in a pathway of their choice and then performing a locomotor step or springlike action, followed by a balanced ending pose.

Children at a mature developmental stage might create gymnastics routines with partners or in small groups that consist of a balanced shape, traveling, rolling, and meeting and parting. They may be asked to include mirroring or matching. The children can write their routines down on paper, practice them, and then perform them for the class. Educational gymnastics differs from traditional or Olympic gymnastics in that children create their own responses to gymnastics problems.

## Educational Dance

The key to educational dance is movement expression. What type of mood or feeling is created when children perform a dance? As implied in figure 2.3, all types of dance forms can be used in the educational dance area. For example, children can apply elements from each of the movement concepts when working on folk or square dances. Applying creative movement is a wonderful way to enhance problem solving. Chapter 13 provides an Umbrella Dance example: students pretend to become umbrellas as they sway in the wind and rain. Once learned, movement elements become part of each core content area.

# Presentation for Learning

The prudent physical educator introduces or reviews movement concepts, categories, and elements very early in the academic year, thus providing a structure to the core content areas to be presented throughout the year. The ultimate goal of the physical educator or elementary classroom teacher administering physical education is to teach children sufficient movement knowledge to help them develop their skill in whatever movement problem is presented. Children should not only develop a movement word bank, or vocabulary, but also be able to transfer this knowledge to how their bodies move and the movement principles involved in all types of movement problems.

Initially, you should begin by providing lessons that focus on building a movement word bank in each of the four concept areas. Although all movement concepts and elements should be covered and will eventually be presented as you move into the core content areas, there are critical categories and elements that should be taught prior to implementing any lessons in educational dance, educational gymnastics, and educational games. These critical elements provide a foundation for acquiring a movement word bank (content knowledge) for future movement elements and tasks. The critical concepts include neither all of the movement categories nor all of the movement elements—only the most essential movement elements are included in this list. For example, learners first need to become familiar with the body concept categories of body parts, body shapes, and some actions of the whole body. As noted in chapter 7 (Body Activities), activities may include body part identification, making body shapes, and holding those shapes for a count of 3.

The critical categories and elements include the following with the corresponding pocket chart card alphanumeric reference in parentheses.

### Critical Body Concept Elements

- Body parts—Head, neck, ears, eyes, nose, mouth, shoulders, elbows, wrists, hands, fingers, belly, chest, spine, back, bottom, hips, knees, ankles, feet, and toes (B1)
- Body shapes—Narrow, wide, round, and twisted (B2-B5)
- Actions of the whole body
  - Nonlocomotor—Stretch, curl, twist, dodge, and balance (B13-B15, B24, B25)
  - Locomotor—Run, leap, hop, skip, jump, gallop, and slide (B33-B39)

### Critical Space Concept Elements

- Location—Self-space and general space (S1-S2)
- Direction—Forward, backward, and sideways (S3-S5)
- Levels—Low, medium, and high (S10-S12)
- Pathway—Straight, curved, and zigzag (S13-S15)

### Critical Effort Concept Elements

- Time—Fast, slow, and acceleration (E1-E3)
- Force —Hard and soft (E4-E5)

### Critical Relationship Concept Elements

- People—Partners, even groups, and uneven groups (R3-R5)
- Position—Above/below, over/under, beside, alongside, and near to/far from (R14, R15, R19, R20, R27)
- Timing—Taking turns, movement sequence, and lead/follow (R32, R33, R37)

Within the space concept, learners should first acquire an understanding of location, direction, level, and pathway. For example, becoming familiar with personal and general locations and high, medium, and low levels will help in future activities such as dribbling and throwing and catching. Use of directions can later be applied to passing.

Similarly, in the effort concept area, learners should first acquire movement knowledge of fast, slow, and acceleration (time), and strong (hard) and light (soft) force. Once this knowledge is established, they can apply these elements as they practice locomotor skills, dribble a ball, or develop a movement sequence in gymnastics.

Finally, in the relationships concept learners should first develop partner relationships, work in small groups, and understand the positional relationships of above, below, in front of, and behind. In the timing category, children need to be able to take turns (or work one after the other). This will also help with classroom management. Movement sequence is a critical element as children can work independently starting from the initial stage of development to put two movements together (e.g., wide balance followed by step-like action of walking). In order to be successful in the three core content areas, children need to learn how to combine movements together. Lead/follow is important to include early as children need to be able to follow a partner's movement in the three core content areas. More advanced learners apply these elements in gamelike situations as they relate not only to equipment and apparatus, but also to other learners. Specific applications of these critical elements to core content areas are provided in chapters 11, 12, and 13 with lessons and unit examples.

## Teaching From the Movement Education Perspective

The movement education perspective differs from other teaching approaches in its focus on problem solving. Although the problem-solving approach has often been employed over the years in teaching physical education, movement education uses it in a unique way by incorporating a cognitive body of knowledge: the movement word bank. By achieving a cognitive understanding and applying the movement elements, learners discover ways their bodies can move and how they can solve movement problems. We provide examples of how to include problem-solving activities (chapters 7-10) and lessons (chapters 11-13).

If you use a process of discovery and the techniques of problem solving, and accept many answers as correct, you will maximize this dual cognitive and motor approach. In this way of teaching physical education, you can present movement problems through a questioning style as follows:

- Show me how you can . . . .
- Can you think of a different way to . . . ?
- How many different ways can you . . . ?

The movement education approach contributes to the total education of the child: physically, affectively, and cognitively. Along with the cognitive and motor advantage, the movement education approach enhances the affective domain as well by encouraging learners to build working relationships with partners and small groups. Learners also acquire working and applied definitions of cooperation and collaboration, as well as competition.

## Summary

This chapter is really the heart of the book. It is in this chapter that the movement education content of teaching in elementary physical education is given. A tree roots analogy for the movement concepts is set up early and is expanded upon later to complete the entire MEF conceptual model. A set of organization terms (i.e., concepts, categories, and elements) is laid out to help clarify the way that movements and ideas in our presentation of the MEF are grouped. The majority of the chapter is dedicated to the details of definitions, descriptions, and examples of the entire MEF. Our pocket guide to the MEF, which we fondly call the Flip 'n' Fold, is unveiled here along with encouragement for readers to refer to the glossary (available in both English and Spanish).

# Developmentally Appropriate Teaching and Assessment

One of the challenges in physical education is to teach developmentally appropriate activities and lessons. Without well-designed learning opportunities, children are unlikely to progress to mature patterns of movement. Without any instruction, encouragement, or practice, children will hit a wall (Gallahue, Cleland, & Donnely, 2003, call this the "proficiency barrier"; see figure 3.1 on page 32) and remain at the immature level instead of progressing to a mature level of performance.

Consider the scenario of a seven-year-old child in the second grade who is performing below the level of her peers or is at an immature, or initial, developmental stage. If her physical education teacher used age or grade level to determine the types of activities to include in lessons, the child would be given tasks that were far beyond her capacity. The opportunity for success would be slim because the child would probably not be able to do any of the tasks!

The knowledge amassed by motor development specialists can help you create developmentally appropriate learning experiences that will be more likely to increase your students' chances of successful learning and improved performance. Researchers in the field of motor development have identified the performance criteria that

define stages of development (initial, elementary, and mature). Good teaching progressions are not only based on knowledge of motor development, but also include the application of motor learning. Key theories and practice methods that help the teacher design efficient and effective practice activities will be presented in this chapter.

## Stages of Motor Development

The stages of motor development can be related to phases and levels of motor development (see figure 3.1 on page 32). The two phases are the fundamental movement phase and the specialized movement phase. The fundamental movement phase is "an organized series of basic movements that involve the combination of movement patterns of two or more body segments . . . and are categorized into stability, locomotor, or manipulative movements" (Gallahue, Cleland, & Donnely, 2003, p. 52). "The specialized movement phase typically begins around the age of seven . . . and frequently continues through adolescence and into adulthood" (p. 64) and "is a fundamental movement skill or combination of fundamental movement skills that have been applied to the performance of a specific sport-related activity" (p. 52).

The stages of motor development that are likely of most interest to readers of this book are contained in the first group: fundamental movements. However, some children are more advanced, and hopefully most or all of them will progress to the second group of specialized skills. For this reason, you should have the big picture of where children begin and where they will progress.

Motor development specialists have classified the fundamental movement skills (nonlocomotor, locomotor, and manipulative) into three stages: initial, elementary, and mature (Gallahue & Ozmun, 2006). This three-stage approach, although simple, accurately and adequately describes the development of most fundamental movement patterns. Also of practical value is that these three terms are easily understood and can be used effectively in planning instruction. Figure 3.1 shows the interrelationship of the two phases and the three stages of motor development. Gallahue, Cleland, and Donnely (2003) included the three commonly used levels of learning as well.

Table 3.1 presents some characteristics of the initial, elementary, and mature stages of motor development. These translate nicely into nonverbal signals and verbal cues that many teachers use (also shown in table 3.1). In the initial stage you can use the thumbs-up signal with a verbal "Good try!" added to support the child in just attempting the skill. In the elementary stage you can bring the thumb and index finger close together while communicating a verbal "Almost!" telling the child that he is making progress. Finally, clapping hands in applause is a signal that the child is meeting the performance criteria; a verbal "Looks good" emphasizes the message. Ages and grade levels are not included in this table intentionally because the characteristics, not age, are the most important.

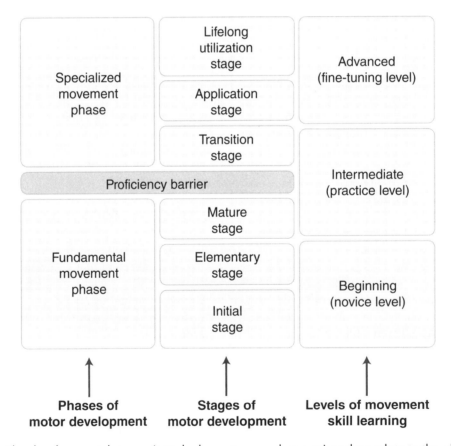

**Figure 3.1** The developmental stages (initial, elementary, and mature) as they relate to the phases of motor development and the levels of movement skill learning.

Reprinted, by permission, from D. Gallahue and F. Cleland, 2002, *Developmental physical education for all children*, 4th ed. (Champaign, IL: Human Kinetics), 69.

**Table 3.1**  Progression of Motor Developmental Stages

| Stage | Movement characteristics | Nonverbal signals with verbal cues |
|---|---|---|
| **Fundamental movement phase: all three stages** | | |
| 1. Initial | Characterized by the child's first observable attempts at the movement pattern. Many of the components of a refined pattern, such as the preparatory action and follow-through, are missing. | "Good try!" |
| 2. Elementary | A transitional stage in the child's movement development. Coordination and performance improve, and the child gains more control over movements. More components of the mature pattern are integrated into the movement, although they are performed incorrectly. | "Almost!" |
| 3. Mature | The integration of all the component movements into a well-coordinated, purposeful act. The movement resembles the motor pattern of a skilled adult, in terms of control and mechanics, but is lacking in terms of movement performance as measured quantitatively. | "Looks good!" |
| **Specialized movement phase: first stage only** | | |
| Transitional | Greater form, accuracy, and control over fundamental movement skills. Application of the fundamental movement patterns in slightly more complex and specific forms. New combinations of fundamental movement skills | "Now you're getting there!" |

## Initial Stage

Children make their first, or initial, movement attempts in this stage, which are characterized by missing or improperly sequenced parts of the movement. The body movements are either exaggerated or restricted. There is little effective rhythmic flow or coordination. Children may be at the initial stage in some skills and at higher stages in others. In general, though, most of a child's skills will be at this stage at the beginning of new skills. Although the initial stage of many movements should (and generally does) occur at the preschool level, many elementary school children are still at this stage, at least in some skills, so elementary school teachers should be aware of these characteristics. Table 3.2 on page 34 presents the time frame of typical emergence of some motor skills.

## Elementary Stage

During this stage a child still shows the exaggeration and restriction of movements of the initial stage. However, the timing and spatial elements of movements have improved, so the performance of the typical preschooler gets better and more coordinated.

**Table 3.2** Emergence Order of Some Nonlocomotor, Locomotor, and Manipulative Skills

| Grade level | Age | Emergence order (time) | Nonlocomotor | Locomotor | Manipulative |
|---|---|---|---|---|---|
| Pre-K | 4 months to 4 years | First (earlier) | Axial movements (stretch, bend, twist, turn, etc.), static balance | Crawl | |
| | 1 year | | | Walk | Throw |
| | 1.5 years | | | Run | Kick |
| | 2 years | | | Jump, gallop, slide | Catch, strike |
| | 2.5 years | | Dynamic balance | Hop | |
| | 3 years | | | Gallop, slide | |
| K | 5 years | Last (later) | | Skip | |

The primary reason for this change is thought to be simply physical maturation. Some children mature slower or faster than others, which may account for some differences in performance. Many children and adults perform skills at the elementary stage. According to Gallahue and Ozmun (2006), many never get beyond this elementary stage in many movement patterns. This is because instruction, practice, and encouragement are absent.

## Mature Stage

Children typically reach the developmental *potential* for mature performance in most nonlocomotor and locomotor skills by about age 6 (see table 3.3). However, there is a great deal of variation in the rate individual children reach each motor developmental stage. Unlike the elementary stage, in which simple physical maturation leads to skill progression, to reach the mature stage of performance, children must have an appropriate learning environment, opportunities for practice, encouragement, and effective instruction. The use of motor learning practice methods can make a significantly positive difference in the amount of learning that can take place at this critical stage. Because children have a great range of developmental differences, using the age of 6 as a benchmark for reaching the mature stage is a mistake. Mature performance is generally characterized by mechanically efficient, coordinated, and controlled performances that, once the physical potential is present, gradually unfold with good instruction and lesson design.

**Table 3.3** Potential Achievement at the Mature Stage of Performance

| Grade level | Age | Development order (time) | Nonlocomotor | Locomotor | Manipulative |
|---|---|---|---|---|---|
| Pre-K | 6 months to 4 years | First (earlier) | Axial movements (stretch, bend, twist, turn, etc.) | | |
| K | 5 years | | | Walk, run | Throw (boys) |
| 1 | 6 years | | Static balance (6-10 years) | Gallop, slide, skip | |
| 2 | 7 years | | | Hop | Catch, strike (7-8.5 years) |
| 3 | 8 years | | | | Throw (girls), kick |
| 4 | 9 years | | | | |
| 5 | 10 years | Last (later) | Dynamic balance | Long jump | |

Because skills vary in their level of difficulty, children reach the mature stage in some skills before reaching that stage in other skills. Table 3.3 depicts when fundamental movement patterns present themselves. Notice that in a very general way the nonlocomotor skills are the first to emerge followed by most of the locomotor skills; the most complex skills (manipulative skills) emerge last. Thus, the axial skills and static balance (nonlocomotor) are first, followed by the locomotor skills (walk, run, jump, and hop), and then the throw, catch, and strike (manipulative) skills. The more difficult nonlocomotor skill of dynamic balance comes a little later and, along with leg strength, can facilitate the attainment of the ability to hop and skip (which uses the hop).

Again, each fundamental motor skill seems to require a unique amount of time to develop. Thus, the skill that emerges first is not necessarily the one that will mature first. Elementary movement educators must continue to provide meaningful challenges to children because they will be at different stages with each and the goal is to have as many students as possible reach a mature stage. Table 3.2 (which shows the emergence order of skills) presents the same skills as table 3.3 does (which shows potential achievement at the mature stage); however, table 3.3 shows the approximate age at which 60 percent of children are likely to reach the mature stage. Note that there are exceptions and that skills can overlap, but you can feel confident using this scheme when creating movement sequences and teaching progressions.

Although the three-stage approach is most helpful and will be used in the activities and lesson and unit plans presented in this book, the elementary teacher should consider one more stage, the transitional stage.

## Transitional Stage

The transitional stage (along with the application stage and lifelong utilization stage) is part of a more advanced general grouping called the specialized movement phase. (See figure 3.1 for a visual presentation of where this stage fits into the overall picture.) People are not likely to progress to the transitional stage without reaching the mature stage in the fundamental movement skills. This inability to progress in skill has been termed the proficiency barrier (see figure 3.1). In other words, a significant movement limitation and lack of continued progress will result with-

out forming the movement foundation created in the earlier developmental stages (i.e., initial, elementary, and mature). As we will discuss in chapter 4, this is a very real threat to developing an active lifestyle.

Some children advance much faster than others and are ready to move beyond the fundamental movements of the initial, elementary, and mature stages and into more specialized movements. This is a very fun and exciting time because they are combining and applying movement fundamentals to sport and recreational skills. Often these children receive lots of opportunities from their physical education teacher who works with them to combine and apply these fundamentals to other skills. A whole new movement world is opened up! As well, children developing at slower rates should also be provided with more difficult challenges of combining skills and attempting to apply fundamentals to specialized situations to help them continue to develop. If you are aware of these stages and their interrelationships, you will be more confident about and efficient in designing effective individual learning experiences. Chapters 11, 12, and 13 provide examples of lessons that show good progression using each of the stages.

## Stages of Motor Development Criteria

You may find yourself thinking, *But I am not a motor development specialist! How do I know at what developmental stage my students are performing?* This may be a concern particularly with less experienced teachers. Not to worry! If you observe performers carefully, you can determine at what stage they are performing. Knowing what to look for simplifies this process.

Research about the development of fundamental motor skills is limited, so use the criteria presented in tables 3.4 through 3.7 (on pages 36-39) only as a general guideline. You can use these tables as examples to see how the authors made applications for each of the movement education concepts and categories to the stages of motor development. The guidelines presented in this chapter contain information from the motor development textbooks by Payne and Issacs (2007) and Gallahue and Ozmun (2006). These guidelines will be helpful when you are looking at the core content chapters (11, 12, and 13); you

**Table 3.4** Developmental Stages Applied to Body Concepts

| Movement element | Developmental stage | | | |
|---|---|---|---|---|
| | **Initial** | **Elementary** | **Mature** | **Transition** |
| Body parts | Is able to identify some body parts | Is able to identify most body parts | Is able to identify all body parts | Is able to identify which body parts are important to performing a skill |
| Body shapes | Most body shapes look very similar (e.g., wide and round look similar) | Can perform examples of each body shape (e.g., round, wide, narrow, twisted) | Can perform multiple examples of body shapes (e.g., round, wide, narrow, twisted, symmetrical, asymmetrical) | Changes body shape or shape of body part to accomplish a goal (e.g., making a wide body shape to block a defender or making a round or curled shape to accomplish a body roll) |
| Actions of body parts | Performs action accidentally, not intentionally (e.g., may be able to move like a horse, but may not be able to keep front foot leading in the gallop or know that the front foot is leading the action) | Performs most of the actions, but may not know the term (e.g., is able to demonstrate galloping [front foot leading], but may not be able to identify the front foot as the body part which is leading the action) | Knows and performs each action (e.g., can gallop with either foot leading and can identify which foot is leading the action) | Can identify which action is important for successful performance (e.g., applying force becomes the important element, rather than leading the action if gallop is used in a foot race) |
| Actions of whole body | Nonlocomotor skills are the most advanced, lack of physical development may limit quality of performance (e.g., lack of leg strength reduces ability to jump ) | Most nonlocomotor skills are performed well with many locomotor skills and basic manipulative patterns identifiable (e.g., there is a clear difference between hop, jump, leap) | Patterns are smooth and outcomes are achieved with some regularity (e.g., broad jumps a consistent distance and does not fall backward) | Selection of skill to situation can be made, skills can be combined into new combinations, increased speed, force, direction demands are responded to regularly (e.g., child can combine a run with a jump to create a running long jump) |

**Table 3.5** Developmental Stages Applied to Space Concepts

| Movement element | Developmental stage | | | |
|---|---|---|---|---|
| | **Initial** | **Elementary** | **Mature** | **Transition** |
| Location: self-space | Is able to stand in hula hoop or on carpet square when directed by teacher and understands this is self-space | Is able to move off identified self-space and may or may not touch others while moving | Is able to move within general space while maintaining self-space (i.e., moves without touching others) | Is able to identify open space and moves purposefully to or through it |
| Location: general space | Moves randomly through available space; stays in local area or does not use all space available for movement | Demonstrates inconsistent use of entire space available for movement; may or may not stay within identified boundaries (i.e., lines or cones) | Regularly uses available space for movement and can stay within marked boundaries | Can identify and is able to move within sub-areas of general space (e.g., half-court, a serving area) |

| Movement element | Developmental stage | | | |
|---|---|---|---|---|
| | **Initial** | **Elementary** | **Mature** | **Transition** |
| Directions | Can perform and understand one direction at a time (e.g., does a forward movement) | Moves more randomly than directed; changes with prompting (e.g., teacher reminds quick direction changes to avoid being tagged) | Makes clear and sharp changes without prompting (e.g., moves to avoid being tagged without comment from teacher) | Can combine directional elements to achieve new goals in core content tasks (e.g., creates a fake and moves into an open space to avoid another person) |
| Level | Can perform and understand one level at a time (e.g., bounces a ball at a low level, a medium level, or a high level) | Can perform a skill at a variety of levels (e.g., performs overhead pass at a high level, chest pass at a medium level, and bounce pass at a low level) | Can perform skill with mechanical efficiency at appropriate level when directed (e.g., performs a sharp, direct chest pass at a medium level) | Can choose level at which skill needs to be performed and can perform it to achieve new goals in context of core content tasks (e.g., chooses overhead pass to get above a defender at a high level) |
| Pathway | All pathways look similar; hard to tell one pattern from another (e.g., running around the playground) | Pathway is detectable but not exact (e.g., wandering from side to side while attempting to run in a straight path) | Distinct differences among pathways (e.g., landing on a straight line the entire distance of the path) | Can identify and perform a pathway for a specific movement situation (e.g., a straight line is most direct to the finish line, a curved path is effective in setting a performer up for a high jump) |
| Plane | Primarily uses ideas of self-space; develops an understanding that the body can be divided further (e.g., there are three unique areas through which the body moves) | Is likely able to do one movement in each plane (e.g., jumping jacks in the frontal plane, hula hooping in the transverse plane, galloping in the sagittal plane)<br><br>Understands terms enough so teacher feedback using planes terms is meaningful (e.g., keep arms in sagittal plane while running) | Can do several movements in each plane (e.g., jumping jacks, snow angels, and sliding in the frontal plane)<br><br>Can also use planes terms to communicate about movement (e.g., my arms are in the sagittal plane when I run) | Can identify movements for most joints in most planes (e.g., I am flexing and extending my shoulder when my arms drive when I run)<br><br>Can identify a purpose for planar movement (e.g., sagittal arm drive reduces trunk rotation and helps drive legs) |
| Extension | No real difference in how close or far movements occur to or from the body (e.g., does not adjust racket swing to a ball that is closer to or farther from the body) | Begins to vary the size of body movements; either close to or far away from the body (e.g., may be able to overhand rally five consecutive times in badminton) | Adjusts body parts and implements to location of object and target (e.g., pulls racket in toward body to do a volley from a return that is hit toward your body) | Knows when to use an extension purposefully to achieve a goal (e.g., reaching to full extension during an overhead tennis serve can help to achieve a faster and more powerful serve) |

**Table 3.6** Developmental Stages Applied to Effort Concepts

| Movement element | Developmental stage | | | |
|---|---|---|---|---|
| | **Initial** | **Elementary** | **Mature** | **Transition** |
| Time | Performs movements at about the same rate no matter what the situation demands; not much change in speed (e.g., throws a ball with the same speed) | Begins to change rate of movements (e.g., throws are limited to fast and slow) | Able to make distinct differences in rates of movements (e.g., has a range of speed control of throws between slow and fast) | Able to adjust speed at rate of movement that is appropriate for situation (e.g., throws slow to toss from pitcher to first base versus throwing fast from third base to first base) |
| Force | Performs only one dimension of hard or soft, even if a harder or softer tension is needed | Demonstrates inconsistent ability to display soft versus hard force (e.g., sometimes strikes ball too hard, losing control) | Has ability to control amount of tension (e.g., has a range of tension control and can display both hard and soft taps to control plastic puck with hockey stick) | Able to adjust amount of muscle tension for a situation (e.g., striking a plastic puck with less force in a floor hockey game versus using much more force in grass on an outdoor field) |
| Flow | Performs movements that appear jerky or unrelated to each other (e.g., a body shape, a travel, and a body shape are performed one after the other with a pause separating each movement) | Performs movements that appear related to each other (e.g., a body shape, a travel, and a body shape are performed one after the other without a pause most of the time) | Has control over fluidity in motion, creating a smooth and coordinated appearance of movement  Has a greater number of movements that may be included (e.g., a body shape seamlessly moves into the travel that is followed by a roll and then completed by another body shape) | Has greater consistency of flow that can be used to generate movement outcomes (e.g., creation of floor exercise routine that includes a balanced body shape, a travel, a roll, another travel, and an ending balanced body shape that is held for at least three seconds) |
| Focus | Wastes effort and expresses effort randomly (e.g., team members in a tug-of-war game exhibit scattered energy because pulling is not synchronized) | Expresses effort randomly (e.g., children in a tug-of-war game sometimes are pulling together and sometimes are not) | Can control effort for a movement and channel it (e.g., all children in a tug-of-war game are pulling in the same direction) | Uses the energy to accomplish complex goals (e.g., children playing tug-of war work cooperatively to pull together and collaboratively to watch the opposing team in order to decide when to use the most focused energy to pull the other team over the line) |

will realize the practical applications of these guidelines when making teaching decisions. For example, rather than use grade level or age, you can use developmental stage to create appropriate learning sequences or progressions because of the wide variation of physical development, maturation, and movement experience of young children. Because the motor development process reveals itself in behavior, use students' behaviors to help you choose appropriate lessons.

Knowledge of motor development, identification of the stage of development of a child are great first steps to preparing a developmentally appropriate lesson. Designing activities that are appropriately progressive for the stage of the child is a good next step.

**Table 3.7** Developmental Stages Applied to Relationship Concepts

| Movement element | Developmental stage | | | |
|---|---|---|---|---|
| | **Initial** | **Elementary** | **Mature** | **Transition** |
| People | Works best alone (e.g., solo or alone in a mass) | Begins to work with others in simple combinations (e.g., partners); finds working in complex arrangements challenging | Works in combination with others and in a variety of geometric arrangements (e.g., triangle, circle, spokes of a wheel) | Identifies when to work alone or with others; can use geometric arrangements to achieve a movement goal (e.g., uses a triangle to participate in fungo hitting: softball batter, fielder, catcher) |
| Position | Does not know many of the position elements; can perform some of the elements (e.g., above/below, support/supported) | Can identify and describe most of the position elements but can only perform some of the position elements (e.g., above/below, support/supported) | Can perform all of the positioning elements (e.g., in front of/behind, meet/part) | Knows when to apply elements of position in a movement situation. Can perform the positioning skill in a situation (e.g., knows that the ball should be thrown in front of the receiver in flag football) |
| Timing | Builds on previous life experiences (e.g., takes turns and claps to a beat in unison) | Begins to use simpler simultaneous timing patterns and movement sequences (e.g., mirror, match, contrast, lead/follow) | Achieves more complex successive timing patterns (e.g., canon, question/answer, act/react) | Uses timing to achieve a specific goal (e.g., question/answer where the question is the lob and the answer is the smash) |
| Goal | Is able to work alone, but not able to collaborate or cooperate with others on a consistent basis; does not know or understand the elements of cooperation, collaboration, and competition | Is able to cooperate with self (e.g., working independently on a Lummi stick routine); is able to compete with self (e.g., improving the number of successful throws and catches in a row) | Is able to compete (e.g., win/lose), cooperate (e.g., help others), and collaborate (e.g., strategize) with others (e.g., everyone participates together in a Lummi stick routine in a class) | Is able to work cooperatively, collaboratively, or competitively in complex situations (e.g., doing a formal performance of a Lummi stick routine for an audience) |
| Environment | Works well in static environment (e.g., kicking a stationary ball) | Handles static environments well; begins to adapt to some dynamic environments (e.g., kicks a stationary ball well and is beginning to attempt kicking a variety of rolled balls) | Handles dynamic environments well (e.g., can kick a variety of balls [soccer or playground] rolled on ashphalt, dirt, grass, or indoor floor) | Continuously changes from static to dynamic and back relative to the context of the performance situation recognized by performer (e.g., can perform a soccer kick-in or kick a ball passed by a teammate to another teammate) |

# Progression Tools: Motor Program and Schema Theories

Application of technical theories to teaching movement education in the gymnasium provides the opportunity to help children learn in efficient ways. A brief understanding of motor program theory and schema theory provides the necessary background for the teaching methods that follow.

In motor program theory, generalized motor programs refer to what motor developmentalists like to term *fundamental motor skills* (e.g., cartwheel, slide). A class of movements in motor learning contains all of those fundamental motor skills. However, each class is separated by the type of invariant features they share. For example, a class of movements in motor learning typically corresponds with the movement elements in categories or subdivisions of a movement concept such as steplike actions or roll-like actions in the Body Concept. See table 3.8 for examples of how these movement education terms apply to motor learning. It may be helpful to have a copy of the Flip 'n' Fold available as you view table 3.8.

In schema theory, the rules for a particular outcome for a generalized motor program (motor skills, such as cartwheels) are termed the *schema*. The set of rules comes from practice. Practice of various parameter values (e.g., distances) helps a performer learn how far he needs to throw a ball. Teachers can help to set up practice situations that emphasize certain parameters of a motor skill (e.g., force, speed, distance). Knowing which parameters (e.g., distance) and what parameter values (e.g., 30 m, 90 m) are important for the actual performance of the skill in the real-life situation (e.g., target archery) is key to designing a great practice activity. The goal of practice, then, is to develop a very broad and stable set of variant parameters for a generalized motor program.

The main thing to note is that, no matter which theory or framework you use, it all boils down to having different ways to describe the same movements. Motor program theory uses fundamental motor skills and classes of movements. Schema theory uses schemas and parameter values. In the movement education framework, instead of fundamental motor skills, we use the phrase *movement elements* that are a part of a category. Specifically, the movement elements we present as part of the category of actions of the whole body are the same as the ones described in a generalized motor program as fundamental motor skills. But in the end, all three, despite the different labels, describe the same movements.

## Motor Learning Practice Method: Contextual Interference

A practice method called contextual interference is a way in which parameters can be organized that will result in much higher learning. It is thought that when a teacher uses a teaching technique of interference, the learner is challenged in new ways, which is possibly why there is greater learning. Performance tends to worsen initially, so preparing your learners and encouraging them so they know that the challenge will ultimately lead to better performance and may motivate them to try their best with this teaching technique. There are three common methods of organizing practice to create an environmental (contextual) desired interference for the performance:

**Table 3.8** Application of Motor Learning Terminology to Movement Education Terminology

| Motor learning terms | Movement class | Generalized motor program | Invariant features of skill | Schema (set of rules or variant parameters) |
|---|---|---|---|---|
| Movement education terms | Steplike actions | Cartwheel | Contact with support surface, weight transfer via hand-hand-foot-foot pattern | Direction: clockwise, counterclockwise |
| | Springlike actions | Slide | Foot strike, flight, toe-off | Level: low, medium, high |
| | Roll-like actions | Body roll | Approach, delivery, follow-through | Direction: sideways, forward, backward |
| | Send away | Throw | Backswing, foreswing, release, follow-through | Force: hard, soft |
| | Gain control | Catch | Flex, reach, hands, flex | Level: low, medium, high |
| | Propel | Dribble | Manipulate, run | Time: fast, slow |

1. blocked and constant,
2. random, and
3. variable (see table 3.9).

The simplest form of this practice is called blocked practice. It occurs when someone takes a single skill and repeats it several times in the same way, such as catch, catch, and catch. This method is often overused, and when it continues, it will result in less learning and lower performances. However, it is a great tool to use in early learning (initial and early elementary motor developmental stages), during warm-up, or for the first few minutes of performing a skill.

Random practice has the greatest potential for yielding learning. It involves practicing skills so that a single skill does not repeat itself. This is common for most real-life applications of motor skills and lifelong activities. An example in movement education might include creating an obstacle course where children must begin by walking, then jumping over a hurdle, and finally rolling. Walk, jump, and roll are three distinct skills that the child must perform. The change from one skill to another makes the performer do an internal comparing and contrasting (interference) that are thought to contribute to higher learning. Because of the potential for greater learning, it may be tempting to just implement the random practice method; however, the blocked and variable methods have an important place in the learning process.

The random method is thought to be so effective because changing the skill on each repetition forces the learner to rethink or remember how to perform the skill rather than just repeat a movement sequence without thinking (the forgetting hypothesis). The other common explanation for higher learning is that movements become more meaningful or more distinct to the performer because of the constant comparing and contrasting that occur due to the change in activity. Designing the practice activity with this in mind can be very effective. For example, having a child perform a forehand racket swing followed by a backhand racket swing presents the child with clues about why each skill is named the way it is (backhand is with the back of the hand facing the net) and also helps the child see that fewer steps are needed when pivoting for the backhand. Many other kinds of movement problems can be presented with the use of the random practice method.

Variable practice can be used alone and eventually should be used in combination with the random method. For example, throwing short, medium, and long distances in the same drill is variable practice; the variable emphasized is distance (see table 3.8). Throwing at different levels or with differing amounts of effort is also a good example of variable practice; level or effort is the variable that is manipulated (see table 3.8). A random variable application must combine more than one movement element (e.g., catch, throw) and more than one parameter (e.g., level, effort). If we put the previous example together, your practice might be catch high, throw softly, catch low, throw medium, and so on. It is most helpful to determine which variables are most important in the core content activities or complex movement applications you have and to use those in designing the practice situation. This method of practice builds the schema. Remember that a schema is a set of rules created by trying different parameters of the skill via variable practice.

Use each of these practice methods (blocked, random, and variable) when the situation calls

**Table 3.9** Teaching Progression Using Contextual Interference

| Developmental level | Methods of practice presentation | When to use practice method |
|---|---|---|
| Initial | Blocked | *First few minutes of a skill<br>*Warm-up<br>*Introducing new skills or concepts |
| Elementary | Variable | Working on movement elements in isolation |
| Mature | Random | Combining multiple movement elements |

Wrisberg, 2007, p. 104

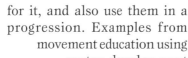

for it, and also use them in a progression. Examples from movement education using motor development and contextual interference methods are presented in table 3.10. This progression will create a natural environmental challenge that makes the performer work and think to solve a movement problem (a positive interference in the context of the activity). The ability to generate solutions to movement challenges with slightly greater difficulty will lead learners to greater movement success. This success can be motivating and can encourage children to make physical activity part of their lifelong habits, which is discussed more thoroughly in chapter 4.

## Motor Learning Practice Method: Part–Whole

Another method that can be used to create a teaching progression is the part method, also known as the part–whole method. This method is helpful when certain components of learning a motor skill need attention. Thus, part practice is usually used when complex movements are involved.

The three techniques for part practice are fractionalization, segmentation, and simplification.

These methods are presented in table 3.11 with an example from movement education and with an explanation of how that method was applied. All are very useful in teaching movement concepts, movement categories, and movement elements. More detail of these motor learning methods with easy-to-understand descriptions can be found in Wrisberg's textbook *Sport Skill Instruction for Coaches* (2007).

Use fractionalization when teaching a single movement element by itself. For example, the concept of self-space is often first taught in isolation with children on a poly spot or carpet square. General space is another movement element that is taught as one piece of the whole idea of space. This is a great tool for teaching a difficult section of the movement. Sometimes organizing the practice session for fractionalization is difficult or may seem like an inconvenience, but it may be necessary for the poorly skilled students. For example, when teaching throwing and catching, there is a natural tendency to combine these two elements; however, it may be better to work on each separately. Instead of pairing people to throw and catch back and forth, it might be better to organize it so that the children practice throwing to a wall or net instead of to a partner so that the catching does not become a barrier to throwing success, nor is catching a safety issue.

Segmentation (also called progressive part practice) is a popular tool in which the learner practices one component of a skill, then adds another related component to the practice, and so on, until the learner is performing the whole skill. Teaching the step and the hop might precede teaching

**Table 3.10** Sample Progressive Relationship Using Motor Development and Motor Learning

| Stage of motor development | Methods of practice presentation | Example of developmental progression in movement education |
|---|---|---|
| Initial | Blocked | *Self-toss and catch<br>*Seated toss and catch with partner |
| Elementary | Variable | One partner tosses and other partner catches at different distances |
| Later elementary | Random | Toss, catch, run: finding the open space |
| Early mature through transitional | Random and variable | *Toss, catch: working in triangles<br>*While playing a modified Ultimate Frisbee game, the various skills of toss, catch, run, and finding the open space |

**Table 3.11**  Part Practice Methods

| Part practice method | Visual representation of method | Example from movement education | Explanation |
|---|---|---|---|
| Fractionalization | | Self-space | Work on only one part of the space concept: self-space |
| Segmentation | | Skipping | Add a step plus a hop to make a skip |
| Simplification | | Striking—use a batting tee instead of a live pitch | A stationary ball is easier to hit than a moving pitch |

the skip to create a nice segmentation method in which students practice the step (each foot strike in a walk) and then the hop. The performers could take fewer steps and fewer hops until they alternately perform just one step followed by one hop (defined as a skip). Segmentation is an excellent tool in facilitating the learning process in the core content area of educational dance. You can teach each part of the dance separately and then put the steps or parts together to create the entire dance.

Modifying a particular piece of the movement or activity to make it easier to perform is the beauty behind the simplification method. Many pieces of equipment are designed specifically for this purpose. For example, teaching striking with the use of a batting tee makes it easier to contact the ball because it is stationary. You can also change the rules or guidelines of an activity to result in simplification. For example, allowing children to run and carry a basketball (typically a traveling violation of the rules) while working on passing to open spaces removes the difficulty of dribbling. When the difficulty of dribbling is removed, the focus can shift to the pass and looking for an open space.

# Tools for Observing and Assessing

The use of assessment in physical education can be a nice companion to the MEF. You must know whether your students are acquiring the knowledge you are imparting. Reporting student progress based on specific rubrics will enhance the viability of the profession. Assessments in relation to a movement education approach to teaching physical education can show students how well they are implementing the elements being presented, let you know whether students are understanding what you are teaching, and give parents and caregivers information about what their children are learning in physical education. The use of assessment in physical education can help you determine outcomes you can eventually measure. In addition, assessments in a movement education program can show administrators how grading or evaluation was conducted in the program.

This section provides samples of assessments to use in everyday lessons for the movement concept areas as well as the core content areas. The first is PE Metrics, a new assessment tool promoted by the National Association for Sport and Physical Education. The second set of assessments comes from actual teachers of physical education who have been involved with teaching movement education for many years. Finally, some tests from the field of motor development are discussed as additional options. It is critical to understand that the purpose of assessing students is to measure what they know and have learned, not to determine the full success, or lack thereof, of a physical education program.

## PE Metrics Assessment

*PE Metrics: Assessing the National Standards* (NASPE, 2008) was published to provide educators with valid and reliable rubrics or measures to assess some of the skills physical educators teach throughout the school year. NASPE suggests it is "important to use pre-assessment and formative assessment to communicate to students important skills and knowledge and to properly prepare students for summative assessment" (p. 3). Formative data may be gathered prior to or early in the delivery of instruction to answer the question, What do students already know?

Another tool to help develop formative assessment is the task analysis, in which teachers identify the outcomes they want to see at the end of a lesson or unit. Chapter 6 provides examples of task analyses for movement education. The movement elements and skills identified in the task analysis become the content for assessment.

Summative assessment occurs at the end of a lesson or unit and answers the following questions:

- How much did students learn as a result of the lesson or unit?
- Do I need to reteach the elements or skills?

## Sample Teacher and PE Metrics Assessments

The assessment tools presented in this text were obtained from two sources: elementary physical education teachers in the Madison Metropolitan School District of Madison, Wisconsin, and *PE Metrics: Assessing the National Standards*

(NASPE, 2008). We present a minimum number of assessment tools to give you an idea of the types of tools you might use to determine students' acquisition of movement framework elements. Assessment tools are provided for lower developmental stages (grade 2), and higher developmental stages (grade 5).

### Body Concept

An assessment rubric is provided in the Body Concept Assessment: Locomotor Sequences Rubric on page 49, and the Body Concept Assessment: Locomotor Sequences Score Sheet is provided on page 50. You may need to adapt how they assess students because the opportunity to videotape and analyze each student's performance may not be available. A station format may be more practical for many elementary physical educators. The same type of assessment tool and rubric may be used for other locomotor skills (e.g., steplike actions) as well. An example of an assessment tool for skipping (from a Madison, Wisconsin, teacher) is provided in the Body Concept Assessment: Skipping on page 51. This tool can be altered to fit other springlike actions as well. A rolling assessment is on page 52.

The worksheets on pages 53-59 are examples of assessments of manipulative skills for both lower and higher developmental stages (elementary and mature). We chose examples from grades 2 and 5 of underhand throwing, striking, catching, kicking, and volleying. A variety of assessment examples are provided. You may choose to alter these to fit your needs as well as to substitute other manipulative skills.

## Space Concept

The Space Concept Assessment: Pathway on page 60 provides an example of an assessment of the pathway category in the space concept. The student is asked to list and draw a picture of three pathways. This assessment may be adapted to fit other categories in the space concept area. Students may be asked to draw pictures of directions or levels. They may also be asked to write about what tasks they have done that demonstrated moving in different directions or at different levels. Students at higher developmental stages may be asked to demonstrate written or pictorial knowledge of moving in various planes. Some uses of planes are found in the educational gymnastics and dance assessments as well on pages 64 and 68.

## Effort Concept

The Effort Concept Assessment: Action Words on page 61 is an example of an action word story. An action word story encourages students to write a story using movement action words. Students can move like the identified words. For example, if a student chooses the word *crush,* they might move with strong, powerful movements. Students will identify action (movement) words and then write a story about these movements. Students choose action words to represent categories in the effort concept area. For example, from words that relate to the force category, students might choose *pow, poof, slash, crush, smash, fluff,* or *pause.* From the time category, students may choose words that represent different ways to move that depict slow, fast, and changes in speed (e.g., *slither, inflate, bounce, stride, shuffle, crawl, run, waddle*). In addition to (or instead of) writing the action words, younger children might create pictures of the actions they choose. As noted on the assessment sheet, the action words are then placed in a story format (either written or drawn), thus addressing sequencing as well.

## Relationships Concept

The Relationships Concept Assessment: Working With a Partner, Relationships Concept Assessment: Basketball Ball-Handling Routine, Educational Games Assessment: Game Creation, and Educational Games Assessment: Movement Relay on pages 62, 63, 69, and 70 provide assessments for the relationships concept. Because this concept

area has multiple elements, providing assessment tools for each category was not possible. We chose to provide assessments for the people and goal categories. The assessments provided address partner work and small group or cooperative work. Partners can demonstrate how they worked together by helping each other succeed. Groups can identify how they cooperated in creating a basketball routine or designed a game in which everyone was successful.

## Educational Games

The Educational Games Assessment: Floor Hockey Rubric on page 71 presents examples of assessments in floor hockey from the educational games core content area. Included are skill assessments for dribbling and shooting for grade 5 (mature developmental stage). Adapt these assessments to your own needs.

## Educational Gymnastics

The Body Concept Assessment: Rolling (Body) on page 52 and the Body Concept Assessment: Balancing on page 48 provide examples of assessments from the educational gymnastics core content area. Students are asked to provide examples of rolling and balancing. Other educational gymnastic assessments might include students demonstrating knowledge of steplike actions such as the bear walk, the cartwheel, or the rolling actions of rocking. Students might also provide examples of a routine as demonstrated in the Educational Gymnastics Assessment: Creating a Routine on pages 64-65 and the Educational Gymnastics Assessment: Peer and Teacher Observation on page 66. This type of assessment emphasizes the problem-solving approach that is critical to the movement education perspective.

## Educational Dance

Assessments in educational dance may be focused on specific elements such as rising and sinking (actions of the whole body in the body concept), flow (free versus bound in the effort concept), question and answer, or act/react (timing in the relationships concept). You may also choose to ask children to demonstrate a dance or movement routine that shows rhythmic step content as in the Educational Dance Assessment: Rhythm Step Evaluation on page 67. This may be appropriate for children at an elementary developmental stage.

The Educational Dance Assessment: Rhythmic Dance and Gymnastics Routine on page 68 is an example of an assessment for children at a mature developmental stage. This type of routine or creative dance asks children to demonstrate knowledge of more complicated elements such as symmetrical, asymmetrical, group formations, and counterbalance.

## Other Assessment Tools

Many other types of assessment are available in addition to the assessment tools discussed in this chapter. The *Test of Gross Motor Development—2* (Ulrich, 2000), for use with children without disabilities and those suspected of developmental delays, is a simple but validated system with clear behavior descriptions and a set of norms to help interpretation. Ignico (1992) created a very helpful set of DVDs in which educators can observe 8 to 10 children performing 12 different fundamental movement patterns. The set provides a simple verbal and visual analysis using stop action and yes or no answers after viewers are asked to make their own assessments based on their own observations. More written practical examples of performance criteria can be found in the NASPE *Moving Into the Future* (2004a) document. Finally, additional insight can be found in motor development textbooks such as those by Payne and Issacs (2007) and Haywood and Getchell (2009).

## Putting It All Together in the Gym

You must be able to observe children and identify the motor developmental stage they are operating at to provide lessons that span these developmental stages. Children in various grades and of various ages operate at multiple stages of development (initial, elementary, mature, and transitional). To provide lessons for children that are not only developmentally appropriate, but also allow all children to be successful, you must determine their developmental stages using the motor development stage criteria blended with the performance criteria. You must look at tasks and activities that are labeled for particular grade levels and determine whether they will truly be appropriate for the developmental stages of your students.

## Summary

The developmental perspective provided in this chapter is based upon both motor development and motor learning theories. We chose ideas that can be useful and practical in the field. We began with a presentation of four motor development stages (initial, elementary, mature, and transitional). We then provided a series of unique tables (3.4-3.7) that provide specific examples of how the movement elements can be applied to each of the motor development stages. We addressed the issue of creating teaching progressions using ideas from motor learning (generalized motor program schema theory). Practice methods using blocked, random, and variable aspects of skills are applied to the MEF. Three different methods of part/whole practice (segmentation, fractionalization, and simplification) are also applied to the MEF. This chapter closes with assessment tools and examples, PE Metrics (NASPE, 2008), the four movement concepts, and the three core content areas as applied to the MEF.

# Quick-Find Table: Examples of Movement Education Assessment Forms

| | Assessment | Page number |
|---|---|---|
| **Movement concepts** | | |
| Body | Balancing | 48 |
| | Locomotor sequences rubric and score sheet | 49-50 |
| | Skipping | 51 |
| | Rolling | 52 |
| | Striking with body parts | 53 |
| | Put the bat swing in order | 54 |
| | Underhand throw | 55 |
| | Throwing knowledge | 56 |
| | Kicking | 57 |
| | Volleying | 58 |
| | Catching | 59 |
| Space | Pathway | 60 |
| Effort | Action words | 61 |
| Relationship | Working with a partner | 62 |
| | Basketball ball-handling routine | 63 |
| **Core content areas** | | |
| Educational gymnastics | Creating a routine | 64 |
| | Peer and teacher observations | 66 |
| Educational dance | Rhythm step evaluation | 67 |
| | Rhythmic dance and gymnastics routine | 68 |
| Educational games | Game creation | 69 |
| | Movement relay | 70 |
| | Floor hockey rubric | 71 |

# Body Concept Assessment: Balancing

Name _____

Draw two different balances.

From K. Weiller Abels and J.M. Bridges, 2010, *Teaching Movement Education: Foundations for Active Lifestyles* (Champaign, IL: Human Kinetics). J. Koval, K. Myers, and L. Vande Sande, 1995, Elementary Physical Education Assessment and Portfolio Potpourri, (Madison, WI: Madison Metropolitan School District).

# Body Concept Assessment: Locomotor Sequences Rubric

Name _____

| Level | Locomotor pattern | Transitions |
|---|---|---|
| 4 | Performs 3 locomotor movements with mature patterns and with fluid motion. | Smooth fluid transitions throughout the sequence. |
| 3 | Performs 3 locomotor movements with mature patterns. | Transitions between locomotor movements are smooth. |
| 2 | Performs 2 of 3 locomotor movements with mature patterns. | One transition is not smooth. |
| 1 | Performs 1 or no locomotor movements with a mature pattern. | More than one transition is not smooth. |
| 0 | Violates safety procedures or does not complete the assessment task. | |

From National Association for Sport and Physical Education, an association of the American Alliance for Health, Physical Education, Recreation and Dance, p. 70.

From K. Weiller Abels and J.M. Bridges, 2010, *Teaching Movement Education: Foundations for Active Lifestyles* (Champaign, IL: Human Kinetics).

# Body Concept Assessment: Locomotor Sequences Score Sheet

Name _____

| Student name | ID number | Gender | Locomotor patterns (0-4) | Transitions (0-4) | Total score (0-8) 6 = competent |
|---|---|---|---|---|---|
| | | | | | |
| | | | | | |
| | | | | | |

From National Association for Sport and Physical Education, an association of the American Alliance for Health, Physical Education, Recreation and Dance, p. 72.

From K. Weiller Abels and J.M. Bridges, 2010, *Teaching Movement Education: Foundations for Active Lifestyles* (Champaign, IL: Human Kinetics).

# Body Concept Assessment: Skipping

Name _____

This is what I know about skipping.

1. Each foot gets to be the leader when you skip.   Yes    No

2. You step and hop on the leader foot.    Yes    No

3. You land on the back of your foot.     Yes    No

4. Skipping can go forward or backward.    Yes    No

5. I am a good skipper.         Yes    No

From K. Weiller Abels and J.M. Bridges, 2010, *Teaching Movement Education: Foundations for Active Lifestyles* (Champaign, IL: Human Kinetics). J. Koval, K. Myers, and L. Vande Sande, 1995, Elementary Physical Education Assessment and Portfolio Potpourri, (Madison, WI: Madison Metropolitan School District).

# Body Concept Assessment: Rolling (Body)

Name _____

I am learning how to roll in physical education. I showed my two best rolls to a partner and this is how I did!

| | | | |
|---|---|---|---|
| Log roll | 🙂 | 😐 | ☹️ |
| Egg roll | 🙂 | 😐 | ☹️ |
| Forward roll | 🙂 | 😐 | ☹️ |

My detective was _____

From K. Weiller Abels and J.M. Bridges, 2010, *Teaching Movement Education: Foundations for Active Lifestyles* (Champaign, IL: Human Kinetics). J. Koval, K. Myers, and L. Vande Sande, 1995, Elementary Physical Education Assessment and Portfolio Potpourri, (Madison, WI: Madison Metropolitan School District).

# Body Concept Assessment: Striking With Body Parts

Name _____

## How Many Body Parts Can You Strike With?

Use a large punch-ball balloon or a very soft ball to practice your striking skills at home. Circle the skills you did at home. On the blank next to the skill you circled, write the name of the body part you used to strike the balloon or ball.

Body parts: elbow, knee, head, arm, shoulder, hand

Underhand strike _____   Strike with shoulder _____

Strike with elbow _____   Strike with knee _____

Overhead strike _____   Strike with head _____

Parent's signature _____

From K. Weiller Abels and J.M. Bridges, 2010, *Teaching Movement Education: Foundations for Active Lifestyles* (Champaign, IL: Human Kinetics). J. Koval, K. Myers, and L. Vande Sande, 1995, Elementary Physical Education Assessment and Portfolio Potpourri, (Madison, WI: Madison Metropolitan School District).

# Body Concept Assessment: Put the Bat Swing in Order

Name _____

The pictures below are in the wrong order. The striking swing is not done like this. Using the numbers 1-4, put the swing back in the right order. Put the numbers above the pictures. The first is already in place for you.

From K. Weiller Abels and J.M. Bridges, 2010, *Teaching Movement Education: Foundations for Active Lifestyles* (Champaign, IL: Human Kinetics). J. Koval, K. Myers, and L. Vande Sande, 1995, Elementary Physical Education Assessment and Portfolio Potpourri, (Madison, WI: Madison Metropolitan School District).

# Body Concept Assessment: Underhand Throw

Name _____

1. Can you throw a ball underhand?

   😊        😐        ☹️

2. How do you throw a ball underhand?

3. Do you like to throw underhand?

   😊        😐        ☹️

From K. Weiller Abels and J.M. Bridges, 2010, *Teaching Movement Education: Foundations for Active Lifestyles* (Champaign, IL: Human Kinetics). J. Koval, K. Myers, and L. Vande Sande, 1995, Elementary Physical Education Assessment and Portfolio Potpourri, (Madison, WI: Madison Metropolitan School District).

# Body Concept Assessment: Throwing Knowledge

Name _____

1. What does your body do in a good overarm throw?

2. What games or activities use an overarm throw?

3. What can you do to get more force and make a ball go farther?

4. List the types of balls you can throw overarm.

Teacher's box

Critical elements: ____/5
Force: ____/2
Complete: ____/3
Total: ____/10 ____
Lists: ____

From K. Weiller Abels and J.M. Bridges, 2010, *Teaching Movement Education: Foundations for Active Lifestyles* (Champaign, IL: Human Kinetics). J. Koval, K. Myers, and L. Vande Sande, 1995, Elementary Physical Education Assessment and Portfolio Potpourri, (Madison, WI: Madison Metropolitan School District).

# Body Concept Assessment: Kicking

Name _____

## How to kick

Place an X on the parts of the foot you can kick with.

List games and activities that use kicking.

## Making the skill of kicking

Easy                                    Hard

_____    _____

_____    _____

_____    _____

_____    _____

_____    _____

_____    _____

_____    _____

From K. Weiller Abels and J.M. Bridges, 2010, *Teaching Movement Education: Foundations for Active Lifestyles* (Champaign, IL: Human Kinetics). J. Koval, K. Myers, and L. Vande Sande, 1995, Elementary Physical Education Assessment and Portfolio Potpourri, (Madison, WI: Madison Metropolitan School District).

# Body Concept Assessment: Volleying

Name _____

Score

    *   Did it every time       +   Did it sometimes       O   Never did it

_____ Ball held at waist level

_____ Striking arm straight

_____ Hits with heel of hand

_____ Big, fast arm swing

_____ Steps with opposite foot

_____ Arm follows through straight ahead

Checklist tester _____

Score

    O   Good       X   Oops!

| 1 | 2 | 3 | 4 | 5 | 6 | 7 | 8 | 9 | 10 |
|---|---|---|---|---|---|---|---|---|---|
| 1 | 2 | 3 | 4 | 5 | 6 | 7 | 8 | 9 | 10 |

The net tester _____

Best total = _____

From K. Weiller Abels and J.M. Bridges, 2010, *Teaching Movement Education: Foundations for Active Lifestyles* (Champaign, IL: Human Kinetics). J. Koval, K. Myers, and L. Vande Sande, 1995, Elementary Physical Education Assessment and Portfolio Potpourri, (Madison, WI: Madison Metropolitan School District).

# Body Concept Assessment: Catching

Name _____

My partner(s) today was (were) _____

1. Circle the types of equipment you tried catching with today.

   Yarn ball      Foam ball

   "Mush" ball     Football

   Nerf ball      Tennis ball

   Beanbag

2. Which equipment type(s) worked best for you? Why?

3. Did your partner(s) like the same equipment you did?

4. If not, how did your group compromise on choosing equipment so everyone in your group could be successful?

From K. Weiller Abels and J.M. Bridges, 2010, *Teaching Movement Education: Foundations for Active Lifestyles* (Champaign, IL: Human Kinetics). J. Koval, K. Myers, and L. Vande Sande, 1995, Elementary Physical Education Assessment and Portfolio Potpourri, (Madison, WI: Madison Metropolitan School District).

# Space Concept Assessment: Pathway

Name _____

List three pathways and draw a picture of each.

1.

2.

3.

From K. Weiller Abels and J.M. Bridges, 2010, *Teaching Movement Education: Foundations for Active Lifestyles* (Champaign, IL: Human Kinetics). J. Koval, K. Myers, and L. Vande Sande, 1995, Elementary Physical Education Assessment and Portfolio Potpourri, (Madison, WI: Madison Metropolitan School District).

# Effort Concept Assessment: Action Words

Name _____

## Directions

1. Pick six action words and write a story that uses all six words.

2. Write the story in the space below, underlining the action words.

3. Think of movements to show the story and the six underlined action words.

4. Practice the story with actions.

5. When you are prepared to share, come see the teacher.

Write your story here:

From K. Weiller Abels and J.M. Bridges, 2010, *Teaching Movement Education: Foundations for Active Lifestyles* (Champaign, IL: Human Kinetics). J. Koval, K. Myers, and L. Vande Sande, 1995, Elementary Physical Education Assessment and Portfolio Potpourri, (Madison, WI: Madison Metropolitan School District).

# Relationships Concept Assessment: Working With a Partner

Name _____

1. While working in class today, I changed something so my partner or classmate could succeed or learn.

   Yes          No

2. I changed:

   _____ Equipment

   _____ Rules

   _____ Other

3. I still had fun doing the activity because _____

   _____

   _____

From K. Weiller Abels and J.M. Bridges, 2010, *Teaching Movement Education: Foundations for Active Lifestyles* (Champaign, IL: Human Kinetics). J. Koval, K. Myers, and L. Vande Sande, 1995, Elementary Physical Education Assessment and Portfolio Potpourri, (Madison, WI: Madison Metropolitan School District).

# Relationships Concept Assessment: Basketball Ball-Handling Routine

Team members

_____    _____    _____

Our routine includes six moves. The routine includes two from each ball-handling area: dribbling (D), passing to a partner (P), passing around the body (BP), and two-arm strength (S) moves. We can repeat our routine for the length of the song, and we can do the routine in a synchronized fashion (all together).

|    | Number of times | Kind of move (see above—D, P, BP, or S) |
|----|-----------------|-----------------------------------------|
| 1. |                 |                                         |
| 2. |                 |                                         |
| 3. |                 |                                         |
| 4. |                 |                                         |
| 5. |                 |                                         |
| 6. |                 |                                         |
| 7. |                 |                                         |
| 8. |                 |                                         |

Music: Wipe Out or Sweet Georgia Brown or Surfin'

Completed correctly: _____

Neatness: _____

Synchronized: _____

Creativity: _____

From K. Weiller Abels and J.M. Bridges, 2010, *Teaching Movement Education: Foundations for Active Lifestyles* (Champaign, IL: Human Kinetics). J. Koval, K. Myers, and L. Vande Sande, 1995, Elementary Physical Education Assessment and Portfolio Potpourri, (Madison, WI: Madison Metropolitan School District).

# Educational Gymnastics Assessment: Creating a Routine

Name _____

I need to have at least:

| | |
|---|---|
| Two balances | 1. |
| | 2. |
| Two rolls | 1. |
| | 2. |
| One travel | 1. |
| One jump or leap | 1. |

I can add up to four more moves if I want to.

## Routine Ideas

**Beginning and ending shapes and balances (choose 4)**

Lunge
Stretch
Squat
Straddle
Pike
V-sit
Knee lunge
Scale
Knee scale
Passe
Candle
Tuck
Arabesque
Tripod
Headstand
Other _____

**Tumbling moves (choose 3)**

Egg roll
Forward tuck roll
Forward straddle roll
Mule kick
Cartwheel
Round-off
Other _____
Other _____

From K. Weiller Abels and J.M. Bridges, 2010, *Teaching Movement Education: Foundations for Active Lifestyles* (Champaign, IL: Human Kinetics). J. Koval, K. Myers, and L. Vande Sande, 1995, Elementary Physical Education Assessment and Portfolio Potpourri, (Madison, WI: Madison Metropolitan School District).

Connectives and locomotion (choose 3)

Walk

Run

Gallop

Jump

Leap

Skip

Slide

Chase

Turn

Spin

Interesting changes

Directions: forward, backward, sideways

Levels: high, low, medium

Speeds: fast, slow, medium

Planes: sagittal, frontal, transverse

Shapes: curled, straight, wide

I changed these things to make my routine interesting:

My routine is (include all of the above in a special order):

1.

2.

3.

4.

5.

6.

7.

8.

9.

10.

## Evaluation

Have a friend watch, score, and sign.

| Practice 1 | 1 | 3 | 5 | |
|---|---|---|---|---|
| Practice 2 | 1 | 3 | 5 | |

From K. Weiller Abels and J.M. Bridges, 2010, *Teaching Movement Education: Foundations for Active Lifestyles* (Champaign, IL: Human Kinetics). J. Koval, K. Myers, and L. Vande Sande, 1995, Elementary Physical Education Assessment and Portfolio Potpourri, (Madison, WI: Madison Metropolitan School District).

# Educational Gymnastics Assessment:
## Peer and Teacher Observations

Name _____

1. _____

2. _____

3. _____

4. _____

5. _____

6. _____

7. _____

8. _____

9. _____

10. _____

## Evaluation

1. Show your routine to another group.

1     2     3     4     5     6     7     8     9     10

2. Show your routine to the teacher.

| | | | |
|---|---|---|---|
| Requirements | 1 | 2 | 3 |
| Flow | 1 | 2 | 3 |
| Group work | 1 | 2 | 3 |

From K. Weiller Abels and J.M. Bridges, 2010, *Teaching Movement Education: Foundations for Active Lifestyles* (Champaign, IL: Human Kinetics). J. Koval, K. Myers, and L. Vande Sande, 1995, Elementary Physical Education Assessment and Portfolio Potpourri, (Madison, WI: Madison Metropolitan School District).

# Educational Dance Assessment: Rhythm Step Evaluation

Name _____

| Does the routine show the safe use of steps? | Yes | No |
|---|---|---|
| Is the routine creative? | Yes | No |
| Does the routine have at least 24 counts of music? | Yes | No |
| Does the routine have at least four different steps? | Yes | No |
| Do the movements match the rhythm of the music? | Yes | No |
| Are there three or fewer people in the group? | Yes | No |

If the answer to any one of these is no, please find a solution that will make the answer a yes.

From K. Weiller Abels and J.M. Bridges, 2010, *Teaching Movement Education: Foundations for Active Lifestyles* (Champaign, IL: Human Kinetics). J. Koval, K. Myers, and L. Vande Sande, 1995, Elementary Physical Education Assessment and Portfolio Potpourri, (Madison, WI: Madison Metropolitan School District).

# Educational Dance Assessment:
# Rhythmic Dance and Gymnastics Routine

Name _____

During the rhythmic dance and gymnastics unit, I chose to do a routine with the:

hoop    ball    ribbon

My routine was:

☺          😐          ☹

Write the following planes under the correct picture:

S = sagittal    F = frontal    T = transverse

From K. Weiller Abels and J.M. Bridges, 2010, *Teaching Movement Education: Foundations for Active Lifestyles* (Champaign, IL: Human Kinetics). J. Koval, K. Myers, and L. Vande Sande, 1995, Elementary Physical Education Assessment and Portfolio Potpourri, (Madison, WI: Madison Metropolitan School District).

# Educational Games Assessment: Game Creation

Name _____

Name of game: _____

Name of evaluator: _____

Was the game fun? _____

Was the game safe? _____

Did everyone get equal playing time? _____

Did everyone work together for a common goal? _____

From K. Weiller Abels and J.M. Bridges, 2010, *Teaching Movement Education: Foundations for Active Lifestyles* (Champaign, IL: Human Kinetics). J. Koval, K. Myers, and L. Vande Sande, 1995, Elementary Physical Education Assessment and Portfolio Potpourri, (Madison, WI: Madison Metropolitan School District).

# Educational Games Assessment: Movement Relay

Name _____

Directions: You and your partners need to come up with four different legs of a relay using a different locomotor skill element and two different space elements for each person. If it helps, you can name them all here:

Locomotor (7):          Directions (3):          Levels (3):          Pathways (3):

You must write out what each person is doing in each leg of the relay. You will turn these plans in before the relay and each person in your group must do one of the legs you chose. If someone does not do it as you have stated, they may have to return to the beginning and do it over. Remember, you are trying to come up with combinations that will get you to the end the fastest while still performing the movements correctly.

Person 1:

Person 2:

Person 3:

Person 4:

From K. Weiller Abels and J.M. Bridges, 2010, *Teaching Movement Education: Foundations for Active Lifestyles* (Champaign, IL: Human Kinetics). J. Koval, K. Myers, and L. Vande Sande, 1995, Elementary Physical Education Assessment and Portfolio Potpourri, (Madison, WI: Madison Metropolitan School District).

# Educational Games Assessment: Floor Hockey Rubric

Name _____

| Level | Dribble | Shoot |
|---|---|---|
| 4 | Displays all the essential elements with fluid motion. | Shoots using all the essential elements with fluid motion |
| 3 | Dribbles the hockey puck with all essential elements.<br>a) grip of hockey stick with dominant hand lower, thumbs pointing to ground, hands apart<br>b) continuous dribble<br>c) uses both sides of stick<br>d) maintains slow jog | Shoots using all the essential elements.<br>a) sets up for shot by trapping or controlling the puck<br>b) uses a push shot<br>c) follows through to target |
| 2 | Dribbles with 3 of 4 essential elements present. | Shoots using 2 of 3 essential elements |
| 1 | Dribbles with 2 or fewer essential elements present. | Shoots using only 1 of 3 of the essential elements. |
| 0 | Violates safety procedures or does not complete the assessment task. | |

From National Association for Sport and Physical Education, an association of the American Alliance for Health, Physical Education, Recreation and Dance, 2008, p. 95.

From K. Weiller Abels and J.M. Bridges, 2010, *Teaching Movement Education: Foundations for Active Lifestyles* (Champaign, IL: Human Kinetics).

# Foundation for an Active Lifestyle

The scientific and empirical evidence is indisputable—life-long participation in physical activity has a significant positive impact on people's health and well-being" (NASPE, 2005, p. 3). The current view of the importance of physical activity suggests that the process, or behavior, of physical activity should be promoted, rather than the product, or outcome (fitness). The reason is that physical activity (e.g., exercise walking) can continue into adulthood, whereas the product of developing fitness (e.g., aerobic endurance) is maintained only if the person maintains the same level of physical activity. Those in the physical education profession have been clear about the role of physical education for children: to promote a lifetime of physical activity (Meredith & Welk, 2007). A summary of the general statement in the *National Standards for Physical Education* states that "Physical activity is critical to the development and maintenance of good health. The goal of physical education is to develop physically educated individuals who have the knowledge, skills, and confidence to enjoy a lifetime of healthful physical activity" (NASPE, 2004, p. 11).

## Working with Physical Activity Guidelines for Children

The National Association for Sport and Physical Education (NASPE) has published guidelines for recommended levels of physical activity for children (2004).

- Guideline 1. Children should accumulate at least 60 minutes, and up to several hours, of age-appropriate physical activity on all, or most, days of the week. This daily accumulation should include moderate and vigorous physical activity with the majority of the time being spent in activity that is intermittent in nature.

- Guideline 2. Children should participate in several bouts of physical activity lasting 15 minutes or more each day.

- Guideline 3. Children should participate each day in a variety of age-appropriate physical activities designed to achieve optimal health, wellness, fitness, and performance benefits."

Guideline 1 in the previous bulleted list makes an important note: "This daily accumulation should include moderate and vigorous physical activity with the majority of the time being spent in activity that is intermittent in nature." Teachers are beginning to measure moderate to vigorous physical activity (MVPA). Although it is not totally clear what constitutes moderate or vigorous physical activity for elementary school children (Guinhouya et al., 2006), the Walk4Life (model M4L MVP) is an example of a pedometer designed to measure MVPA (hence the name MVP). More information on the NASPE guidelines related to pedometer use is presented in chapter 5.

Of the total physical activity time that young children should get, "the time allocation for elementary physical education [is] a minimum of 150 minutes per week of instructional physical education across the school year" (NASPE, 2009, p. 1). Further, "the length of the daily class period was described as appropriate to the needs and maturation of the learner with 30 minutes as the suggested minimum" (NASPE, 2009, p. 1). Classroom teachers, too, can use many of the methods described in this book to contribute to the total number of students' physical activity minutes. Throughout the day or in physical education, both classroom and physical education teachers can then coordinate their data to create meaningful report cards as suggested in the proposed FIT Kids Act, which is discussed in more detail later in this chapter (NASPE, 2008). Pedometers can be an excellent tool for assessing how long students are active by translating time into a number of steps. Lessons in chapters 11 through 13 are approximately 30 minutes long. You can use these lesson times to help build units and a curriculum that will meet NASPE guideline 2 of obtaining several bouts of at least 15 minutes of physical activity during the day. You can also make sure that you are meeting the NASPE instructional minimum for elementary children of providing at least 150 minutes of physical activity during the week (NASPE, 2004a).

Even though the NASPE guidelines for and the goal of developing physically educated and physically active people are clear, it does not appear that these are being successfully met, especially for children. According to data from the Shape of the Nation Report (NASPE, 2006, p. 8):

- The percentage of young people who are overweight has more than tripled since 1980. Among children and teens aged 6 to 19 years, 16 percent (over 9 million young people) are overweight.
- About 10 percent of children aged 2 to 5 years are overweight.
- Four in 10 Mexican-American and African-American youth age 6 to 19 are overweight or at risk of being overweight.
- Approximately 60 percent of obese children ages 5 to 10 years have at least one cardiovascular disease risk factor, such as elevated total cholesterol, triglycerides, insulin levels, or blood pressure, and 25 percent have two or more risk factors.
- Children and adolescents who are overweight by the age of 8 are 80 percent more likely to become overweight or obese adults.

From *Shape of the nation report: Status of physical education in the USA,* with permission from the National Association for Sport and Physical Education (NASPE), 1900 Association Drive, Reston, VA 20191, USA.

## Connecting Fitness With Academic Learning

In addition to providing health benefits, an active lifestyle has positive influences on the brain and cognitive learning. The California Department of Education (2005) used the Fitnessgram test of physical fitness and the California Standardized Tests for English-Language Arts and Mathematics to evaluate the relationship between physical fitness and academic achievement. Results showed that "there was a strong positive relationship between physical fitness and academic achievement" and that "this cumulative evidence indicates that conditions that improve general health promote both a healthy body and improved intellectual capacity" (p. 6).

Legislators are also recognizing the link between physical activity and academics. "The statistics on childhood obesity are staggering, and we need to get them going in the other direction. Research shows that healthy children learn more effectively and achieve more academically. The proposed FIT Kids Act also ensures a strong emphasis on physical education to help bolster academic performance and provide students with the physical activity and education to lead healthy lifestyles," said Congressman Wamp, founder and co-chair of the Congressional Fitness Caucus (NASPE, 2007).

The No Child Left Behind (NCLB) Act would allow for the integration of the physical aspects of learning for both academic and health-enhancing reasons if the new proposed FIT Kids Act (H.R. 3257) is passed. The FIT Kids Act would require schools, districts, and states to include the quantity and quality of physical education in report cards sent to parents (NASPE, 2007). If a national physical education report card documented the number of minutes of physical activity achieved by a student per week, the nation would have a better knowledge of whether or not NASPE's 150-minute recommendation is being met.

# Movement Education and Active Lifestyles

The significant issue of inactive and overweight youth can be addressed effectively in a movement education program. Success for all and movement for all are philosophies inherent in a movement education and fitness approach to teaching. The development of health-related fitness is not a separate goal, but one that is built naturally into the movement education program. Health-related fitness includes components of cardiovascular fitness, muscular strength and endurance, body composition, and flexibility. Thus, a separate fitness unit, while valued, is not needed in movement education. Because movement education is fitness based, teachers using this approach make efficient use of the often minimally allotted time for physical education.

Heart rate monitors and pedometers can be used to create exciting problem-solving activities, which are so important in movement education. The inclusion of these technologies directly supports the development and assessment of the cardiovascular component of health-related fitness. The movement elements included in the body concept (e.g., body parts) provide multiple opportunities to teach about body composition. Height and weight are ideas related to the Body Concepts and both of these are used to calculate body mass index (BMI), a useful body composition assessment. The fitness component of flexibility connects well with the nonlocomotor skills and body shapes content from the movement education framework (MEF). For example, making a wide body shape, which usually involves expanding, and the nonlocomotor stretch are typically parts of flexibility. Finally, muscular strength and endurance aspects of health-related fitness find a nice home in all of the effort concepts. Chapters 11 through 13 include more specific examples of how to include fitness components as a natural extension of movement concepts in a movement education lesson.

# Using Pedometers to Measure Physical Activity

To help you determine the degree to which movement education activities contribute to the attainment of physical activity guidelines, lessons in this book (chapters 11-13) provide approximate physical activity time (PAT) values. These were attained from a pilot study of 713 children performing the activities wearing the Walk4Life (model W4L MVP) pedometer.

We used a field test using the lessons in chapters 11 through 13 to assess the viability of the MEF pocket chart cards and pedometers, as well as to suggest that the MEF approach to teaching physical education can result in children's being physically active while providing them a content-based approach to learning movement. Research assistants trained in movement education conducted the lessons and collected the data. Children at two elementary schools, grades K through 5, in the Dallas-Fort Worth, Texas, area participated in the study. It was our goal to identify how much physical activity time (PAT) children received during movement education lessons.

The graphs in figure 4.1 on page 77 show the results from both elementary schools. Reported are the lesson core content area, the grade level, and the percentage of the total class time during which the children were physically active (PAT).

- Educational games: There were two games in which children engaged for the core content area of educational games. At school 1, all students in grades 1 through 4 achieved 50 percent PAT available for movement during game 1. However, for game 2, students in grades 1 through 3 did not achieve 50 percent PAT, but students in grades K and 4 did. At school 2, students in grades 2 through 5 achieved 50 percent PAT during both games.
- Educational gymnastics: In educational gymnastics, students at school 1 achieved 50 percent PAT available for movement in this core content area. At school 2, only students in grades 2 and 3 achieved 50 percent PAT.
- Educational dance: As demonstrated in the graphs, children at school 1 achieved 50 percent PAT available for movement during educational dance in grades 1, 2, 3, and 4. However, at school 2, only students in grades 2 and 3 achieved this 50 percent goal.

Although total possible activity time was limited for many classes because of a variety of factors, children were still able to achieve 50 percent PAT during many of the lessons. These preliminary data demonstrate that fitness goals in all core content areas can reasonably be achieved. At least one bar in one of the graphs for each grade and each core content area is above the 50 percent level. We hope that future research studies will provide more specific data regarding any unique characteristics among the core content areas, the movement elements, and the use of pedometers in tracking physical activity. Additional practical suggestions on how to best implement teaching strategies as well as how to apply assessment using pedometers in the promotion of positive health-related fitness benefits in a movement education program need to be developed.

# Youth Physical Activity Promotion Model (YPAPM)

Welk's Youth Physical Activity Promotion Model (1999), shown in figure 4.2 on page 78, complements the MEF. The traditional individual, or interpersonal, model of physical activity and fitness education focuses only on the student, with instruction and feedback given to students only. The obesity epidemic, along with the discovery of the cognitive benefits of lifetime physical activity, indicates the need for a philosophical model with a broader focus than fitness or the individual. The YPAPM, which is recognized in the *Fitnessgram Test Administration Manual*, is such a model; it philosophically attends to the broader socio-cultural needs of children in the United States. The following sections address the predisposing, enabling, and reinforcing factors of the YPAPM and explain how they are connected to the MEF.

## YPAPM Predisposing Factors

What makes a child want to participate in physical activity are the predisposing factors. Meredith and Welk (2007) suggest that both feeling like physical activity is worth it and competence are critical motivators that predispose someone to exercise. Enjoyment of the physical activity is extremely important to making participation worth it. The MEF approach allows children to discover benefits to participation, such as enjoyment, that are relevant to them personally. Thus the MEF approach can be a strong motivator for children to choose physical activity.

A child's perception of her skill is competence. Essentially, she is asking, "Am I going to be successful?" Children in sport or competition-based physical education programs can easily feel unsuccessful and thus may not enjoy and may not want to participate in physical activity. The basic philosophy of a movement education program focuses on everyone having success and opportunities for problem solving. Because success is more a matter of experience than of determining winners and losers, the movement education approach can result in very high rates of self-perceived success.

As noted in chapter 2, essential to the MEF is providing knowledge that forms a foundation for movement. This important piece provides an opportunity for those who are not as physically gifted as others to demonstrate cognitive proficiency in solving their own movement problems. MEF lessons that encourage children to solve movement problems and develop skills based on movement knowledge result in more positive answers to the questions Am I able? and Is it worth it?

## YPAPM Enabling Factors

What elements help children be physically active? According to Meredith and Welk (2007), access to facilities, equipment, and programs that promote

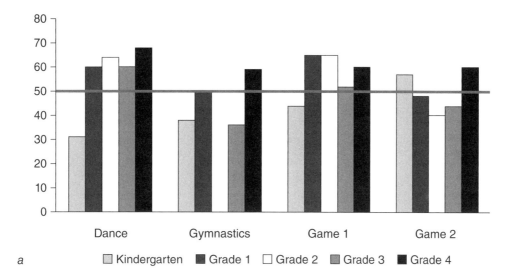

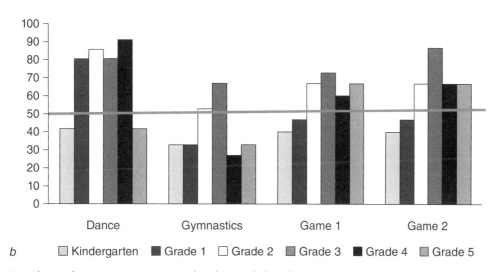

**Figure 4.1**  Physical activity time at *(a)* school 1 and *(b)* school 2.

opportunities for physical activity are influential enabling factors. Although these variables are important for all physical activity models, they do not guarantee that children will participate.

Perceiving oneself as physically fit and skilled is an enabling factor. A child with this self-perception is likely to be physically active. The reverse also occurs: children who are not physically fit and do not perceive themselves as skilled are less likely to want to participate in physical activity. Good instruction and good feedback from teachers are enabling factors too.

Because children in a movement education program are likely to answer the question of Am I able? in the affirmative, they are likely to perceive themselves as physically fit or skilled—a powerful physical activity motivator. Not only are children physically active throughout movement education lessons, but they are also empowered with knowledge of movement and the perception that they can be successful in their movement experiences. Newly available teaching technologies specifically designed for movement education also serve as exciting enabling factors (see appendix C for more details).

## YPAPM Reinforcing Factors

Who reinforces a child's level of interest? According to Meredith and Welk (2007), important socializing agents such as parents, peers, teachers, and coaches are critical reinforcing factors. In a

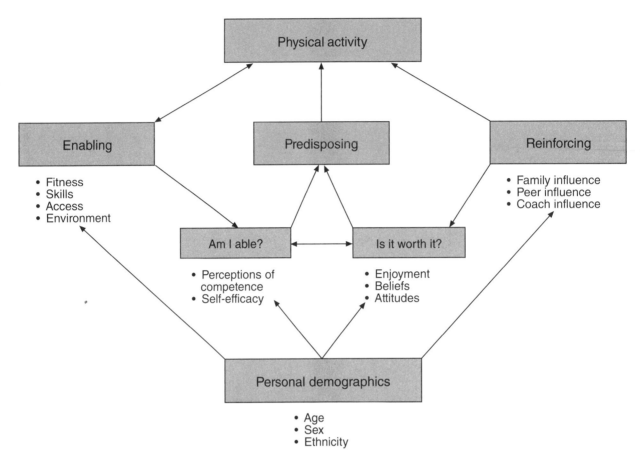

**Figure 4.2** The Youth Physical Activity Promotion Model.

Reprinted, by permission, from The Cooper Institute, 2005, *FitnessGram/ActivityGram test administration manual,* Updated 3rd ed. (Champaign, IL: Human Kinetics), 18.

school setting, teachers and peers are the most critical reinforcing factors. Positive reinforcement, feedback, and programs that promote success foster a more positive response from young learners. Similarly, encouraging children to solve their own movement problems encourages peer support and positive outcomes, thus promoting an interest in physical activity. In a movement education approach, although children learn how to throw, catch, kick, and so on, the focus on solving movement problems leads to greater success and less focus on one correct response, which is common in a command style of teaching. In addition, as children learn about various types of relationships that can occur, such as partner, cooperation, and collaboration, they have greater opportunities for success.

# Applying NASPE Standards to the Movement Education Framework

Developing an active lifestyle is part of being physically educated. NASPE's (2004) definition of a physically educated person is separated into six standards. The movement education approach most directly relates to standards 1 and 2 and indirectly supports the other four standards. (To read all six of the NASPE standards, see NASPE, 2004, or visit www.aahperd.org/Naspe/.)

Standard 1 is really about the physical performance of motor skills. Being active for a lifetime is greatly facilitated by developing solid fundamentals, which is a major function of movement education. This idea is supported in the NASPE document *Moving Into the Future* (2004, p. 12): "Mastering movement fundamentals establishes a foundation to facilitate continued motor skill acquisition and gives students the capacity for successful and advanced levels of performance to further the likelihood of participation on a daily basis."

When is the best time for development of these skills? Again, this is addressed in the national standards: "In the primary years, students develop maturity and versatility in the use of fundamental motor skills (e.g., running, skipping, throwing, striking) that are further refined, combined, and varied during the middle school years. These motor skills, now having evolved into specialized skills (e.g., a specific dance step, chest pass, catching with a glove, or the use of a specific tactic), are used in increasingly complex movement environments through the middle school years" (NASPE, 2004, p. 12). Thus, children in elementary schools would benefit most from the movement education approach. Himberg, Hutchinson, and Roussell (2003) presented a diamond-shaped framework showing how the elementary years fit into the entire K-12 curriculum and contribute to children's becoming active for life (see figure 4.3 on page 80).

During grades K through 2, NASPE standard 1 can be met very nicely using the movement education approach. In fact, the NASPE expectations and movement education expectations are almost identical. This is evident in the first step of the movement education tree in chapter 2 (figure 2.1). The body concept category, actions of the whole body, includes all of the nonlocomotor, locomotor, and manipulative skills that form the basis of most of the examples provided in the *Moving Into the Future* document. Essentially, in grades K through 2 the desire is to develop form in the locomotor skills and simple manipulative skills (e.g., the underhand throw).

*Moving Into the Future* (2004, p. 17) provides student expectations and performance outcome examples for grades 3 through 5. The expectation is for all of the fundamentals (nonlocomotor, locomotor, and manipulative skills) to be performed at a mature level by the end of fifth grade. As well, children should be able to combine these skills as they move in complex and dynamic environments.

The relationships concept of the MEF addresses this quite well in that fundamental skill elements in all categories may be used not only in combination, but in dynamic environments in which a variety of relationships are occurring.

NASPE standard 2 is an extension of standard 1. Whereas standard 1 addresses physical competency, standard 2 lays out what the student should know in a cognitive way. In a further discussion of standard 2, *Moving Into the Future* states that a "[k]nowledge of these concepts and principles and of how to apply them enhances the likelihood of independent learning and therefore more regular and effective participation in physical activity" (p. 12). Thus, developing an understanding of movement language and being able to use movement terms appropriately is deemed part of encouraging an active lifestyle. Lifetime activity depends on knowledge as well as learning the actual movements. Additional classroom activities and supplementary learning tools, such as pocket charts, pocket chart cards, and other technologies (see appendix C for resources), can enhance the achievement of NASPE standard 2. Chapter 5 discusses innovative teaching and the use of technology in further detail.

The student-centered nature of movement education creates a very positive environment. Students are rarely in lines and rarely waiting. The more effective formations of circles, triangles, and partnerships keep students active during class and help them meet NASPE standard 3.

In movement education, students often work at their own intensity levels, which makes moving more comfortable than when trying to keep pace with others in competition-based programs. Keeping track of data such as physical activity time (PAT), MVPA (level of moderate to vigorous physical activity), MVPA bouts, and the number of steps (using pedometers) can help document student progress and ensure that NASPE standard 4 is addressed.

An active lifestyle appears to be related to physical fitness. The greater the level of physical fitness, the more likely the person is to have an active lifestyle. Knowing the factors that contribute to the ability to increase physical fitness helps you determine which activities are important in developing a successful fitness unit.

Stodden, Langendorfer, and Robertson (2009) studied the association between motor skillfulness

# National Standards and Guidelines

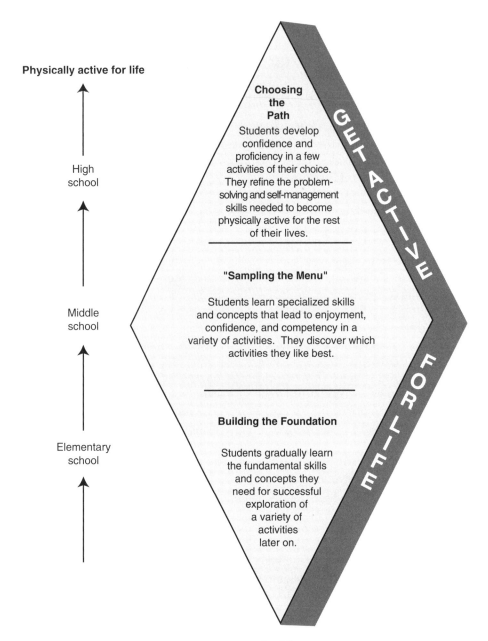

**Figure 4.3** Childhood to adulthood: physically active for life.

Reprinted, by permission, from C. Himberg et al., 2002, *Teaching secondary physical education: Preparing adolescents to be active for life* (Champaign, IL: Human Kinetics), 19.

and physical fitness, saying that "children who attain a certain level of proficiency in FMS and continue to become skillful during middle childhood and adolescence have more options to participate and be successful in activities requiring adequate FMS as adults" (p. 228). What this means is that although the development of motor skills (e.g., kicking, throwing, and jumping) in childhood may not be reflected in levels of physical fitness during childhood (e.g., 12-minute run/ walk, percent body fat, curl-ups, grip strength, and maximum leg press strength), the importance of the lifelong carryover is significant! Because a movement education program emphasizes competence in motor skills, along with a strong movement content foundation and enjoyment of the activity, it is likely to result in positive levels of physical fitness that will carry over to adulthood (Stodden, Langendorfer, & Robertson, 2009).

Building positive self-esteem in children is critical (Gallahue & Ozmun, 2006). Because movement education programs allow for many correct solutions to movement problems, and because success is a major theme, building self-esteem for each child comes rather easily. In addition, students learn about their own self-space and how to stay there, a nice beginning for developing competence in NASPE standard 5.

The term *self-space* can be used as a classroom management tool outside of the gymnasium as well. In addition to identifying and becoming comfortable in their own self-space, children learn how to take this self-space with them as they move throughout the general space. Responsible social behavior is also enhanced as children learn to work in various organizational and situational patterns as described in the relationships concept. The MEF helps children learn to respect each other's contributions to the movement questions posed in each lesson.

NASPE Standard 6 is a general outcome of a movement education program. As children recognize their success at their individual levels, they positively answer the questions posed by the YPAPM model. By being assured of movement knowledge and movement success, children value physical activity as well as the challenges it provides.

## Summary

This chapter has attempted to provide a rational link between teaching movement education and the goal of preparing children with a foundation for an active lifestyle. We began with describing the NASPE guidelines (2004b) that identify the recommended levels of physical activity for children. Generally we want children to be active for at least an hour or more every day doing a variety of physical activities, each one lasting at least 15 continuous minutes. We then brought out some of the accumulating data about the growing link between physical activity and enhanced academic performance. We presented some preliminary research data we have collected using pedometers in movement education lessons. This research documents that movement education can contribute positively to the total amount of physical activity

that children acquire in a physical education class, although we encourage much more research in this area. We described in specific detail which aspects of movement education serve as predisposing factors, enabling factors, and reinforcing factors to being physically active in the youth physical activity promotion model presented in Welk (1999). We ended the chapter with a presentation of how movement education can be used to meet all of the current NASPE standards (2004a).

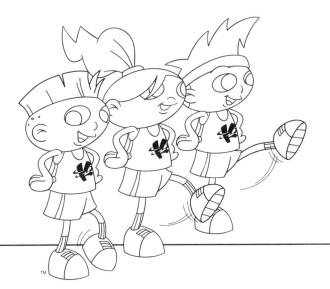

# Innovative Teaching Ideas for Movement Education

Making learning engaging and providing multiple avenues for presenting information help increase children's opportunities to be successful. This chapter presents practical suggestions, through the use of tools and innovative ideas, for movement educators. The first of these tools are pocket charts and pocket chart cards designed specifically for use in physical education. This chapter provides a variety of activities that can be done using the pocket chart cards. Word walls are also great tools that bridge the gap between the gymnasium and the classroom. Word wall activities that may be useful for the classroom teacher may be found in Word Wall Activities by Sportime (www.sportime.com). These activities accompany the Word Wall poster set by Sportime. Pedometers are also helpful to use with movement education content, as are learning centers. We conclude the chapter with a discussion of interdisciplinary approaches to teaching movement education.

Commercial equipment made for movement education that has stood up to the rigors of the school environment, is cost friendly, and is meaningful to both children and teachers is available. Appendix C provides a list of teaching aids directly relevant to movement concepts, including vendor names, Web sites, and product numbers.

## Pocket Chart Cards and Word Walls

Pocket charts and cards are old standbys for elementary classroom teachers. They are simple, inexpensive, and effective materials used to deliver information using both visual and manipulative approaches. These two tools help to reinforce cognitive content of almost any subject matter: literacy (letters, words, sentences), mathematics (numbers, shapes, basic functions), or science (animals, weather, plants). Elementary classroom teachers also use pocket charts for practical things such as class organization (task assignments, calendar, birthdays).

Pocket charts come in a wide variety of shapes, sizes, and colors and are available at a relatively low cost at almost any local or name-brand teacher's store. Sets of pocket chart cards designed for specific subject matters are also available. Blank pocket chart card decks and sentence strips made specifically to fit pocket charts are also available at very reasonable costs at the same stores.

Using pocket cards and charts for teaching movement education will help elementary classroom teachers by allowing them to work within a content delivery system they already know and use. This is a real benefit since elementary classroom teachers are often responsible for fulfilling mandated physical education minutes.

The use of pocket charts and cards in physical education, while a rather new idea, is logical and natural. In fact, the gymnasium offers an exciting environment in which to use them. Figure 5.1 shows a pocket chart with movement education cards placed in the pockets for a lesson. An entire deck of movement concepts cards is shown in figure 5.2. Later in this chapter are descriptions of pocket chart card activities that you can use to

**Figure 5.1** Teaching with pocket chart cards in the gymnasium.

Photo courtesy of Karen Weiller-Abels.

**Figure 5.2** A movement education pocket chart card set.

teach movement education; chapters 7, 8, 9, and 10 offer much more detailed descriptions of specific activities for each of the four movement concepts.

The word wall is another common tool used in the elementary classroom. Many elementary classroom teachers use this versatile tool to reinforce vocabulary words, to assist children with spelling words, and to emphasize words from stories being read in class. Word walls can be used in the gym as well. Figure 5.3 shows a word wall designed specifically for gymnasium use, as well as classroom use. Although many poster sets for physical education focus on the motivational aspects of movement, word wall poster sets are a colorful way to deliver movement content to students right on the gym wall. A word wall poster set designed by the authors of this book is commercially available at www.sportime.com.

## Who Can Use Pocket Charts or Cards and Movement Word Walls?

Pocket cards and word walls are effective tools for professionals who develop literacy in the content area of physical education in numerous settings,

including K-12 physical education teachers, elementary classroom teachers, preservice teachers, and university teacher educators. Teachers can choose from a variety of methods of implementation, from directed teaching to guided discovery and self-discovery, depending on the learning situation and children with whom they are working. These approaches allow teachers of physical education and classroom teachers to apply not only physical education terminology in both movement and cognitive formats, but also content from other curricular areas (e.g., language arts, math, science, music, art).

## Pocket Chart Card and Word Wall Activities

The needs of the lesson, as you develop it, should drive your choice of when and how to include the activities presented in this section. Following are some things you might want to consider:

- You can conduct these activities in either the classroom or the gymnasium.
- The activities can be done prior to teaching each word or set of words.

Photo courtesy of Lynn Vande Sande.

**Figure 5.3**   Use of a word wall in the gymnasium.

- You may want to do one or some of these activities as part of a lesson introduction or to begin new activities and ideas in a lesson.
- You can use these activities when recovery, rest, or settling down are needed during class (in either the gym or the classroom).
- The pocket chart and movement cards can be used as review or as an assessment of the previous lesson.

## Identification of Movement Concepts

Introduce the movement education framework (MEF) in one of your first lessons using a pocket chart card deck. It is helpful to organize the material into a few big chunks that the children can remember.

1. To begin, place the movement concepts card at the top center of the first pocket in the chart. Similarly, you can point to the words *movement concepts* on a word wall.

2. Explain to the children that they are going to be learning about four big ways in which the body moves. Share with them that they will be learning some new uses for words they probably already know. What is new is that the words are used to help them understand more about how people move.

3. Tell the children that there are four words that are called *movement concepts,* and that every way people move fits into one of these concepts.

4. Now place each of the four movement concepts on a separate line of the pocket chart (i.e., body, space, effort, and relationships) or point to them on the word wall. Ask the children to read the words or describe the picture of the KinetiKid. Ask them to give examples or descriptions of what they know about each of these words as you place them in the pocket chart or point to them on the word wall, taking as much or as little time as needed or available.

5. You might engage the children even more by inviting a child to go up to the pocket chart and flip over the first card to reveal the definition (Body—What the body is doing). You might use the pocket chart for the definitions and the word wall for identifying the movement concept, category, or element you are discussing. You can emphasize the word *what* for the body definition, *where* for space, *how* for effort, and *connections* for relationships. Continue this process until all four concepts have been revealed.

After you have introduced the MEF and the four concepts, challenge the children to remember them. You can place the four movement concept cards among 10 or so other cards from the deck randomly within a circle on the floor, faceup. You can make this memory task more challenging by not telling the children the number of cards they should find. You can start again with the cards flipped over, now facedown, asking children to then find the definition (now faceup) of each movement concept. It might be helpful to provide an analogy: "Movement is like soup; we can put all kinds of things in our soup. Let's see if you can find the four basic movement soup ingredients from the pot of soup on the floor." A teacher in Madison, Wisconsin, created simple pictures that she taped to the wall to make her movement soup analogy (see figure 5.4).

Photo courtesy of Karen Myers.

**Figure 5.4**  Movement Soup from elementary physical education teacher Karen Myers.

## Progression of Movement Concepts

You can also use the movement education tree (see figure 2.1 on page 10) as an early movement education lesson. The Blank Movement Education Tree Worksheet is available on page 100.

1. Ask a child to pick up the body concept card and place it in a pocket in the lower center part of the pocket chart. Have the child write the word *body* on the center taproot, or have her draw a picture of a body to add the labels to (a circle for the head and a line for the body will do).

2. Direct another child to pick up the space concept card and place it in the pocket directly above the word *body*; encourage him to write the word *space* and to draw a spaceship or several stars out in space to represent the idea of space on the root next to the center body concept root.

3. Select a different child to pick up the effort card and place it in the pocket chart directly above the space card; have her write the word *effort* on the worksheet on the root on the other side of body and also ask her to give ideas of things she might draw to represent effort (muscle man, hammer, superhero).

4. Finally, pick one last child to place the relationships card above the effort card on the pocket chart. Again, have the child write the word *relationships* on the right and left side roots that are nearest the surface of the ground and then ask him for ideas of what he might draw on the tree worksheet to represent the movement concept of relationships (two or more people, a heart, a team with a ball).

5. A completed worksheet might look something like the Completed Movement Education Tree Worksheet on page 101.

6. Ask the children questions about their drawings and help them notice that it was harder to come up with pictures for the last two concepts. The tree begins with the simplest idea and becomes more complex with each set of roots. Now the children have the basic idea of the order of the movement concepts from simple to complex. A clean copy of this worksheet can be used for review or assessment.

Once all four concepts have been pointed out on the word wall, children can draw the items on their worksheets in the same way they did for the pocket chart cards. Use the back side of the pocket chart card, with the definition on it, to help you reinforce the idea of the definitions of the four major concept areas with the children. Reviewing the MEF using the Blank Movement Education Tree Worksheet and definitions of movement terms in the classroom prior to an MEF lesson is a great way to reinforce the learning of this content for children.

### Rainy Day Activities

Physical education teachers are always looking for things to do on rainy days. The pocket chart card deck can be used for this purpose. For example, children can use the pocket chart cards to create their own games, with or without the pocket chart, in small groups in a hallway or at their desks.

### Integrating Game Cones Into Instruction

Pocket chart cards also work really well when placed in cone sleeves or cones with a slotted top (cones are designed to hold signs, posters, and cards). Figure 5.5 shows an example of this.

**Figure 5.5** Using pocket chart cards with game cones.

Whereas a pocket chart stays in one location, cone markers with slotted tops can be put in a variety of places throughout the learning space. Thus, cards can provide directions about what movement to perform or how to perform it, or serve as visual reminders of the cognitive concepts on which students are working. Although pocket chart cards work well with cones, larger (8.5-by-11-inch) elementary task cards by Bonnie's Fitware (www.pesoftware.com) also fit nicely into slotted cone tops making for visually exciting stations. Other commercially available tools include locomotor directions and animal cone caps. Gopher Sport (www.gophersport.com) sells cone caps that you can use to teach locomotor and movement direction skills. These caps come with directions and locomotor movements pre-printed for easy use or are blank so that you can make your own.

## Movement Learning Centers

Essentially, a learning center is a physical space with items that enhance the opportunity to learn a particular subject or concept. Although the use of learning centers is common practice in the classroom, it is not as popular in the gymnasium. Why not have them both places? Having a movement learning center in the classroom will help to create a more seamless connection with what goes on in the gymnasium. Whether physical education is taught by the physical education specialist or the classroom teacher, a classroom learning center creates a physical space in which students can learn about movement without having to rely on the availability of a movement teacher. In addition, a gymnasium learning center can be a welcoming place where students can access movement content.

## Classroom Learning Center Materials and Methods

Pocket charts and cards, as well as word walls, can be used in many ways to support the content of movement education. Classroom teachers can immediately integrate movement concept cards into ongoing activities in literacy learning centers. A learning center for physical education within the classroom can give really active or kinesthetic learners a strong sense of relief and belonging.

A classroom movement learning center might include a physical education pocket chart and movement concepts deck (see figure 5.1 on page 84), Move Cubes for movement education (www.gophersport.com),12-sided It's Your Move locomotor dice which allow teachers and students to roll through various movements (www.gophersport.com), and a computer to log pedometer steps (Log It is available free from www.peclogit.com). In the university setting, a pocket chart card deck can show elementary education majors in their teaching methods classes and physical education majors and minors a way to emphasize literacy in physical education.

## Gymnasium Learning Centers

You can have a physical activity learning center that is available at all times rather than one that you have to set up and take down. The first step is to identify a space for a permanent physical education learning center. Involving the children and even the classroom teachers in creating, defining, and managing this space will contribute to their investment in the learning that will take place there. Although physical space in the gymnasium is usually at a premium, there are some ways to create a learning center for physical education content in or near the gym.

Consider using a section of the physical education office, a small area in a second floor gymnasium or gym overlook area, an oddly shaped corner, entry, or exit, or a part of the equipment room for your movement learning center. How

about an area near the bleachers? Many gymnasiums have such "dead spaces" that can be used for a movement learning center. With larger classes, children can be active in the movement learning center while others are participating in the main lesson. In addition, children who are unable to participate in the physical portion of the lesson due to injury or recent illness can work in the movement learning center on a movement assessment or other written activity. Students with special needs might find this a place where they can excel and as a result may feel more of a part of the movement experience along with their peers.

Once you have identified a physical space, add materials that will facilitate learning, such as a movement pocket chart and card deck, all or part of a movement word wall, and elementary task cards (see appendix C for more detailed product information). Comfortable seating (e.g., a couple of beanbag chairs) or even a physical learning arcade system (e.g., the Smart Cycle by Fisher-Price or a music video dance platform such as DDR by Konami) could be added to encourage children to relax and engage in fun learning activities at their own pace. Make sure it is an inviting space. How about putting in a computer with Web access limited to assigned sites (e.g., http://kidshealth .org/kid, www.kidnetic.com, www.bam.gov, www .kidsrunning.com/, www.peclogit.org/kidsquiz .asp)? In addition, assessment or problem-solving activities (either written or participatory) may be located in the movement learning center. Examples of assessments are provided in chapter 3.

# Materials for Enhancing Movement Education Lessons

Lots of new products are available in the movement marketplace, and many gymnasium standbys have been modernized. We provide a few suggestions including specialized music CDs that can help with time issues and organizing movement activities (Station to Station), movement beach balls, a variety of parachutes, soft floor discs, and pedometers.

## Specialized Timed Music Interval Movement CDs

Great motivation and management tools for movement education activities are found in the Station to Station music CDs (www.shopstationpe.com). There are six paired time intervals to choose from on each CD to facilitate the rotation or work schedule of movement station activities:

- 30 seconds of music, 15 seconds of silence
- 30 seconds of music, 30 seconds of silence
- 1 minute of music, 15 seconds of silence
- 2 minutes of music, 15 seconds of silence
- 3 minutes of music, 15 seconds of silence
- 3 minutes of music, 30 seconds of silence

Having the CD do the timing frees you up to interact with the children and maximize your movement feedback. The "Swift Sounds" CD could be used nicely with lessons that focus on the effort concept, although any of the CDs would be a great addition to any movement education lesson. The Station to Station CDs could be used to expand children's movement repertoires rather than focusing on "right" and "wrong" ways of moving.

## Movement Beach Balls and Parachutes

Writing selected movement terms with permanent or washable marker on beach balls (see figure 5.6) or purchasing specific movement education beach balls (see the resources listed in appendix C) is another fun way to provide manipulatives to reinforce cognitive learning. Movement terminology beach balls bouncing or rolling around in a

**Figure 5.6** Interactive beach balls with movement terms written on them.

stretched-out parachute during an activity reinforce the use and retention of movement terms. Children can also make up movement concept games using the parachute. For example, a child can use the terms on the ball as content reminders. When a child sees a movement element term (e.g., forward) on the ball, he can shout it out loud, and all of the children might need to move forward two steps in unison while holding on to the parachute. Between parachute activities you could engage students in further discussion of selected terms or give them movement problems that they must work on cooperatively to solve.

## Soft Floor Discs (Jellyfish)

The soft floor discs shown in figure 5.7 can be used as classroom organizers, self-space identifiers, or targets for balancing or jumping and leaping activities. A variety of inserts (see the resources in appendix C) can be placed into the jellyfish center (e.g., KinetiKidz movement pictures, fruit pictures, numbers, and even blank writable inserts). If you have children moving from one disc to another disc, you might ask them to verbally identify the picture on the insert of each disc when they arrive. You can also use simple poly spots for the same purposes.

Photo courtesy of AMEP.

**Figure 5.7**  Soft floor discs with movement-related content.

## Pedometers

Pedometers are readily available and inexpensive so that even programs with low budgets can use them. Many resources are available to help you get started with using pedometers. PE Central (www .pecentral.org) is a great place to find all kinds of information about teaching physical education. You can find elementary lessons that use pedometers by using the PE Central search feature and typing in "pedometers."

Pedometers can facilitate the use of problem solving in movement education. By phrasing challenges as questions, you can direct your students toward discovery through developmentally appropriate movement analysis. For example, you might ask students to compare the number of steps they get when walking compared to running versus leaping. Leaping should use the fewest steps, and walking should use the most. They can record this data during several class meetings and even create a graph of their data. At the completion of data collection, provide them with a written set of questions to direct their thinking toward some important aspect of movement analysis. You might guide them toward discovering the important locomotor concept that springlike actions have flight (a momentary time of being airborne), but steplike actions always have one foot in contact with the supporting surface. You can ask one developmentally appropriate question (or a list of them) to encourage the students to discover the idea of your choosing (e.g., flight is part of all springlike actions) based on the data they have gathered with their pedometers.

You can use other topics to create interesting pedometer-centered lessons that use similar directions, data collection, data graphing, and questioning to teach key ideas and relationships within and among movement concepts, and also to encourage and track fitness. Many possibilities are available, so don't feel limited to these suggestions. One idea is to have students compare the number of steps of moderate to vigorous physical activity among the following:

- Body elements for a set of nonlocomotor, locomotor, and manipulative skills
- Body elements for a variety of manipulative skills

- Space elements of location (self-space vs. general space)
- Effort elements of time (fast, slow, acceleration)
- Effort elements of focus (direct and indirect)

# Integrating Subject Matter Into Movement

As an important part of the teaching staff, the physical educator should understand the basic ideas of other content areas (e.g., reading, writing, music, math, and science). Likewise, the classroom teachers should be a basic movement educator, as should other specialty teachers. Although it isn't practical to expect classroom teachers to function at the level of physical education specialists, it is reasonable to expect them to know and be able to teach the content from the Flip 'n' Fold. Using all of the Flip 'n' Fold movement elements or just a limited selection from the critical elements (on page 28), the physical educator and elementary classroom teacher can work together!

## Combining Literacy With Movement

The activity presented here may be more appropriate for younger children. Begin by choosing movement words presented during classroom activities, maybe as spelling or vocabulary words (e.g., low level, forward direction, and self-space; body shapes of narrow, stretched, and curled). Then place these words in the gymnasium pocket chart and ask the students to draw what a child doing these movements would look like. The drawing activity can be done before, after, or both before and after students physically perform the movements. The drawings may significantly change once students have experienced the movements. Drawings are helpful forms of assessment and can facilitate parents' and guardians' understanding of the movement education program.

Another creative approach to combining movement and a traditional subject is to apply learning the letters of the alphabet to a movement lesson. Certainly, this is one of the basic tenets of this approach. A creative lesson by Joannie Kellum

in North Carolina serves as the basis for this example.

The lesson is divided into four lessons: (1) letters A–H, (2) letters I–Q, (3) letters R–Z, and (4) Alphabet Soup (a review of any stations). Large classes can be divided into working groups. Kellum applied tasks to each letter (see the Alphabet Letters on the Move worksheet on page 103). To further apply this activity to movement education, we added a movement application in the last column. In addition to setting up directions for each station, you might want to post the movement framework elements and directions as well. For children who are not yet reading well, or those whose first language is not English, use the KinetiKidz pictures using pocket chart cards or add symbols to the chart. The movement elements examples provided in table 2.1 are options from which you may choose to do an activity with your class. It is not vital that all MEF elements (i.e., the Flip 'n' Fold) be included for each portion of this lesson. Rather, choosing particular elements for each lesson will focus the lessons.

Another fun way to combine literacy with movement is to include matching activities at the close of a movement lesson.

1. You or your students place each of the movement concept terms on the top left of the pocket chart followed by each of the definitions to the right (not in the correct order).
2. Students then match the definitions to the correct words.
   - Body: What the body is doing (B)
   - Space: Where the movement takes place (S)
   - Effort: How the body is performing the movement (E)
   - Relationships: Connections with whom or what the body is moving (R)
3. For students operating at lower developmental stages or students whose first language is not English, you can read the word and definition or ask them to work together. You may also point to the terms on the movement word wall, hold up definition cards, and ask students to match the appropriate definition to the word on the word wall.

4. Give each child a card (from a list you have created) from the group of cards you have created and ask them to perform the movement. As children perform the movements, see if they can identify elements that would be classified within each category. For example, you might have children performing bound, free, hard, and soft movements. The correct match would be bound and free because they are both types of flow; and hard and soft should be matched because they are both types of force. You can design your matches any way you like to highlight movement concepts that you want your students to learn or to create a discussion rather than seeking correct answers.

5. Photo matching is another fun activity. Show pictures of children who are doing the movement elements being covered that day. You can take pictures at conferences or in-service workshops (if legally appropriate) of students demonstrating movement elements and enlarge them so all students can easily see them. Ask the students to identify what is being done in the photo. You can call on students individually or ask groups to respond. Ask the students why they chose their responses. This will help you identify areas of strength or weakness in prior learning.

Reprinted, by permission, from Joannie Kellum.

## Writing or Drawing in Response to Movement Education Lessons

Having children write about how they felt during a movement lesson enhances not only the movement aspect, but also their writing skills. For example, following a lesson on moving at various levels through all the general space, children may write that they felt free while doing it. Younger children may add that they felt as though they were moving like particular animals that move at those levels. As in the drawing examples in figure 5.8, children may choose to illustrate their writing with movement pictures.

## Movement Phrases

Movement phrases (which you might also think of as movement sentences or sequences as they are all very similar) and movement stories can also be used to link literacy with movement.

1. Select movement elements from one (or more) of the four concept areas and have students create phrases as they do in the classroom.

2. Each phrase should have a beginning, middle, and ending, much like a sentence.

3. This activity may begin as a teacher-directed activity and then progress to a student-directed activity.

4. As shown in figure 5.9 on page 94, you can distribute extra sets of pocket chart cards and ask the children to make movement phrases. As noted earlier, emphasize that movement phrases are just like phrases created in the classroom: each has a beginning, middle, and ending.

Following are some examples of how you can ask students to create movement phrases:

- "Show me a movement phrase that starts at a high level and then travels in different directions and finishes at a low level." You would place the following in the pocket chart: Start at a high level, travel in different directions, finish at a low level (pocket chart terms: *high level, directions, low level*). You may also be more descriptive by specifying directions.

- Shapes can also be a part of a movement phrase. Children can start their phrase or sentence with a beginning shape, travel in a direction or pathway at a level, and then finish with an ending shape.

- Sentences or phrases can also be student directed. Ask students (either individually, in pairs, or in small groups) to select a minimum of three movement words from one or more categories within the space movement concept to form a movement phrase (e.g., general space, forward, low level). They then place these in the pocket chart. Students then demonstrate their understanding of this movement phrase by creating a sequence of movements that demonstrates this phrase.

- If you are using a word wall, you can also have sets of pocket chart cards. Creating pocket cards of particular elements (steplike actions,

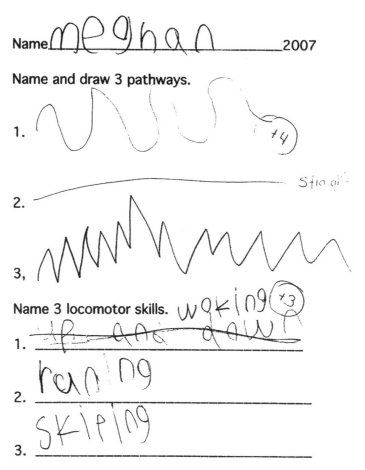

**Figure 5.8**  Drawings by a child in response to a movement lesson.

springlike actions, body shapes, pathways, levels, or directions) might be a great way to help younger students choose cards to create movement sequences. Students may choose a way to travel, a body shape, and another way to travel to create their movement sequences.

## Movement Story, Poem, or Rhyme

Having students create movement stories is an additional way to incorporate literacy with movement, and it's fun! Once you have presented the idea of movement phrases, or sentences, and students have practiced them, you can move on to movement stories. Ensuring that movement is a major theme of the story is essential. Movement stories should first be done in a teacher-directed manner within concepts or between concepts. Students will begin to make the association that a movement story has a definite beginning, middle, and ending, much like sentences that make up a story and movement sentences. The movement story can be placed on the pocket chart as a whole or in part and then demonstrated through movement in class.

To write movement stories, students identify and demonstrate movement elements found in nursery rhymes, poems, or stories read in class. The following examples lend themselves well to this type of activity:

- Peter Rabbit hiding in a pile of leaves
- Leaves in the fall
- A very windy day (e.g., a blustery day for Winnie-the-Pooh)
- Animals in a zoo (e.g., elephant, giraffe, gorilla)
- Frogs jumping on lily pads

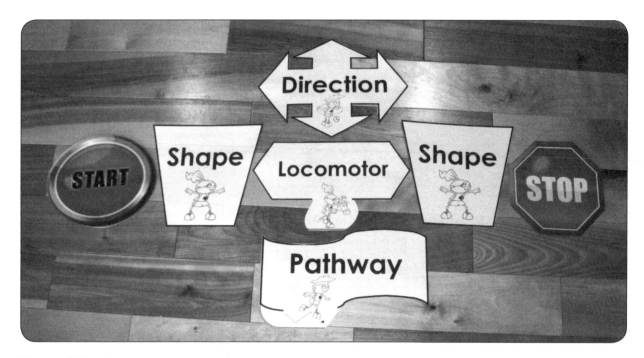

**Figure 5.9**  A generic movement phrase.

Having students select and place pocket chart cards in response to hearing a poem is a great activity for either the physical education class or regular classroom, and it's an activity that physical educators and classroom teachers can do together! You can modify this activity for children at various developmental stages by reading shorter or longer poems to them. You can also have them read a poem silently and then complete the activity.

Have students work in small groups while you read a movement story. They should place movement words on pocket chart cards in the pocket chart in a sequential order as they occur in the movement story. Help students identify the movement concepts, categories, and elements in the movement story. They can then demonstrate their understanding by combining these movement phrases into a story through their actions. Ask the students, "Can you place the movement words in the order they occur in the story?"

Prior to guiding children through the following movement story, make certain that students know there is not one right way to do the movements. Rather, the focus is on the movements and how the body is performing the movements, not finding the correct way. Movement stories are discussed in greater detail in chapter 13, Educational Dance.

This activity may also be done from a student-directed perspective. Ask students to work in small groups and give them topics from which they can create their own movement stories. Older students who are operating at a higher developmental stage can write their movement stories. Younger students can talk about their stories or draw pictures of some of the actions or movements. Each group of students (working with a pocket chart) then identifies the movements in their story and practices them in sequential order.

## Movement Flow Map

You can also combine literacy and movement by having students in the classroom create a movement flow map that they can then use in a physical education lesson in the gym. A movement flow map focuses on movement concept combinations and helps students work on sequencing the order of a movement story (see figure 5.10 on page 97). This is different from using words to capture ideas. In the same way that a global positioning system in a car provides a visual map of the places the driver arrives at in a certain order for the driver to follow, so the movement flow map provides a visual outline of the order (or flow) in which movements occur.

## Tropical Jungle Movement Story

Following is an example of a movement story that you can share with your students:

*Picture yourself in a tropical jungle. You are suddenly stuck in quicksand, and you slowly start to sink. Try to pull yourself out in different ways.*

As a teacher-directed activity, you would first place the following concepts, categories, and elements in the pocket chart for students to review. You could follow this review by having the children identify the card terms relating to the story on the word wall. After that, you could have them perform the movements to create the story. You could help them discuss their performance, the terms, and the story as a culminating activity.

- Body (body shapes—narrow, twisted, wide, round)
- Space (areas—self-space; directions—variety; levels—low, medium, high)
- Effort (time—slow, fast; force—strong, light; flow—bound)

The following list may assist you in teaching children how to create their own unique movement flow maps. Remember to encourage originality and creativity over correctness.

1. Make a written list of all of the movement elements in the story (we encourage children to use the Flip 'n' Fold during this stage of analysis).

2. Put all of the movement elements in the order in which they appear in the story (from first to last).

3. Represent each of the movement elements with a picture; this can be a simple geometric shape (e.g., a square, circle, or triangle) or something meaningful (e.g., a stick figure or drawing of the main topic).

4. Students should be able to recreate the story as a movement performance using the movement flow map they created. Other students should then be able to do the same using that movement flow map.

Students can work in small groups or individually to make their movement flow maps. Older children could first identify what movement elements are in the story. Younger children might do better if you direct the activity. Once the students have identified the movement concepts, you (or they) can place the movement concepts and movement element cards in the pocket chart. This helps to visually facilitate the movement analysis process for the children and to help keep the activity concrete and less abstract. Older students can create a movement map on paper and then demonstrate their application of the movement concepts, categories, and elements. It might be a fun challenge for older students to take someone else's movement flow map and take turns presenting their interpretations of them to the class.

You might also direct older children to make up their own written stories, either as a classroom activity or as physical education homework. You can direct younger children (e.g., on a marker board) to identify the components of their movement flow maps (see the preceding list). Following this, they can then demonstrate their understanding of the movements and their movement flow maps.

## Math and Science

Although there are a great number of possibilities for exploring the link between math and science and movement education, here are just a few suggestions to get you started thinking about math and science interdisciplinary lessons. You can have students create geometric shapes with their bodies; roll one die or two dice and add the numbers to find out how many times they should do a movement. You might also have students use movement elements to represent objects in nature such as wind, clouds, falling leaves, or growing flowers. See if they can write or draw their movement elements, making the science connection.

Linking math and geometry to movement is a natural interdisciplinary avenue of discovery for students. You can also take the topic of spatial

# Creating a Movement Flow Map

## Baby Bird Story

*You are a baby bird standing on the ground in your own space. Now, move as if you were just starting to fly. Gradually grow until you are a full-grown bird and fly at different speeds. Now you are flying very high in the air, way above the clouds.*

## Analyzing the Story

Movement element responses may include round shape; stretched shape; self-space; general space; low, medium, and high levels; slow; and fast.

You can discuss with the students both the order of events of the movement flow map as well as the movement content of the map. There should be a beginning, middle, and end to the sequence, as presented in the movement sequence element from the relationships concept. What would be the order of the story? You might ask, "Can someone tell me the correct order?"

Movement elements can be determined from the story line. For example, from the preceding baby bird story the students may choose to demonstrate a rounded shape at a low level in their self-space. Or, they may choose to demonstrate this in the beginning of the story at a medium level rather than a low level. Perhaps the baby bird they are imagining is a baby hawk! Ask students to identify what type of movements a baby bird might make if it were starting to fly. Would it be free or bound? Would it be quick or slow? Would acceleration be part of the movement?

You may choose to have students list the movement elements along with the flow map. This can help them transform their movement story from a written form to a movement form. Here are some additional questions that you might ask to help stimulate the students to make links to movement elements: "As the baby bird begins to grow, what happens? Does it rise? Does it move to a medium and then a high level? How can you show this? Think of ways to demonstrate the bird growing. How can you show the bird flying at different speeds? Which of our movement elements would you choose? Acceleration?"

As the bird travels, you want students to think of using all of the general space in a free-flowing motion. Does the bird travel softly or forcefully? Close the lesson by asking children what movement concepts and categories they used. Again, you might need to lead them into this type of thinking with questions such as: "Did you use effort? Did you use force? How about flow?"

## Sample Movement Flow Map for the Baby Bird Story

1. The list of the movement elements we chose from the baby bird story that we randomly picked out during our group discussion:

   Round shape, low level, self-space, fast, general space, medium level, stretched shape, acceleration, bound, free, and high level

2. Our reorganized list, which puts the movement elements in the order in which they appear in the story:

   Round shape, low level, self-space, bound, acceleration, free, medium level, general space, stretched shape, high level, and fast

3. To create our movement flow map (see figure 5.10), we grouped together the movement elements that occur about the same time in the story.

   a. Within a rectangle, we put these movement elements: round shape, low level, and self-space. (These come from the body and space concepts.)

b. Within a triangle, we put these movement elements: bound, acceleration, free, and medium level. (These come from the space and effort concepts.)

c. Within a circle, we put these movement elements: general space, stretched shape, high level, and fast. (These come from the body, space, and effort concepts.)

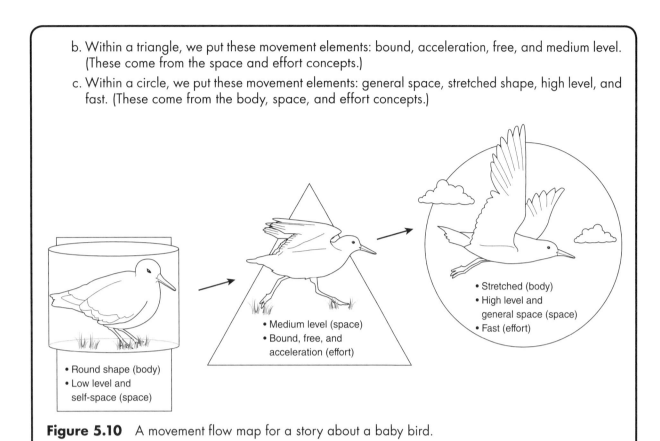

- Round shape (body)
- Low level and self-space (space)

- Medium level (space)
- Bound, free, and acceleration (effort)

- Stretched (body)
- High level and general space (space)
- Fast (effort)

**Figure 5.10** A movement flow map for a story about a baby bird.

planes (sagittal, frontal, and transverse) and explore the mathematical and scientific aspects in relationship to physical movement in very simple ways (or even more complex ways if the students are curious). In addition to the space concept is the body concept: elements within the category of actions of body parts (weight bearing, force application, weight transfer) make super topics for a lesson that blends science and movement.

## Music and Art

Music and art content can be integrated easily into movement education. Using musical instruments in physical education is an opportunity to include the content of music. Ask children to listen to a variety of musical instruments, either played by you, on a CD, or even live by their peers! These instruments can be formal (cymbals, drums) or as simple as lummi sticks, plastic bottles, and rice

shakers. Thinking about how these instruments make them feel, students, with your help, can identify movement element words. For example, a sharp drumming, lummi stick, or Boomwhackers beat might make some children feel the movement element *bound*. A plastic flute might make others feel the movement element *free*. You can place these words (*bound, free*) in the pocket chart or discuss them as you or the student(s) point to the terms on the word wall.

The art specialist can really add some fun to the movement lessons. Throwing paint-filled balloons at a giant wall of paper might be part of a lesson on hard (black paint) and soft (peach-colored paint). Students might express effort in both *direct* and *indirect* ways and culminate the experience by creating a chalk drawing on pavement that captures, for them, the opposite of these movements. In the art classroom or even as physical education homework, students might make a collage of pictures (from magazines, advertisements, photos, clip art, cereal boxes) to present the ideas of movements that they are learning about in the gymnasium.

## Summary

In this chapter we provide practical suggestions for new ways to teach movement education that are relevant to current technology. One of the primary tools we describe is the pocket chart and its related pocket chart cards, which are designed specifically for use in physical education. Word walls and learning centers addressing movement education content can also be used in both the gymnasium and the classroom. We also suggest the use of specialized timed music interval CDs, beach balls, parachutes, soft floor discs (jellyfish), and pedometers in movement education programs. The chapter ends with a discussion of interdisciplinary approaches to movement education.

# Quick-Find Table: Worksheets

| Worksheet | Page number |
|---|:---:|
| Blank Movement Education Tree Worksheet | 100 |
| Completed Movement Education Tree Worksheet | 101 |
| Pedometer Data Comparisons of Walk, Run, and Leap | 102 |
| Alphabet Letters on the Move | 103 |

# Blank Movement Education Tree Worksheet

Name _____

Directions: Place the name of the movement concept in the box provided. Each box is placed on top of the roots that are showing one concept.

From K. Weiller Abels and J.M. Bridges, 2010, *Teaching Movement Education: Foundations for Active Lifestyles* (Champaign, IL: Human Kinetics).

# Completed Movement Education Tree Worksheet

Name      Merchelle

Directions: Place the name of the movement concept in the box provided. Each box is placed on top of the roots that are showing one concept.

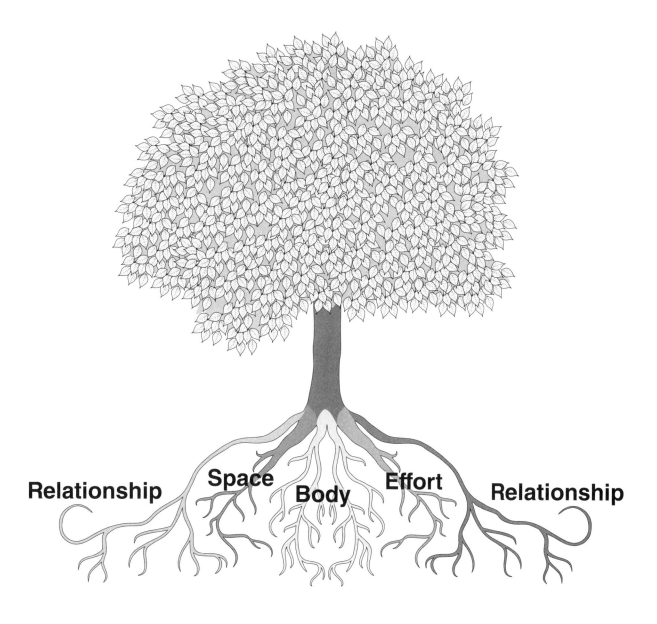

Relationship        Space    Body        Effort        Relationship

From K. Weiller Abels and J.M. Bridges, 2010, *Teaching Movement Education: Foundations for Active Lifestyles* (Champaign, IL: Human Kinetics).

# Pedometer Data Comparisons of Walk, Run, and Leap

Name _____

Directions:

1. In the table below, write the name of the locomotor skill (walk, run, or leap) that had the lowest, middle, and highest number of steps on your pedometer.
2. In the table below, write the name of the locomotor skill (walk, run, or leap) that had the lowest, middle, and highest speed.
3. In the table below, write the name of the locomotor skill (walk, run, or leap) that had the lowest, middle, and highest distance per step.
4. Complete the graph for your data.

|  | Number of steps | Speed | Distance |
|---|---|---|---|
| Lowest |  |  |  |
| Middle |  |  |  |
| Highest |  |  |  |

From K. Weiller Abels and J.M. Bridges, 2010, *Teaching Movement Education: Foundations for Active Lifestyles* (Champaign, IL: Human Kinetics).

# Alphabet Letters on the Move

Name _____

| Alphabet letter | Lettered movement theme | Link to movement concept and performance suggestions |
| --- | --- | --- |
| A . . . | . . .is for Animal Movements (perform any animal movements) | Body and effort concepts: Have children move slowly, quickly, softly, and more forcefully for the animals you choose. Encourage a variety of body shapes and nonlocomotor movements. |
| B . . . | . . .is for Bowling/Bats and Bases (swing bat and run bases in order) | Body concept: Children may choose to focus on a variety of locomotor movements. |
| C . . . | . . .is for Crawl Through the Shapes (crawl through large foam shapes trying not to touch)/Catch Ball (resembles a jack, toss and catch, can add numbers up at end) | Space concept: Children can apply directions (forward, backward, sideways); levels (low, medium, high); and pathways (straight, curved, zigzag). |
| D . . . | . . .is for Dot-to-Dot (jump from ABC poly spot to poly spot recognizing letters, thinking of words that begin with those letters or spelling words)/Dribble (practice dribbling soccer ball or basketball) | Body and effort concepts: Jumping dot to dot could incorporate various types of jumps (one foot to two feet, two to two, or two to one). Additional springlike actions of leaping, hopping, skipping, galloping, and sliding might be applied. Dribbling could include organization (people) as students dribble in a triangle or square, or match dribbling actions. Effort concept: Timing could be applied as well. |
| E . . . | . . .is for Exercise (perform various exercises from the poly spots or pictures posted) | Body, space, effort, and relationships concepts: Reviewing a variety of exercises (perhaps those part of a fitness testing) might include all four movement concepts. |
| F . . . | . . .is for Frog Fun (toss and catch Velcro insects with frog-shaped mitt)/Foam Frisbee | Relationships concept: Use the partner element in relationships as well as cooperation in the goal category. |
| G . . . | . . .is for Gym-I-Nee (shoot mini-basketballs into mini-goal and can add up points from the numbers on each chute)/Grab Ball (toss and catch or kick and grab balls) | Body and effort concepts: Body part, and levels, as well as the force category within the effort concept. |
| H . . . | . . .is for Hopscotch (practice hopping and jumping on mat)/Hula Hoops | Effort and relationships concepts: The categories of time and force are great here, as is the position category (elements of beside, near to/far from). |
| I . . . | . . .is for Individual Stunts (perform stunts on poly spots—crab kick, body fold, bicycle, etc.)/Instant Exercise (roll large dice and add up numbers and perform any exercise that many times) | Body concept: You may choose a variety of concepts, categories, and elements from those listed: body—body parts, body shapes; actions of the whole body—nonlocomotor (stretch, curl, twist, turn, spin, push, pull). |

*(continued)*

From K. Weiller Abels and J.M. Bridges, 2010, *Teaching Movement Education: Foundations for Active Lifestyles* (Champaign, IL: Human Kinetics). Courtesy of Joannie Kellum, Eastern Elementary School, www.pecentral.org/lessonideas/ViewLesson.asp?ID=8864.

| Alphabet letter | Lettered movement theme | Link to movement concept and performance suggestions |
|---|---|---|
| J. . . | . . .is for Juggling (toss-toss-catch-catch with juggling scarves)/Jump Ropes | Space, effort, and relationships concepts: Levels (high, medium, low); directions (up, sideways); time (slow, fast); force (soft, hard); position (above, below); timing (mirror, match). |
| K. . . | . . .is for Koosh Ball and Gloves (practice tossing and catching alone or with a partner) | Space, effort, and relationships concepts: Levels (high, medium, low); force (soft, hard); people (partner). It is important to add learning cues for throwing/catching as well. |
| L. . . | . . .is for Lifting Weights (lift 1 lb [0.5 kg] dumbbells to work biceps and triceps)/L and M together (for outside) is for Locomotor Movements (practice locomotor skills pictured— walk, hop, skip, jump, gallop, slide, leap, run) | Body concept (locomotor—springlike actions): Emphasis on hop (one foot to same foot), skip (step-hop), jump (two feet to two feet, one foot to two feet, two feet to one foot), gallop (step-close in a forward direction), slide (step-close in a sideways direction), leap (one foot to opposite foot), run (longer flight pattern). Biceps/triceps might include body parts as well as effort (slow, controlled). |
| M. . . | . . .is for Move to the Music (dance or do specific exercises to the music playing)/Marching | Space, effort, and relationships concepts: Directions (forward, backward, sideways); pathways (straight, curved, zigzag); time (slow, fast, acceleration); flow (bound, free); people (partners, even/uneven groups, triangle [or other geometric shapes]) |
| N. . . | . . .is for Number Ring Toss (toss rings around poles, recognize numbers and add up)/Number Dash (run from cone to cone in numerical order) | Body, space, effort, and relationships concepts: Locomotor skills (springlike actions); directions (forward); levels (medium [release ring at a medium level]); time (slow, fast, acceleration [run in a different speed from cone to cone]); people (partner, even, or uneven group); goal (cooperative or competitive). |
| O. . . | . . .is for Octopus Beanbag Toss/Over the Hurdles (jump or leap over hurdles set up) | Body, space, effort, and relationships concepts: Actions of the whole body (locomotor—springlike actions [jump or leap]); levels (low, medium, high); time (fast, slow); flow (bound); people (partners or small groups); position (over); goal (cooperative). |
| P. . . | . . .is for Puppets/Playground Balls | Body, space, effort, and relationships concepts: Actions of body parts (receiving weight or force); locomotor (springlike actions); levels (low, medium, high); focus (direct, indirect); timing (taking turns). Beanbag toss would be similar to ring toss. Puppets— relationships concept; timing (question/ answer; act/react). |
| Q. . . | . . .is for Quiet Time (sit and read or look at healthy/sport books)/Quarterback (practice throwing a football) | Space, effort, and relationships concepts: Levels (high, medium, low); force (hard/soft); people (partners). As in other tossing/catching activities, learning cues for throwing and catching should be included. |

| Alphabet letter | Lettered movement theme | Link to movement concept and performance suggestions |
|---|---|---|
| R. . . | . . .is for Ring Toss | Ring toss was discussed under N. |
| S. . . | . . .is for Scooters/Stompers (walk around on stilts) | Body, space, effort, and relationships concepts: Body parts (stomach, knees, seat); directions (forward, backward, sideways, clockwise, counterclockwise); pathways (straight, curved, zigzag); time (slow, fast, acceleration); focus (direct, indirect); people (partners); position (near to or far from); timing (mirror, match, taking turns); goal (cooperation). |
| T. . . | . . .is for Target (toss beanbags or small balls at target)/T-Ball (practice hitting a ball off a tee) | Body (manipulative—throw [underhand]). Target location: effort and relationships concepts: force (soft, hard); position (near to or far from). Striking off a tee: space and effort concepts: plane (transverse); force (soft/hard); focus (direct). |
| U. . . | . . .is for Under (to under hurdles of various heights) | Body and relationships concepts: Body parts (variety); position (under). Other relationships element options include partner work and cooperation. |
| V. . . | . . .is for Volleyball (balloons for inside) | Body, space, effort, and relationships concepts: Body parts (variety); actions of body parts (applying force); levels (high, medium, low); force (soft/hard); people (partner, even or uneven groups); position (above/below); goal (cooperation). |
| W. . . | . . .is for Working Together (put life-size skeleton together)/Wobble Ball | Relationships concept: Goal (cooperation). |
| X. . . | . . .is for X Marks the Spot (toss beanbags to turn over Xs on tic-tac-toe board) | Body, space, and effort concepts: Manipulative (sending objects away). Note: Sending objects away can be used for other tossing/throwing lessons. |
| Y. . . | . . .is for Yarn Ball (tossing and catching with oneself or a partner) | Space, effort, and relationships concepts: Levels (high, medium, low); force (soft/hard); people (partner). |
| Z. . . | . . .is for Zigzag Pattern (hop on hoppity hop following the Z shape or zigzag pattern made with poly spots or tapeline) | Space concept: Pathways (straight, curved, zigzag). |

From K. Weiller Abels and J.M. Bridges, 2010, *Teaching Movement Education: Foundations for Active Lifestyles* (Champaign, IL: Human Kinetics). Courtesy of Joannie Kellum, Eastern Elementary School, www.pecentral.org/lessonideas/ViewLesson.asp?ID=8864.

# Activity Analysis
## Application to the Movement Education Framework

What is an activity analysis, and how do teachers use it in teaching? An activity analysis is a process to help you understand what movement concepts, movement categories, and movement elements are being emphasized in the presentation of a task or activity within a lesson. A variety of techniques are used to break down (analyze) an activity (task). The process we suggest to facilitate the development of effective lessons is presented in the Movement Activity Analysis Worksheet on page 114. But how do you decide what tasks to include in lessons?

Effective teachers know exactly what they want students to accomplish by the end of the school year, unit, and even individual lesson. One way to determine what you want your students to accomplish is to use NASPE's national standards (NASPE, 2004) and perhaps additional guidelines provided by your state and school district. These guidelines may provide a more focused review of expectations for various grade levels or developmental stages. Using the national standards and state or district guidelines as a basis, you can then establish lesson objectives, again identifying what students are to accomplish by the end of each lesson or unit.

The purpose of this chapter is to guide you through the activity analysis process as it relates to the design and development of movement education, movement concepts, and activities and lessons. We also relate effective teaching techniques to using the activity analysis process. A blank activity analysis worksheet is available on page 114.

## The Seven-Step Process

Here is a description of the short seven-step process for the activity analysis.

1. Name the task.
2. Write the current objective of the task or create one (i.e., what is the overall intent?).
3. Using the name and objective, identify and list the most important movement concept or concepts.
4. Identify and list the most important movement category or categories based on the previous list.
5. Identify and list the most important movement element or elements based on the previous list.

6. Write a brief analysis of what you really want to see in the movement performance. You might pose this analysis as questions to help you think more critically.

7. Create the actual movement activity or activities using the previous lists.

Step six is where the actual analysis is occurring. If you are revising or updating an older task or even a task you got somewhere else, this is the step where you will list changes that you might make to improve its ability to address what you are really wanting the movement experience to be for the performer or performers.

## Movement Objectives

Movement objectives may focus upon what students are to accomplish within one or more of the four movement concept areas and in all three learning domains: motor, affective, and cognitive. For example, a lesson for children at the elementary developmental stage may include nonlocomotor balancing actions. A movement objective for this lesson might read, Students hold body shapes very still for a count of three when balancing or Students can identify how to move on and off balance. A movement objective in the affective domain might read, Students will demonstrate the ability to stay in personal space,

to travel safely, and to share space. The examples in this chapter will focus on the motor domain. You may determine, through the activity analysis process, that you desire to revise your objective.

## Applying Activity Analysis

During lessons, effective teachers observe students' movements to determine if they are exhibiting identified movement objectives for the lesson as well as specific elements presented in each task. This is not always as easy, or as simple, as it sounds. The question you may be asking is, How do I know whether my students are exhibiting the movement elements that I intend for this lesson? If you are a preservice or first-year teacher, the activity analysis format presented in this chapter will help you identify if your activity is designed as you intended. If you are an experienced teacher, you may benefit from activity analysis because it can help you review current lessons to determine if your tasks really are focused on the movement elements you think you are addressing. Activity analysis can also help all teachers develop appropriate feedback to give students based upon the tasks on which they are focused.

Table 6.1 presents an example of how to use activity analysis to design a lesson using the location category in the space concept area. When using this activity analysis process to design a

**Table 6.1**  Activity Analysis for Space Concept, Location Category: Self- and General Space Elements

| Steps | Description |
|---|---|
| **Step 1:** Select an activity | Teaching elements of self- and general space |
| **Step 2:** Write objective or objectives | Students will demonstrate an ability to stay in self-space while moving in general space. |
| **Step 3:** Movement concept | Space |
| **Step 4:** Movement category | Location |
| **Step 5:** Movement element | Self-space; general space |
| **Step 6:** Create questions about movement element performance | 1. Can students move in general space while staying in self-space? <br> 2. Can students stop and start on signal while moving in general space? |
| **Step 7:** Create tasks | 1. Now that you can start and stop on signal, we will explore all our general space. Remember, general space is all our available space for moving. On the signal, see how many places you can go in our general space without touching each other. <br> 2. See how many ways you can move in the general space. When you hear "Freeze," stop right away and stay on your feet. |

lesson, it may help to clarify the application of steps six and seven of the seven-step process. The movement analysis in step six during the design process can be guided by creating a list of questions that develop the ideas surrounding the movement elements you selected. Instead of simply ending the analysis in table 6.1 with identifying movement elements of self-space and general space, it is much more illuminating to write, Can students move in general space while staying in self-space? Because you have made it really clear what you are looking for in step six, step seven (Create development of the movement task by saying, Now that you can start and stop on signal, we will all explore our general space. Remember, general space is all our available space for moving. On the signal, see how many places you can go in our general space without touching each other.) really meets your intention! You can follow the same process for the movement elements in all four concept areas. Examples from each of the core content areas are also provided in this chapter. We also discuss how to use the activity analysis method to enhance activities that you may gather from outside sources and potentially need to revise to meet your true intentions.

## Core Content Area: Educational Games

Educational games can include a variety of skill themes. Movement education framework (MEF) elements foster content understanding as well as improved skill acquisition. The example provided in table 6.2 on page 110 is a compilation of several lessons and is provided to demonstrate the application of activity analysis to the design of educational games movement tasks.

Other movement elements, while they appear in the movement tasks presented in table 6.2, are not excluded from the actual analysis. For example, students should already be able to demonstrate an understanding of self-space and general space. In addition, you may have already focused on partner relationships and so may not need to revisit that topic. Finally, students should be able to demonstrate an understanding of the relationships elements of leading and following. These movement elements may be part of the movement language you use with students yet not be the main focus of your lesson.

## Core Content Area: Educational Gymnastics

Table 6.3 on page 111 is also a compilation of several lessons for demonstration purposes of how to use the activity analysis process in designing movement tasks. As with the other core content areas, additional movement elements appear in the movement tasks presented but are excluded from the actual activity analysis. Prior work would have included body shapes and balances, with a discussion of base of support and moving on and off balance. Students would need to know elements in steplike actions and springlike actions. Students should also have an understanding of self-space, general space, and bound and free flow.

## Core Content Area: Educational Dance

As noted in chapter 13, educational dance can encompass a wide variety of tasks. You may choose to teach more traditional dances or to focus on a more creative approach but the emphasis is on self-expression. In this chapter, we present a task that lends itself to a more creative approach to teaching educational dance. However, the same process applies to traditional dances. The example provided in table 6.4 on page 112 is a compilation of several lessons in educational dance. We have consolidated these lessons to demonstrate the activity analysis in designing movement tasks.

The following movement elements, while important to delivery of the lesson presented in table 6.4, were intentionally not included in the activity analysis. Examples of what has been left out include:

- Can students continue to work in their self-space?
- Can students move to the beat of a drum?
- Do students understand how to rise and sink?
- Can students apply elements of various levels as they move?

**Table 6.2** Educational Games Activity Analysis

| Steps | Description |
|---|---|
| **Step 1:** Select an activity | Dribbling with either hand |
| **Step 2:** Write objective or objectives | • Students will demonstrate the ability to dribble a ball with either hand when both stationary and traveling.<br>• Students will be able to apply changes in speed as they dribble. |
| **Step 3:** Movement concept | Body, space, and effort |
| **Step 4:** Movement category | Actions of the whole body (manipulative), directions, and time |
| **Step 5:** Movement element | Dribble, forward, backward, sideways, slow, fast, and acceleration |
| **Step 6:** Create questions about movement element performance | 1. Can students demonstrate an understanding of proper dribbling techniques?<br>2. Can students demonstrate an understanding of changes in speed as applied to dribbling a ball?<br>3. Can students demonstrate an understanding of changes in direction while dribbling a ball? |
| **Step 7:** Create tasks | 1a. In your self-space, show me how you can dribble the ball. I see everyone using the whole hand and not slapping the ball with a flat hand. See if you can use enough force to make the ball come to a medium level (at your waist).<br>1b. Let's see if you can begin to move around the general space as you dribble. Keep the ball at a medium level and use your fingertips. You decide how slow or fast to go so you can keep control of the ball.<br>1c. What do you need to do to keep the ball at a medium level? How do you need to use your hands and fingertips? If your ball is getting away from you, slow down.<br>2. Now start dribbling slowly and see if you can speed up and then slow down. Keep changing your speed and keep the ball close to you as you travel. Can you sometimes go slowly and sometimes more quickly? This is accelerating, or changing speed.<br>3a. As you continue to dribble, look for open spaces. If you come close to another person, stop quickly and change direction.<br>3b. See if you can dribble in one direction and then change and go in another direction. I will first give you a signal to change direction, and then you will be able to decide on your own when to change direction. Sometimes you will be dribbling forward, sometimes backward, and sometimes sideways.<br>3c. We are going to play Follow the Leader. Followers will stay behind the leader and carefully watch the direction they are going and the hand they are dribbling with. Be ready to change your direction and your dribbling hand each time you see your leader change. Take turns being the leader and the follower. |

We have chosen to limit the focus of the activity analysis for demonstration purposes. Although all lessons may contain multiple movement elements, we recommend that you highlight a limited number of them in particular lessons. Elements present in many or most lessons include "students working in self-space and general space" and "students demonstrating an understanding of levels." The use and application of movement elements should be inclusive and progressive. That is, there should be a continual building and use of the language of movement. However, although all of the movement elements are important, they may not be the direct intent of a particular lesson. If movement elements are not a direct intent of a lesson, do not analyze or emphasize them in the lesson.

## Applying Activity Analysis to Traditional Activities

While activity analysis is a super technique to help you identify if you are truly using the movement elements in a lesson the way you really intended, it can also be used to analyze individual tasks and to revise older, more traditional activities. Table 6.5 shows a movement activity analysis for a Scooter Tag activity. The first step in doing the analysis is to get as detailed of a picture of the activity as possible. To use this method, write out a detailed description, verbally describe the activity to a colleague, observe a video of the activity, or use any method that will help create an accurate vision

**Table 6.3**  Educational Gymnastics Activity Analysis

| Steps | Description |
|---|---|
| **Step 1:** Select an activity | Counterbalance and countertension |
| **Step 2:** Write objective or objectives | • Students will demonstrate an understanding of counterbalance and countertension with a partner.<br>• Students will demonstrate a gymnastics sequence with a partner showing counterbalance and countertension. The sequence will include traveling and moving into and out of balances showing counterbalance and countertension.<br>• Students will demonstrate an understanding of bases of support needed for both counterbalance and countertension. |
| **Step 3:** Movement concept | Body, effort, and relationships |
| **Step 4:** Movement category | Actions of the whole body (nonlocomotor), flow, and people |
| **Step 5:** Movement element | Counterbalance and countertension, free, and partner |
| **Step 6:** Create questions about movement element performance | 1. Can students demonstrate counterbalance?<br>2. Can students demonstrate countertension?<br>3. Can students work with a partner in creating a gymnastics sequence?<br>4. Can students demonstrate free flow with a smooth gymnastics sequence? |
| **Step 7:** Create tasks | 1a. In counterbalance, your base of support is away from your partner and you lean against each other. Start by leaning against your partner in a standing position. Your shoulders should be touching. As you do this, step away from your partner in a straight path. Keep your shoulders touching and keep your back straight as you press up. You are leaning away from your own base of support and it becomes a wider base. Regain your own balance by stepping in toward your partner.<br>1b. See if you can do other counterbalances with different body parts being the contact point with your partner. You might use your hands, the side of one shoulder, or another body part.<br>2a. In countertension, you and your partner will form or share a small base of support. Clasp each other's hands and put your toes very close together to form a small, or narrow, base of support. Carefully lean away from your base of support, stretching your arms out in a straight line. It is important to work together with your partner. To move back into your own balance position, slowly strengthen your pull and flex or bend your elbows. You can then come to a standing position on your own base of support.<br>    Now, see if you can make a countertension balance with your partner. [Students should find a partner who is about the same height and weight.] Form a narrow base of support with your toes and carefully lean away. Do this several times. You should use the same amount of tension to become balanced.<br>2b. See how straight you can make your hips, knees, and shoulders (no sags).<br>2c. Can you think of a different way to start? Remember, you must have a narrow base of support and lean away from each other. Remember to regain your own balance before you let go.<br>3 and 4. See if you can develop a gymnastics sequence that has either countertension balances or counterbalance balances. Between the balances, each of you chooses a way to travel. You might use steplike actions or springlike actions. Meet and make a second balance. Practice your sequence so it is smooth and flows well. |

of the activity. At a minimum, write a purpose to the activity and a brief movement analysis. The movement analysis should include what you want to see students do in relation to the MEF. Select a movement concept, category, and element that relate directly to the purpose of the activity. When you write your analysis, make sure to link the movement element to the purpose, or objective, of the activity.

Now repeat the preceding analysis process, further exploring other pertinent elements to make this activity fit more closely the movement education view of success for all and activity for all. In addition, bringing in a problem-solving approach enhances student success. As you repeat the process, take the Flip 'n' Fold and look for additional movement elements that enhance this activity. Revise the description of the objective

**Table 6.4** Educational Dance Activity Analysis

| Steps | Description |
|---|---|
| **Step 1:** Select an activity | Designing a movement (dance) sequence with symmetrical and asymmetrical shapes |
| **Step 2:** Write objective or objectives | Students will demonstrate an ability to design a dance sequence (beginning, middle, and ending) using symmetrical and asymmetrical shapes. |
| **Step 3:** Movement concept | Body and relationships |
| **Step 4:** Movement category | Shapes and position |
| **Step 5:** Movement element | Symmetrical/asymmetrical and movement sequence |
| **Step 6:** Create questions about movement element performance | 1. Can students demonstrate an understanding of symmetrical and asymmetrical shapes?<br>2. Can students demonstrate an understanding of a movement sequence (definite beginning, middle, and end)? |
| **Step 7:** Create tasks | 1a. In your self-space, create a variety of symmetrical body shapes using different levels and different bases of support.<br>1b. See if you can keep your symmetrical shapes clear as you rise and sink through the air. Listen to the beat of the drum to tell you when to rise and sink. Sometimes you will move slowly and sometimes more quickly.<br>1c. Select three symmetrical shapes you like best to perform one right after the other. Can you show smooth transitions between shapes? Practice these shapes showing a smooth transition.<br>1d. Now, I want you to think of a variety of asymmetrical shapes using different levels and bases of support.<br>1e. Can you keep your asymmetrical shapes clear as you rise and sink with the drumbeat?<br>2a. Select two of your favorite symmetrical and two of your favorite asymmetrical shapes. The symmetrical shapes will be part I, and the asymmetrical shapes will be part II. Between each part, you will travel. This is our dance movement sequence. In your self-space, practice your dance movement sequence.<br>2b. I am going to put on some wonderful music. Find a starting position. When you are ready, practice your dance movement sequence. I should see clear symmetrical and asymmetrical shapes. |

**Table 6.5** Initial Scooter Tag Activity Analysis

| Steps | Description |
|---|---|
| **Step 1:** Select an activity | Scooter Tag |
| **Step 2:** Write objective or objectives | Students will move fast on scooters trying to tag other players and to avoid being tagged. As students are tagged, they sit on the sidelines until there is one person left. |
| **Step 3:** Movement concept | Effort |
| **Step 4:** Movement category | Time |
| **Step 5:** Movement element | Fast |
| **Step 6:** Create questions about movement element performance | 1. Can students demonstrate an understanding of the element fast (sudden) as they avoid others who are also on scooters? |
| **Step 7:** Create tasks | 1. Can students demonstrate fast or sudden changes in speed as they avoid others who are also on scooters? |

of the activity to include any new or important movement elements not included in the first, often more superficial, objective. Table 6.6 shows what this deeper analysis might look like.

Although the activity in both scenarios is identical (Scooter Tag), the way students move in the second scenario (table 6.6) is very different from the way they move in the first scenario (table 6.5), in which the emphasis is only on moving fast. There is nothing wrong with the first scenario or the first analysis. The point of these two analyses is to show that the name of the activity or task is not enough; you must have a clear idea of which movement elements you want students to perform

**Table 6.6**  Deeper Scooter Tag Activity Analysis

| Steps | Description |
|---|---|
| **Step 1:** Select an activity | Scooter Tag |
| **Step 2:** Write objective or objectives | Students will work on acceleration and dodging as they move quickly and slowly on their scooters to avoid a chaser. |
| **Step 3:** Movement concept | Body and effort |
| **Step 4:** Movement category | Actions of the whole body (nonlocomotor) and time |
| **Step 5:** Movement element | Dodge and acceleration |
| **Step 6:** Create questions about movement element performance | 1. Can students demonstrate an understanding of changing their speed or accelerating or decelerating to avoid a tagger?<br>2. Can students demonstrate an understanding of dodging or changing direction to avoid a tagger? |
| **Step 7:** Create tasks | 1a. Players must stop for a count of 1 whenever they pass a cone marker. This will make them change from a fast to a slow speed or from a slow to a fast speed. Regardless of the taggers, all participants will practice acceleration.<br>1b. When trying to get away in the original activity, children focus only on going fast. Being forced to stop and then go again forces them to make more frequent changes of speed.<br>2a. I would focus on looking for changes in speed and good dodging skills while on the scooters.<br>2b. Students create a Scooter Tag activity that focuses on dodging and has changes in speed. They may choose to include smaller groups of players (no more than five in a group) and changes in direction and pathway. |

during the activity and be able to explain these to the students. Encouraging a problem-solving approach gives students a feeling of success and encourages them to apply movement knowledge as they build their word bank and apply these words to solve movement problems. The deeper analysis reveals the importance of reviewing any activity (task) in light of the movement elements you want to focus on to make sure it lends itself to student success.

## Summary

In this chapter, we have provided a format for analyzing teaching movement elements, core content lessons, and lessons from outside sources. We hope that both preservice and veteran teachers will benefit from this process. We anticipate preservice teachers might best benefit through developing a way of thinking that facilitates how to create lessons and activities that really target the desired objectives and movement outcomes

they are seeking. Veteran teachers often are in a position where they may not be able to get much feedback on their lessons and activities. This activity analysis process may help the veteran put fresh eyes on what they are doing and bring some critical thinking back into the process.

# Movement Activity Analysis Worksheet

Step 1:  Select an activity.

Step 2:  Write an objective or objectives.

Step 3:  Select a movement concept or concepts.

Step 4:  Select a category or categories.

Step 5:  Select an element or elements that relate directly to the objective of the task.

Step 6:  Create short questions that expand your vision of the movement elements as you'd like to see them performed.

Step 7:  Create the actual movement tasks using the previous list of questions to guide you and keep you on track (if first designing a lesson) or create a list of how you would change the activity or activities to better meet your objective (if revising a lesson).

| Steps | Description |
|---|---|
| **Step 1:** Select an activity | |
| **Step 2:** Write objective or objectives | |
| **Step 3:** Movement concept | |
| **Step 4:** Movement category | |
| **Step 5:** Movement element | |
| **Step 6:** Create questions about movement element performance | |
| **Step 7:** Create tasks | |

From K. Weiller Abels and J.M. Bridges, 2010, *Teaching Movement Education: Foundations for Active Lifestyles* (Champaign, IL: Human Kinetics).

# Teaching Movement Education

# Part I

# MOVEMENT CONCEPT ACTIVITIES

Chapters 7 through 10 provide activities that address the four major movement concepts as well as categories and elements.

As discussed in chapter 2, the movement education framework (MEF) is a system for classifying movement. The goal is to provide children with knowledge about movement so they can be successful in executing all aspects of the movement content (Logsdon et al., 1984). Helping children develop an inner feeling for what their bodies can do as they move and apply movement content in all learning situations is the ultimate goal of this approach.

Providing an exhaustive list of activities to use to teach movement elements is not possible in the space available in any book. In addition, each teacher's situation is unique. You need to consider whether your students already have some understanding of the movement education framework (MEF), as well as their developmental stage. If they have little or no knowledge of the MEF approach, you will need to build their movement knowledge. Just as children who are learning to read need to learn words before learning how to write full paragraphs, so, too, those learning about movement need to build a word bank of movement elements before creating movement phrases, sentences, and even stories. This word bank can then be applied to all types of movement situations in each of the three core content areas, as seen later on in chapters 11 through 13.

Students who are new to the MEF approach may need to have elements introduced individually or in small combinations. In one lesson, for example, from the body concept, locomotor/springlike actions, the elements of run, leap, hop, skip, jump, gallop, and slide may be introduced in individual activities. Within the space concept, elements in the directions category of forward, backward, and sideways may also be part of one lesson but introduced in individual activities and then combined as the lesson progresses. The purpose of introducing elements singularly is to ensure that students grasp the application.

Older children operating at a higher developmental stage may be able to handle multiple elements at a time. Using the previous example, in the directions category, activities may combine forward, backward, and sideways. Additional activities would address up and down and clockwise and counterclockwise.

## Initial Introduction and Movement Foundation Word Bank

As you begin to present the MEF approach to students, let them know that they are going to be learning about four big ways the body moves.

- What the body does (body concept)
- Where the body moves (space concept)
- How the body moves (effort concept)
- With whom or with what the body moves (relationship concept)

## Critical Elements

Presenting each concept area by itself will facilitate student understanding. However, although you should cover all concepts and elements, there are critical categories and elements that you need to teach prior to implementing lessons in educational dance, educational gymnastics, and educational games. Not only are these critical elements important for the core content areas, but also you can

use them to introduce your students to the MEF approach to lessons. The list on page 28 in chapter 2 identifies these critical elements, which provide a foundation for acquiring a movement word bank (content knowledge) for future movement elements and activities. We selected these particular elements as critical elements because they are applicable to many, if not all, lessons in the core content areas. Feel free to add or subtract from these critical elements, as you deem necessary.

The critical categories and elements presented correspond with the pocket chart card alphanumeric reference in parentheses. These elements may also be used on the movement word wall. You can find the coding in the glossary and in appendix A.

In chapters 7 through 10, you will find all the critical elements in the order listed on the Flip 'n' Fold. We encourage you to pull out these critical elements prior to teaching other movement elements.

## Communicating About Movement: The Problem-Solving Approach

Communicating with your students about movement is an important step in their acquisition of the critical movement elements as well as the many additional movement elements found on the Flip 'n' Fold that will be included in future lessons. It is important that you provide feedback during lessons, emphasizing what you want to see the children doing (e.g., "I am looking to see if you can travel and stay in your own self-space," or "I really like the way you are staying in your own space as you move throughout the general space"). Continually communicating with students about their work in physical education lessons helps build their movement vocabulary word bank. Also, encourage children to communicate with you and each other using movement terminology.

In a lesson on the movement elements of learning self-space and general space, point to the elements on the word wall or place them in the pocket chart. Ask the children to show their understanding of self-space by thinking of many ways to reach around their bodies in their own self-space. Encourage them to reach up high and sink down low, again staying in their own self-space. Because there are many ways to respond, children can exercise original thinking. As they move around the entire space, they begin to demonstrate their application of general space. Look to see if they can move throughout all the general space while staying in their own space. The key is to use all the open spaces.

This text emphasizes a problem-solving approach. Try to limit your demonstrations to avoid students' mimicking you. Demonstrations may be needed when presenting something new (e.g., throwing, catching, striking; Bilbrough & Jones, 1963; Rink, 2006), but those for the purpose of eliciting one specific response should be avoided.

Once you have presented a movement problem, allow children time to solve the problem and come up with a variety of movement solutions. After a few moments of work, provide praise and feedback. Be sure to observe children as they are working so you will know when to pose additional movement problems or move on to the next task. Statements that encourage children's creativity include: "Can you think of a different way to…" and, "I really liked the way you made a twisted shape. Can you think of another twisted shape?"

Going back to our example of self-space and general space, including some additional movement problems or subproblems can spur children to continue to explore. For example, you might say, "When you hear the signal, stay in your own self-space and see how big your self-space is" and then give them some time to explore. Subproblems may be: "Stretch as far as you can without falling or moving out of your self-space," and, "Can you really stretch to reach all of your self-space?"

Chapters 7 through 10 offer word-for-word suggestions of what you might say. This is for the benefit of preservice and beginning teachers who might need the extra initial guidance. If you are an experienced teacher, we encourage you to make these activities your own. Our intention is to provide examples, not an exhaustive list of activities. As you become more familiar with the MEF approach, you will be able to use your current activities and tasks and integrate into them the MEF and problem-solving approach. We have provided you with sample review activities for chapters 7 through 10. You can adapt these to all elements within these chapters.

# Body Activities

The body concept is the first concept introduced to learners in the movement education framework (MEF). This chapter provides activities for teaching the movement concept, categories, and elements of body awareness. The body concept focuses on what the body is doing in all actions. The four categories within this concept are body parts, body shapes, actions of body parts, and actions of the whole body. These categories help us understand groups of actions, describe the roles various body parts play in movements, name the activity being performed, and define the shape of the body during the activity. Most often, the focus is on the description of the action; however, it is important to understand all roles involved in movement to most fully describe and understand the movement.

Children learning the body concept are taught to become aware of various body parts and the relationship of one part to another, the importance of one body part in leading the movement, taking body weight onto a body part, or transferring body weight from one body part to another. For example, children can balance on one body part (a foot), and then transfer their weight onto the other foot and their two hands. As they do this, their hands are leading the action into the next balance; their body weight is transferred from one foot to the other foot and two hands; they are lifting the body into the air; and they are moving the body in different directions, levels, or ranges (Gilliom, 1970). Children should learn how to move specific body parts, observe and name parts of the body that they or others are moving, make various body parts lead a movement, or use various body parts to support or shift their weight.

For each of the activities in this section we list the equipment you will need. These lists are merely suggestions; feel free to substitute for equipment you have on hand. In some places, we have specifically noted equipment for start and stop signals. In addition, depending on your working space, you may need cones or other types of equipment to denote the space in which the children may work. Because the activities involve partner and small-group work, as well as individual work, you may also need equipment to delineate these spaces.

You may choose to use words (e.g., *go, freeze*), music, or a musical instrument for your start and stop signals. Your focal point should be on the movement elements, which you may teach individually or in combination. Using the appropriate pocket chart cards or a movement word wall helps children focus on the elements and their definitions, as well as apply the elements to other content areas such as reading and language arts.

# Building a Word Bank: Body Parts

Begin by selecting the body parts category card and placing it in the pocket chart. Depending on the developmental stage of your students, you may choose to create and place element cards for each of the body parts being covered in a lesson in the pocket chart, too. Learners at a higher developmental stage may not need this specificity. In that case, you may choose to bypass placing these element cards in the pocket chart and concentrate on providing a multitude of activities that use body parts.

The activities on body part identification are most appropriate for children at the initial or early elementary stage of development, for children whose first language is not English, or for children with learning differences.

## ACTIVITY 1

## First Activity for Body Part Identification
### Topic: Body parts

This activity is appropriate for children at the initial stage of development who are learning to identify body parts. It may also be useful for children whose first language is not English. Have children sit inside their hula hoops and let them know that this is their own self-space.

### Equipment
Hula hoops (one for each child)

### Instructions
1. Everyone find a hula hoop and sit inside that hoop. We are going to learn an element (term) we will cover later, but for now, I want to call this your self-space. Pretty soon, we won't need to use hoops to identify our self-spaces.
2. Raise your hand if you think you know the names of the big parts of your body. See how quickly you can place your hands on the body part I call out. [Call out belly, chest, shoulders, back, hips, knees, feet.]
3. How about other body parts? [Call out nose, ears, mouth, wrists, fingers, ankles, toes.]

## ACTIVITY 2

## Second Activity for Body Part Identification
### Topic: Body parts

This activity is a continuation of activity 1. It is fun for children to see how quickly they can identify body parts and lets you create a fun gamelike activity.

### Equipment
Hula hoops (one for each child, if desired)

### Instructions
1. How quickly can you put your hand in front of your head?
2. How about in back of your neck? [Call out others such as in back of one shoulder, in back of the other shoulder, in front of your belly, in back of your legs.]

## ACTIVITY 3

## Body Part Identification: Partner Fun!
### Topic: Body parts

Once the children at the initial stage of development have learned the words that match each body part, you can ask them to do this activity individually or with a partner. Working with a partner will make this activity much more fun. Make sure you have discussed how to work with a partner. In addition, you can introduce a problem-solving approach by asking children to identify body parts on their own. How many body parts can they identify? Can they create a list of body parts to match with a partner? Some examples are provided for you. Children at the initial and even elementary stages of development may want to write or draw the body parts they are identifying and then do the actual movements.

### Equipment
Hula hoops (one for each child, if desired)

### Instructions
1. Everyone sit in your self-space. I am going to call out combinations of body part words. When I do, see how quickly you can perform the movements asked.

2. Show me your very quickest and safest way to match the body parts.

3. When you are working with a partner or small group, can you move safely in your own space?

| | | |
|---|---|---|
| Chin to chest | Wrist to ear | Foot to leg |
| Nose to knee | Elbow to leg | Toes to heel |
| Hands to hip | Wrist to ankle | Head to knee |
| Ear to shoulder | Arm to leg | Thumbs to toes |

## Variations

These are only examples of possible combinations. See how creative you can be with other body part combinations, or even ask your students to create combinations.

# Building a Word Bank: Body Shapes

Place the category card body shapes in the pocket chart with the element cards of straight, wide, round, and twisted underneath. Explain that in this category the students are learning about four general shapes the outline of the body can make when moving or still. Shapes of the body are related to actions of the body parts (which is the next category). As noted in the final category, an action of the whole body such as stretching might yield a movement of a wide or stretched body shape. Similarly, a whole body action of curling would result in a curled or rounded body shape.

Within the body shapes category, you also want to introduce children to the idea of moving and stopping. For young children, being able to move and come to a stop, whether to completely stop prior to moving again (maintaining stillness) or merely change direction, is critical in learning how to manage their body movements. Often, young children have difficulty completely stopping movements, so a gradual cessation of body movement may be helpful (Maulden & Layson, 1965).

## ACTIVITY 4

## Body Shapes Come Alive

### Topic: Body shapes (narrow, wide, round, twisted)

Students find their own self-spaces and demonstrate body shapes that you request. You are looking for very creative ways to demonstrate the various body shape elements. Ask them to change their body shapes so you can see different narrow, wide, round, and twisted shapes.

### Equipment

Poly spots (these can be round spots or creative ones shaped like animals)

### Instructions

1. This time we are going to use poly spots to mark our self-spaces. You see poly spots all around the gym. When you hear the start signal, walk slowly to find a poly spot. This is going to be your own self-space.

2. As you look around, you will see the poly spots are all very far apart from each other. This means when I ask you later on to find your own self-space, you will know to spread way far apart, right? Give the start signal.

3. Now, that you are all in your own spaces, we are going to work on making various body shapes. We talked about narrow, wide, round, and twisted. Show me how you can make these shapes when I call them out. Make each one very clear.
   • Round
   • Twisted
   • Wide
   • Narrow

## ACTIVITY 5

## Body Shaper

### Topic: Body shapes (wide, round, twisted)

Children are combining their creativity with their knowledge of body shapes. Using music provides a great spark to this activity.

### Equipment

Poly spots or jellyfish floor discs

### Instructions

1. Stay in your own self-space. You do not have to stand right on the poly spot—beside it is fine.

2. We are going to work on changing our body shapes. I will call out two shapes. See if you can make the first one very clearly and then change to the second one.

3. When you are making your shapes, try to move very smoothly from one to the other.

4. Can you show me really interesting shapes?

5. Now, can you make your own body shape combinations? What two shapes will you choose?

Wide—round  Round—wide  Round—twisted
Twisted—round  Twisted—wide  Wide—twisted

# Building a Word Bank: Actions of Body Parts

Children do not need to know the category title "actions of body parts." When introducing this category and the subsequent elements, as a means of discussing the upcoming elements, tell them they are going to be focusing on specific body parts and the roles those body parts play in movement. You could say, for example, "We will be talking about body parts that help us receive weight or force, body parts that help us lead actions we want to do, body parts that help us support our body weight (or others' body weight), and body parts that help us transfer weight."

## Weight-Bearing Activities

Place the weight bearing element card in the pocket chart. Children need to understand that the action of supporting our body weight is sometimes called weight bearing. You may want to mention the term *balancing* so children are aware that supporting body weight is also called balancing. Although you have not yet introduced the element of balance, you have already introduced making body shapes and holding those shapes very still for a count of 3. Tell children you are going to talk about various body parts that help us support weight or serve as a base of support for us.

<hr>

## ACTIVITY 6

### Balancing Body Weight

#### Topic: Actions of body parts

Although children are working on balancing, the focus of this activity is supporting body weight on various body parts.

#### Equipment

Hula hoops or poly spots, if desired, to denote self-space. You may also have children use individual mats or share mats with one or two other children.

## Instructions

1. Show me how you can find your own self-space around the gym.

2. When you hear the start signal, make a shape with your body that uses your hands and feet for support.

3. Now, try using your shoulders and hands for support.

4. Can you balance and support your weight on your knees?

<hr>

## Receiving Force or Weight Activities

Place the receive force or weight element card in the pocket chart or point to it on the word wall. Learners should be aware that another role body parts can play in our activities is to help us receive weight. Prior to introducing this element, make sure children have mastered or become familiar with the ability to bring the body from motion to stillness. Tell them that weight can be received or supported on any number of body parts. You can ask older children to consider various parts of the body that might receive weight. Have them think about jumping and landing or catching a ball that their friend has tossed to them. As they do this, point out that receiving force or weight may be generated by the body itself, such as in landing from a jump, or may be the result of receiving the force of an object, such as in catching a ball. They should also know that we can receive the weight of another person such as when making a gymnastics partner balance.

Teach your students how to properly receive weight or force. For example, remind them that, when landing from a jump, they should absorb the force by bending their feet, ankles, knees, and hips (giving of the joints). After they have absorbed the force, they can then immediately send the

weight back into the air or onto a different base of support.

The same principle applies when absorbing the force of an object. The body part or equipment receiving the force is usually extended toward the approaching object. Upon contact, the body part or equipment is drawn in toward the body to either redirect the object (such as in hockey) or stop the object (such as in catching a ball).

## ACTIVITY 7

### Giving In

#### Topic: Actions of body parts

This activity focuses on force absorption between partners. As one partner throws to the other, your cues highlight catching skills (force absorption).

#### Equipment

Objects to toss and catch such as beanbags, soft coated foam balls, bouncy balls, critters, and yarn balls

#### Instructions

1. You are going to be working with a partner on throwing and catching. Find a partner with whom you can work well.
2. One partner may go get a type of ball and bring it back to your self-space.
3. With your partner, show me how you can throw and catch the ball [or other object]. We are working on absorbing the force of the throw from your partner.

## ACTIVITY 8

### Bring It In

#### Topic: Actions of body parts

As an extension of activity 7, this one encourages children to think about what happens to an object when different amounts of force are applied. What do they have to do when an object is sent at a high level compared to a low level? Do they have to do anything differently to absorb the force at a high level versus a low level or medium level?

#### Equipment

Objects to toss and catch such as beanbags, soft coated foam balls, bouncy balls, critters, and yarn balls

#### Instructions

1. Think about different ways you can pass the ball [or object] back and forth without letting it touch the floor. Can you do high tosses?
2. What do you notice about the difference in the way you absorb the force as you send the object away in different ways? If your partner sends you high tosses or straight tosses, do you absorb the force differently?

#### Variations

Students might respond that they give with their whole body as they reach out for the object. They should reach out with their hands and bring the object into their bodies. Have them mix up tosses—some overhand, some underhand, and some sidearm.

## ACTIVITY 9

### Travel Toss

#### Topic: Actions of body parts

As children become adept at absorbing force in their own self-spaces, add in traveling. The focus of this activity is moving around the general space, staying in self-space while traveling, and absorbing the force of the catch while traveling.

#### Equipment

Objects to toss and catch such as beanbags, soft coated foam balls, bouncy balls, critters, and yarn balls

#### Instructions

1. This time, let's try to toss and catch the ball [or object] as you travel around the general space. Can you walk slowly and toss and catch?
2. Think about absorbing the force of the toss as you catch the object.
3. Toss the object a few steps ahead of you and move to catch it. Can you feel how the force is gradually absorbed?
4. Move in different directions and at different speeds as you toss and catch. Think about using different locomotor movements as you toss and catch the object.
5. Remember, as you travel, keep in your own self-space.

MMSD Elementary School Physical Education Curriculum Committee, A Guide to Curriculum Planning in Elementary School Physical Education, 1986, updated 1991 (Madison, WI: Madison Metropolitan School District).

## Applying Force Activities

Place the apply force element card in the pocket chart or point to it on the word wall. Students should be aware that force is applied by using muscle tension, which may range from light to strong. In receiving force, the body part (e.g., hands) retracts, or gives, with the force of the catch. In applying force, body parts may stretch out or bend and then extend. An example of this is sending an object away. When kicking, the leg retracts and then extends as force is applied to the object being kicked. When throwing an object, the arm retracts and then extends in a follow-through after the object is released. Force may also be applied to an object to redirect it in a different pathway or direction. Finally, force may be applied from one person to another person to "add impetus to or restrict their movement," as in gymnastics, dance, and some games (Logsdon et al., 1984, p. 128).

## ACTIVITY 10

# Race Car Highway
### Topic: Actions of body parts (applying force)

Race Car Highway encourages children to produce powerful movements. It focuses on the application of force as well as the source of the force production. To be successful, however, children must demonstrate good use of both general and self-space.

### Equipment

- Hula hoops, cones, ropes, domes, or critters to denote a highway
- Start and stop signal equipment, if needed

### Instructions

1. We are going to play Race Car Highway. Hold your hula hoop around you like a car and see if you can move forcefully around the general space.
2. Each time you come to another person, move around that person so we don't have crashes.
3. Think about really pushing off with your legs to produce force as you travel all around our highway. Move around the cones and other objects you see.

4. This time, as your car races around our highway, think about pointing your body into empty spaces. Can you make quick turns as you travel?

## ACTIVITY 11

# Symmetry in Motion
### Topic: Body shapes

Once children have learned body shapes of narrow, wide, round, and twisted, you can move to more difficult shapes of symmetrical and asymmetrical. This is a great way to relate to math. See if the children have used these terms in their classroom! You want to see clear distinctions between symmetrical shapes and asymmetrical shapes.

### Equipment

Mats (one for every two children)

### Instructions

1. We are going to continue to talk about body shapes. This time we will focus on symmetrical and asymmetrical shapes. Does anyone know what symmetrical means? [It is the same on both sides.] If I took Suzie and split her down the middle, she would be the same on both sides.
2. Let's start with making shapes that are the same on both sides (symmetrical shapes). Find your self-space on the mat. Can you show me a symmetrical shape? See if you can hold that shape for a count of three (one cherry, two cherries, three cherries).
3. Can you change your symmetrical shape?
4. Now let's talk about asymmetrical shapes. What would these look like? [Different on both sides]
5. In your self-space, can you show me an asymmetrical shape? Can you hold that shape for a count of three?
6. Change your asymmetrical shape and create a new asymmetrical shape.
7. Now I want to see if you can make a symmetrical shape and then move into an asymmetrical shape. Make each shape very clear and distinct.

## ACTIVITY 12

# Same and Different Copy Fun

### Topic: Body shapes

After children have practiced creating symmetrical and asymmetrical body shapes individually, they will now create these body shapes with a partner. You want them to show you clear body shapes for both symmetrical and asymmetrical. See how creative they can be!

## Equipment

Mats (one for every two children)

## Instructions

1. Now that you have shown how you can make symmetrical and asymmetrical body shapes on your own, we are going to make these shapes with a partner.
2. Find a partner with whom you can work well.
3. You and your partner will find your own self-space on the mat. You will each get a chance to be the leader (the first to make a symmetrical or asymmetrical shape).
4. Your partner will copy the shape. You will each get two turns and then switch who is the leader.
5. Show me really distinct symmetrical and asymmetrical shapes.
6. Can you think of ways to make the shapes more interesting? Really exaggerate your shapes.

## ACTIVITY 13

# Stretch and Catch

### Topic: Actions of body parts

Games that involve throwing and catching require children to reach or stretch to catch an object being thrown to them. This activity gives children an opportunity to practice this action, as they consider the body part that is leading the stretching action.

## Equipment

Objects such as yarn balls, soft coated foam balls, critters, and beanbags

## Instructions

1. See if you and your partner can work on reaching, or stretching, catches.
2. When you toss the object to your partner, send it away so your partner has to reach, or stretch, to one side to catch it.
3. Take three turns and change roles.
4. What body part is initiating the action of catching?

MMSD Elementary School Physical Education Curriculum Committee, A Guide to Curriculum Planning in Elementary School Physical Education, 1986, updated 1991 (Madison, WI: Madison Metropolitan School District).

# Weight Transfer Activities

Once you have placed the weight transfer element in the pocket chart or pointed to it on the word wall, ask children what they think it means. They can begin by considering what *transfer* means. Help them understand that weight transfer is moving (or shifting) their body weight from one part to another, or from one place to another. Children may think about various ways they can shift, or move, their body weight. Many of these will be discussed further when we address locomotor springlike actions (e.g., sliding) and the roll-like actions of rocking and rolling. In educational gymnastics lessons children transfer their weight from feet to hands and back to feet.

## ACTIVITY 14

# Shift and Go

### Topic: Actions of body parts

Moving body weight from one part to another is the focus of this activity. You are looking for children who can carefully shift their body weight from a set number of body parts to another set number of body parts. Can they make smooth transitions?

## Equipment

Mats for individual children or ones that children may share

## Instructions

1. Stay in your self-space and see if you can support yourself on three body parts.

2. Now, slowly shift your body weight onto a four-part balance. Although we have not talked about how long to hold balance shapes, let's try to hold it for a count of 3. Make a smooth transition between balance shapes and really think about transferring your weight.

3. Find at least two large body parts on which you can balance, and then find two small body parts.

## ACTIVITY 15

### Up and Down

#### Topic: Actions of body parts

In this activity, you may choose to work with hula hoops. Children can place their hands inside the hoop and their feet outside the hoop. Ask them to think about transferring weight from their feet to their hands. This activity encourages them to solve the movement problem. Using "can you" allows them to consider how they can be successful. Some may only be able to lift one foot to a low level while keeping their hands and the other foot on the ground.

#### Equipment

Hula hoops

#### Instructions

1. See if you can shift your body weight from your feet to your hands and back to your feet.

2. When you shift your body weight onto your hands, can you bring one foot up to a low level?

3. Can you bring both feet up to a low level? If you need to, keep one foot on the floor outside the hoop as you bring the other to a low level. See if you can change the foot you are bringing to a low level.

4. Can you bring one foot to a medium level?

## ACTIVITY 16

### Switch Places

#### Topic: Actions of body parts

This activity may be most appropriate for children at the upper elementary stage of development. However, the wonderful thing about the activities presented in this book is that they offer decision-making opportunities. Children can decide when they are ready to challenge themselves by trying an activity.

#### Equipment

Mats, hula hoops, or both. Younger children may be more comfortable on mats, whereas older children may be able to do this activity using hula hoops.

#### Instructions

1. I want you to think about making your arms very straight and strong. Who can tell me why we need to do this? [To create a strong, stable base of support]

2. Can you get one foot to a high level? How about the other foot? You can decide if you want to try one foot at a high level or stay at a medium or low level.

3. Whichever level you choose, see if you can switch your feet in the air. If you lose your balance, you can collapse and roll out.

# Building a Word Bank: Actions of the Whole Body—Nonlocomotor

Nonlocomotor actions are performed on a fixed base of support, with little appreciable movement from one place to another. You may introduce each nonlocomotor element independently or in combination. Some nonlocomotor movements are best introduced within the applicable core content lesson. For example, spinning, rising, and sinking may be best applied in the educational dance content area. Children can demonstrate rising and sinking as they try to reach upward in a stretching motion and then almost melt into the floor. One involves moving away from gravity, and the other involves giving in to gravity. The key in educational dance is for the performer to express a feeling or a mood and communicate it to an observer.

Children can demonstrate whole body actions that stretch, curl, twist, turn, and spin. Gesturing is described as shaping movements in the air without body parts being supported. Turning involves the entire body moving to face a new direction. This may involve some appreciable movement from a direct base of support. Spinning suggests the entire body turning on a central axis to face a new direction. Momentum in spinning is the result of a single action (Logsdon, 1984).

Dodging is another nonlocomotor movement; it involves quick direction changes and is often used in chasing, fleeing, and dodging games. Balancing involves holding a fixed position (on any number of body parts) very still. We usually tell children to hold a balance shape for at least a count of 3. Counterbalance and countertension round out the nonlocomotor category. Partners or small groups must work together to press against each other as they balance over the wide base of support. Children should demonstrate that they are able to remain balanced over a wide base as they continue to be interdependent for support. Countertension also involves at least two people working to remain balanced over a base of support. Children displaying countertension demonstrate resistance against the partner or group as they pull away from the narrower base of support.

## ACTIVITY 17

## Primary Body Movements
### Topic: Nonlocomotor (primary body movements)

Children love to move their bodies in a variety of ways. Letting them solve this movement problem at their own level of comfort fosters creativity and success. Help children move smoothly from one nonlocomotor action to another. If you are working with older elementary children, encourage them to make their transitions very smooth.

### Equipment
Mats, if desired

### Instructions
1. Can you make a variety of primary body movements? Show me stretch, curl, and twist. Really exaggerate your primary body movements so they are very clear.
2. Can you slowly change your movement from a curl to a twist? Can you add a third movement and make the change smooth?

## ACTIVITY 18

## Letters and Numbers
### Topic: Nonlocomotor (primary body movements)

In this activity, children use primary nonlocomotor actions of the body (stretch, curl, and twist) as they try to make themselves into the shapes of letters and numbers. Ask them to really exaggerate their nonlocomotor actions. You can incorporate math into this activity by having the children use skip counting (skipping by a certain amount of numbers, e.g., 2, 4, 6, and so on) for the number shape you are seeking. Younger children at the initial or elementary stage may also work on letter recognition. Instead of calling out a letter, hold up a very large letter for all to see. Then ask children to make themselves into that letter using the primary body movements they have learned.

### Equipment
Hula hoops or poly spots if you feel children need to denote self-space. Mats may be used as well if children will feel more comfortable.

### Instructions
1. You are going to make your bodies into the shapes of letters that I call out. Try to connect them smoothly.
2. Can you experiment with turning while you are making a letter shape?
3. See if you can travel and, when I give you the signal, move into your letter shape.
4. Now, let's try making our bodies into numbers. When you begin to travel, listen this time for my freeze signal. When you hear it, stop and freeze. I will call out a number. See if you can make your body into that number and hold the shape for at least three seconds.

## ACTIVITY 19

## Swing High, Swing Low
### Topic: Actions of the whole body

Begin by asking the children to remember the last time they used the swings at a park. Their body went back and forth as they were swinging. Now they are going to work on swinging body parts in this activity.

### Equipment

Mats (one for every two children)

### Instructions

1. When we are working on swinging, we are thinking about a body part that moves around an axis (or an object or body part that is fixed or stationary). If you have been to the circus, you may have seen a trapeze artist. The bar on which they are swinging is stationary and they are moving their entire body around the object.
2. We are going to work on swinging body parts. Imagine we are outside and the wind is blowing very hard. Can you swing your arms from your shoulders like they are willow branches blowing in the breeze?
3. As the wind becomes calmer, can you make your arms blow (move) more slowly?
4. Are there other body parts you can swing? Can you swing your legs? How about your fingers?
5. Think of three different body parts you can swing.

---

### ACTIVITY 20

## Traveling, Turning, and Spinning

### Topic: Nonlocomotor

Creating a movement sequence that includes turning, spinning, and traveling in general space can

be fun. See how many different ways children can create a sequence that includes traveling, turning, and spinning. Do they know the difference between turn and spin? Can they spin on different body parts? Can they travel on different body parts as well?

### Equipment

Music that encourages children to spin and turn

### Instructions

1. See if you can create a sequence that has traveling, spinning, and then traveling again.
2. Think of different ways to travel and spin in your sequence. Continue to practice this.
3. Remember to stay in your self-space as you use all our general space.

---

### ACTIVITY 21

## P-U-S-H

### Topic: Nonlocomotor (push)

Pushing a very heavy object requires the application of force. You may want to refer to the prior element of applying force (actions of body parts category). Pushing requires a great deal of force and strong muscle tension. See if children can demonstrate this strong muscle tension as they show you pushing.

### Equipment

None required. You may choose to have music that fosters the element of pushing.

### Instructions

1. In your own self-space, think about pushing away a very heavy object. You would need to exert a great deal of force away from the body.
2. Show me with your arms leading the action how you would attempt to move the very heavy object.

---

### ACTIVITY 22

## P-U-L-L

### Topic: Nonlocomotor (pull)

Directing force toward the body also requires strong muscle tension. You want to see children demonstrating the application of force toward the body as they show you pulling. Ask them to consider whether a narrow or wide base of support is better for directing force toward the body.

### Equipment

Music that encourages the element of pulling

## Instructions

1. When we pull, we are directing force toward the body. You and your partner are working together to pull an imaginary heavy object toward you.
2. Show me with your arms and your legs how you would pull the object toward you. Your arms are leading the action. Think about strong muscle tension as you bring the object toward you.

---

### ACTIVITY 23

## Quicksand
### Topic: Nonlocomotor (rise, sink)

Ask children to pretend they are in quicksand. They work to rise up above the quicksand but somehow keep sinking into it.

### Equipment

Music for rising and sinking

### Instructions

1. As we are traveling, we come upon a huge area of quicksand. Show me how you can rise to a high level with one body part leading the action to get out of the quicksand.
2. When you have risen to as high a level as you can, the quicksand seems to pull you back in, so you sink quickly to a low level leading with the same body part. This is really tricky quicksand, and you keep rising and sinking.
3. Decide which body part should lead the action and show me a very quick sink.
4. Now, change the body part you are using to show rising and sinking.
5. Can you also change the speed at which you are rising and sinking?
6. Can you and your partner use the same body part to rise quickly?

---

### ACTIVITY 24

## Express Yourself
### Topic: Nonlocomotor (gesture)

Gesturing is a difficult element for children to grasp. Ask younger children to make a smiley face and wave their arms in the air at a high level. What feeling does this demonstrate? Then ask them to sink low and make a small, round shape. Again, ask them to consider what feeling or mood this action demonstrates. Gesturing is making motions with our bodies or body parts that demonstrate a mood or feeling.

### Equipment

Music that will assist children in demonstrating the element of gesture

### Instructions

1. In your own space, make a shape with your body and hold it still for a count of 3.
2. See if you can then explore different ways to gesture with free body parts. Remember, gesturing is used to demonstrate a mood or feeling.
3. You can make patterns or shapes in the air with free body parts.

---

### ACTIVITY 25

## Gesture
### Topic: Nonlocomotor (gesture)

Begin by reminding children that they have already worked on making balanced shapes. This activity is an extension of the previous activity in that you ask children to use the free body parts (i.e., those not being used as bases of support in the balanced shapes) to gesture. How can this extend their balanced shapes?

### Equipment

Mats, if desired. You may also choose to use hula hoops or poly spots to denote self-space.

### Instructions

1. You can also gesture while balancing on a base of support. See if you can make an interesting body shape on three body parts.
2. Now use a free body part, or parts (that you're not using for the base of support), to gesture. For example, if you make a wide base of support on your feet and stretch your arms out wide, your arm stretch is a gesture.
3. Show me how you can really extend your balanced shapes by adding in gesturing.

## ACTIVITY 26

# Dodge Away

### Topic: Nonlocomotor (dodge)

Dodging is used in many fun activities and games for children.

### Equipment

- Drum or other musical instrument to use as a signal for dodging
- Cones for dodging around

### Instructions

1. Dodging is fun element to practice. Let's start by finding your self-space.
2. When you hear the start signal, begin traveling around the general space. You can decide how you want to travel. We will start out slowly, however.
3. When you hear the signal [demonstrate the signal], I want you to show me dodging. Dodging is faking, or quickly changing directions.

## ACTIVITY 27

# Partner Dodge

### Topic: Nonlocomotor (dodge)

After children have worked on dodging individually, add in partner work so they can practice dodging a stationary person. They should show you quick direction changes as they dodge. As they work in partners, remind children that their self-space is also the space in which each set of partners has to work.

### Equipment

None

### Instructions

1. Now that you have practiced the movement of dodging, let's see if you can dodge a partner who is standing still.
2. Find a partner with whom you can work well. You and your partner will have your own self-space.
3. Find a spot close to your partner.
4. When you hear the start signal, I want to see if you can move slowly toward your partner.

5. When you get close to your partner, can you quickly change direction?
6. Remember, your partner is standing still and you are dodging your partner.
7. You can use a sideways movement to dodge your partner.
8. Take two turns and then change places.

## ACTIVITY 28

# Get Out of Dodge!

### Topic: Nonlocomotor (dodge)

As children become more adept at dodging, they will be able to dodge in bigger groups. Begin by asking children to walk. Children who are operating at an initial stage of development should stay with walking at a slow speed. As the children demonstrate good dodging skills, they can walk at a faster speed.

### Equipment

Music

### Instructions

1. Find your self-space.
2. When the music begins, show me how you can travel around the general space, dodging others to avoid running into them. We will first travel by walking slowly. I am looking for good dodging skills (quick sideways direction changes). Show me how you can dodge quickly when you come to another person.
3. Remember, as you travel, you are staying in your self-space and using all our general space.
4. Change the way you are traveling. Can you skip, hop, or jump? Again, when you come to a person, show me good dodging. I should see direction changes sideways, forward, and backward.

## ACTIVITY 29

# Avoidance

### Topic: Nonlocomotor (dodge)

The traditional game of Dodgeball is not considered developmentally appropriate for children (NASPE, 2006). However, working on the element of dodging with others and a soft, appropriate piece of equipment can be fun. The intent of this game is not to hit the person with the object, but to focus on their ability to avoid the object. Children at the upper elementary stage of development will enjoy adding their own spice to this game. They might want to see how many dodges they can make within a specific amount of time.

## Equipment

- Soft coated foam balls
- Music or an instrument for a signal, if desired

## Instructions

1. Let's play a game of Avoidance. You will be in a group of four where you will toss a soft object lightly from person to person. One person will be in the middle. The person in the middle will try to dodge or avoid the object as it flies through the air.

2. You keep tossing and dodging until you hear the signal to switch the person in the middle.

The purpose of this game is to work on dodging skills. Feedback to the students is critical to encourage them to work on their avoidance (dodging) movements. You should point out students who are demonstrating good dodging skills.

## Variations

You may add other dodging games, as needed. Resources such as www.pecentral.org provide lessons on chasing, fleeing, and dodging. Remember, though, as children play chasing, fleeing, and dodging games that you focus on dodging skills, as well as chasing and fleeing skills, and not on establishing a winner. Children may also enjoy creating their own dodging games. The group size should be kept as small as possible. Make sure children focus on good dodging, chasing, and fleeing skills in the games they create.

# Building a Word Bank: Actions of the Whole Body—Locomotor

Locomotor actions are those that take the body from one place to another. In the subcategory of steplike actions, at least one body part remains in contact with the floor. We think of steplike actions as being done on the feet, but they can also be done on other body parts such as the hands, hips, and knees. We have chosen to highlight the steplike actions of walking, cartwheels, crawling (a horizontal movement which looks the same as the vertical movement [climbing]), bear walking, and crab walking. Springlike actions result in momentary flight, when all body parts are off the floor. Locomotor movements of running, leaping, hopping, skipping, jumping, galloping, and sliding fall into this subcategory. In roll-like actions (rocking and rolling), although one body part does remain in contact with the floor, weight is transferred along the same body surface or changing body surfaces (Logsdon et al., 1984). As you are introducing each of these elements, place it in the pocket chart or point to it on the movement word wall. It is important for children to become familiar with the definition of each locomotor element.

## ACTIVITY 30

# How Can I Balance?
## Topic: Actions of the whole body

In teaching children to balance, we can help them think about using their core to help them maintain stillness. Staying on balance has been presented when children made body shapes in activity 6. Here we are focusing on the specific aspect of maintaining balance although shapes are included. You are looking for children to maintain stillness for at least a count of three.

## Equipment

Mats (one for every two children)

## Instructions

1. We are going to work on balancing. Everyone stand in your self-space. Think about one of the body shapes we learned (e.g., narrow, wide, round, twisted, symmetrical, asymmetrical). Show me a body shape and see if you can balance or hold that body shape for a count of three without moving. Are you balanced?

2. Now change your body shape and show me another balanced shape. Make sure you are very still for a count of three.

3. Can you make one shape and then move into another shape, staying balanced for both shapes?

## ACTIVITY 31

### Balance With a Partner
**Topic: Actions of the whole body**

As an extension of the previous activity, children are working with a partner or in small groups to create balanced shapes. The focus is not the shape, but rather observing if children can maintain balance. As you begin, ask them what the difference is between being balanced and not being balanced.

**Equipment**

- Mats (one for every two children)
- Hula hoops (one for every two children)

**Instructions**

1. Find a partner with whom you can work well.
2. See if your partner can show how they maintain their balance. Give your partner a number of body parts on which to balance (e.g., two, three, four) and see if your partner can hold their balance for a count of three.
3. Each partner should take two turns and then change roles.
4. You will use your hula hoop now. Can you and your partner create a three-part balance inside each hoop?
5. Create three different balances either inside the hoop, outside the hoop, or a combination.

## ACTIVITY 32

### Partner Counterbalance and Countertension
**Topic: Actions of the whole body**

Ask the children to define counterbalance and countertension. Answers should reflect pushing and pulling equally against another. These elements are done with a partner or in a small group. These elements will be presented in two activities, one with a partner and one in a small group of three.

**Equipment**

Mat (one for every two children)

**Instructions**

1. Find a partner with whom you can work well. You and your partner should find your own self-space on a mat.

2. With your partner, can you show me counterbalance? Can you hold it very still?
3. Now create a different counterbalance. Hold it very still for a count of three.
4. We are going to move on to countertension. How is this different from counterbalance?
5. Show me a countertension balance. Hold this very still.
6. Show me a different countertension balance.

## ACTIVITY 33

### Group Counterbalance and Countertension
**Topic: Actions of the whole body**

As an extension of the previous activity, children will work in a group of three (or four, if needed, depending on the size of your class) to create counterbalance and countertension.

**Equipment**

Mats (one for every two to four children)

**Instructions**

1. You and your group will show me counterbalance. Think about how each person can contribute to the counterbalance.
2. Create a different counterbalance balance.
3. Now show me countertension as a group. Make sure you are holding the balance very still.
4. Let's see if your group can move from one balance to another. You can decide if both are counterbalance or countertension or if you want to show me one of each.

## ACTIVITY 34

### Walk About
**Topic: Locomotor (steplike actions)**

In this activity children travel while keeping at least one body part in contact with the floor at all times.

**Equipment**

None

**Instructions**

1. We are going to work on the steplike actions of walking, crawling, bear walking, and crab walking.

2. Remember when you are moving to keep one body part in contact with the floor. Walking is moving arms and legs in opposition.

3. When you hear the start signal, show me how you can walk in the general space while staying in your self-space. Of course, that is easy for you!

4. Can you walk faster while staying in your self-space? See if you can walk all around finding every corner of our general space. Every time you come to a cone cap, change your locomotor movement.

5. Can you walk in a backward direction? How about in a sideways direction?

6. Listen for my signal and show me how you can quickly change the direction in which you are walking. You will have to listen very closely, because I might be very tricky!

3. Can you show me how a bear might walk if it was very tired? How about if it was very hungry?

4. Show me how a crab might walk if it was scurrying on the ocean floor. What about on the beach in the hot sun?

## ACTIVITY 35

# Crabs and Bears, Oh My!

### Topic: Locomotor (crab walk, bear walk)

Ask children to remember the element of gesturing as they think about how a bear might walk and how a crab might walk. As they are showing you a bear walk and a crab walk, can they gesture with free body parts? Can they use one hand to make the claw of the crab? How about moving in a lumbering manner as if they were a big, brown bear? Classroom teachers can use this activity as well. If you are reading a book about animals that includes bears or crabs, ask the children to do this activity. They will enjoy the movement.

### Equipment

Music to help children with imaginative and creative movement. Think about music that might foster animal movements.

### Instructions

1. Bear walking and crab walking are fun! Bear walking is traveling on your hands and feet with your belly facing the floor. Crab walking is the opposite—your belly faces the ceiling.

2. Choose two obstacles and place them in your self-space. When you are ready, show me how you can crab walk and bear walk around the obstacles.

## ACTIVITY 36

# Give Me a Hand

### Topic: Locomotor (cartwheel)

This activity provides visual cues for where to place the hands to help children with the cartwheel. It is important to recognize children's success at whatever level they choose to bring their feet.

### Equipment

Two poly cue hands for each child

### Instructions

1. You each have two poly cue hands on the floor.

2. Make your body really stretched with your hands reaching toward the sky.

3. Point one foot in the direction you are going to move.

4. See if you can reach down with the hand on the same side as the foot that is pointed in the direction you want to go. Place that hand near to the cue hand on the floor.

5. Your other hand should follow near to the second cue hand.

6. When your first hand is going down, see if you can raise up the opposite foot.

7. As you kick up, see if you can make your legs straight. Keep your arms straight and strong.

8. Can you land on the opposite foot and bring the remaining foot down?

9. Your cues are hand, hand, foot, foot.

10. You choose the level of your feet as you kick up. You can choose a low, medium, or high level.

*Elizabeth Rutherford contributed to the development of this activity.*

## ACTIVITY 37

# Tell Me Why It's Run and Fly
### Topic: Locomotor (run)

Children need to distinguish between a walk and a run. The momentary loss of contact with the floor in a run is what differentiates it from a walk. See if children can show you different ways of running.

### Equipment
- Music to help children distinguish spring-like actions
- Cone caps spread around the gym

### Instructions
1. Find three ways to travel quietly throughout the general space touching the floor with only your feet.

2. Can you show me walking? How about running? Can you run quietly?

3. When you run, I am looking for arms and feet in opposition. What is the difference between a walk and a run? [A run is a faster walk and shows some flight.]

4. Can you travel on different parts of your feet? How about toes, or the toes of one foot and the heel of the other foot?

5. Can you travel with your feet close together and then far apart?

6. When you come to a cone cap, change between a walk and a run.

## ACTIVITY 38

# Locomotor Choo-Choo
### Topic: Locomotor (skip, gallop)

Children at the initial and early elementary stages of development should spend time learning skipping and galloping.

### Equipment
Train music would be lots of fun for children with this activity.

### Instructions
1. This time, let me see if you can show skipping and galloping. Skipping is an alternating step/hop, and galloping is a forward step with the trailing foot closing up to the front foot.

2. Can you show three different ways of traveling that use the locomotor skills we have talked about? We have talked about walking, running, skipping, and galloping, the crab walk, and the bear walk. Pick your favorite two ways and practice those until you hear the signal to stop.

3. Let's see if we can make a locomotor train. Find a partner and stand behind that partner. When I say "Go," show me if you and your partner can create a locomotor train by skipping one behind the other.

4. When you hear the signal, can you change to a gallop?

5. I will tell you when to change the lead person.

6. When you come to a cone cap, change your locomotor skill. If you have been skipping, show me a gallop.

## ACTIVITY 39

# More Locomotor Fun
### Topic: Locomotor (leap, hop, jump)

This activity helps children differentiate between a leap and a jump as well as among the types of jumps. It is important to also help them understand cues for jumping. For jumping, children should focus on swinging their arms, bending their knees and hips to a medium or lower level, and pushing off with the balls of their feet. Remind them to focus on landing on the balls of their feet and bending their knees to absorb the force of the landing following a jump. Ask them to think about showing you quiet, soft landings. Following jumping, add in galloping and sliding. Galloping is a step and a close in a forward direction with the front foot leading the action.

## Equipment

Music that encourages children to demonstrate leaping, jumping, and galloping

## Instructions

1. Let's add in jumping and leaping.
2. There are different types of jumps. We can jump from one foot to two feet, two feet to two feet, and two feet to one foot.
3. Leaping is one foot to the opposite foot, and hopping is one foot to the same foot.
4. Practice all of these locomotor movements as you travel around the general space. I want to see if you can also stop safely on my signal. This means to stay on your feet.
5. Listen for the music, and travel when the music begins.
6. Can you show me leaping? How about different types of jumps?
7. Now, let's add in galloping as you travel around the general space.

## ACTIVITY 40

# Steplike and Springlike Actions
### Topic: Locomotor (steplike, springlike)

In this activity children demonstrate the steplike and springlike actions they have been taught. As you watch them choose their favorite locomotor movements, you may want to refer back to chapter 3 and choose an assessment that works for you. You may use this as an assessment to identify those children who are able to demonstrate the locomotor movements and those who need some additional assistance.

## Equipment

- Hula hoops, jump ropes, noodles, cones with cone caps
- Music for start and stop signals, if desired

## Instructions

1. In the general space you see various objects. We have hula hoops, ropes, noodles, and cones.
2. When you hear the start signal, travel around the general space and use the steplike and springlike movements we have learned. If you want, you can jump into and out of the hoops, leap over the rope, and hop over the noodles. When you come to a cone cap, show me the locomotor skill on the cone cap.
3. Show me how you do your best steplike and springlike actions.

## ACTIVITY 41

# Rock On!
### Topic: Locomotor (rocking)

See how many different body parts children can think to use for rocking. You are looking for children maintaining contact with the floor. Rocking is a form of a locomotor action in which the person maintains contact with the floor (Logsdon et al., 1984). When we rock, we shift our body weight on parts that are next to each other.

## Equipment

Mats for individual children or for children to share

## Instructions

1. On the start signal, see how many different ways you can find (in your own space) to rock back and forth on body parts that are next to each other.
2. Can you rock on your back as well as on your front? How many different places can you find to put your feet and hands while you are rocking?
3. Can you make your rocking smooth? Can you hold your ankles while you rock on your belly?
4. While you are rocking on your back, see how many different ways you can move.
5. Can you change direction while you rock? Can you go side to side as well as front to back?

## ACTIVITY 42

# Copy Rock
### Topic: Locomotor (rocking)

Children enjoy creating rocking movements for partners to copy. Rocking is a form of a locomotor action in which the person maintains contact with the floor (Logsdon et al., 1984). When we rock, we shift our body weight on parts that are next to each other. You may have children demonstrate for each other (half of the class at a time).

### Equipment

Mats for individual children or for children to share

### Instructions

1. Find a mat to share with a partner.
2. We are going to play Copy Rock. Decide who will be the first leader.
3. The leader rocks in different ways, and the follower tries to copy the leader's movements.
4. Once you have had two turns as the leader, switch with your partner.

Encourage children to do rocking movements that their partners can copy. Also, encourage them to make small curled shapes and keep body parts close together.

MMSD Elementary School Physical Education Curriculum Committee, A Guide to Curriculum Planning in Elementary School Physical Education, 1986, updated 1991 (Madison, WI: Madison Metropolitan School District).

## ACTIVITY 43

## Log Roll

### Topic: Locomotor (body rolling)

Encourage children to make long, stretched shapes as they roll. See if they can keep the roll going in one direction. Rolling is a form of locomotor action in which the person maintains contact with the floor (Logsdon et al., 1984). When we roll, we continually transfer our body weight to parts that are close to each other.

### Equipment

Mats for individual children or for children to share

### Instructions

1. Let's change your rock into a roll. To do this, you need to keep going in the same direction. [You may choose to have a student demonstrate.]
2. In your own space on the mat, see if you can rock from side to side in a stretched, narrow position.

3. Can you keep this roll going in one direction? Can you keep your body really stretched? This is called a log roll.

## ACTIVITY 44

## Turtle Roll

### Topic: Locomotor (body rolling)

Another type of roll is a turtle, or curled, roll. Ask children to think about making a very small, round shape, much like a turtle inside its shell. See how many different turtle rolls they can create. Rolling is a form of locomotor action in which the person maintains contact with the floor (Logsdon et al., 1984). When we roll, we continually transfer our body weight to parts that are close to each other.

### Equipment

Mats for individual children or for children to share

### Instructions

1. Show me how you can make a round shape and rock in different directions. This is called a turtle roll.
2. How many ways do you think a turtle might roll?
3. Can you roll slowly or more quickly?

## ACTIVITY 45

## Forward Roll

### Topic: Locomotor (body rolling)

Providing options for children as you introduce a forward roll is important. Many children attempt a forward roll without the ability to be successful. Although providing children with cues is critical, it is also important to encourage children to attempt a forward roll only when they can be successful on their own. Rolling is a form of locomotor action in which the person maintains contact with the floor (Logsdon et al., 1984). When we roll, we continually transfer our body weight to parts that are close to each other.

### Equipment

Mats for individual children or for children to share

## Instructions

1. For those of you who are ready to try this, squat down and curl your body with your hands on the floor just in front of your feet.
2. Tuck your chin to your chest and be very small.
3. See if you can transfer your weight slowly from your feet to your hands (as you raise your hips and look between your legs).
4. Keep transferring your weight onto the back of your shoulders (not your head) as you roll out.
5. This is rolling in a forward direction, or a forward roll. Show me either a great log roll or a forward roll.

## ACTIVITY 46

# Backward Roll

## Topic: Locomotor (body rolling)

Some children may not be ready to do a forward or backward roll. Provide other roll options (e.g., log or turtle roll) for children who are not comfortable doing either a forward or backward roll. Children choose to rock in a backward direction rather than attempting a backward roll. Provide this option so all children can move (rock or roll) in a backward direction. Rolling is a form of locomotor action in which the person maintains contact with the floor (Logsdon et al., 1984). When we roll, we continually transfer our body weight to parts that are close to each other.

## Equipment

Mats for individual children or for children to share

## Instructions

1. If you are comfortable trying this, squat down again, curling your body.
2. Rock forward and backward with a curled body.
3. When your body weight is on your shoulders, drop your feet over your head onto the floor and push lightly with your hands on the floor, helping your body weight to keep the movement going in a backward direction.
4. I am looking for either rocking or rolling in a backward direction. Choose one of those and show me your two best rocks or rolls.

## ACTIVITY 47

# Rock and Roll Creation

## Topic: Locomotor (rocking, body rolling)

Explain to the children that a sequence is a series of movements that have a definite beginning and ending. They may want to start with a beginning shape, or a ready shape, add in the rolls, and finish with an ending shape. After children have practiced their rock and roll sequences, you may choose to have them work with partners to demonstrate their sequences. See if children can identify the various rocking and rolling movements their partners are demonstrating. Rocking and rolling are forms of locomotor actions in which the person maintains contact with the floor (Logsdon et al., 1984). When we rock, we shift our body weight to parts that are next to each other. When we roll, we continually transfer our body weight to parts that are close to each other.

## Equipment

Mats for individual children or for children to share

## Instructions

1. See if you can create a rock and roll sequence.
2. Choose two ways to rock and two ways to roll.
3. Combine these into a sequence and practice this so it is smooth. Each roll should be very clear.
4. Practice your sequence and be ready to show it to a partner.

# Building a Word Bank: Actions of the Whole Body—Manipulative

The manipulative skills of throwing, rolling an object, striking, kicking, volleying, catching, trapping, dribbling, and carrying are divided into the categories of sending objects away, gaining control of objects, and propelling objects.

Sending objects away includes throwing, rolling, striking, kicking, and volleying. Throwing and rolling an object are executed with the hands. Throwing patterns may be underhand, overhand, or sidearm. Rolling is executed with the hands in an underhand motion, with an object released at a medium or low level toward another object or objects such as in bowling. Striking and volleying are executed with the hands, but also may be executed with other body parts as well as equipment. Kicking is executed with the feet. Kicking objects may be done on the ground from a stationary or rolled (dynamic) position or with the object airborne (as in a punt).

Gaining control of an object is presented here with catching and trapping. Catching (Logsdon et al., 1984) suggests reducing an object's speed by grasping or holding it. Trapping an object with the legs or feet is a form of catching because it involves reducing the speed of the object. Propelling can be done with the hands, the feet, or a piece of equipment such as a hockey stick. Propelling an object involves keeping the object under control while moving it from one place to another like dribbling, or carrying it, such as in American football.

To become good games players, children need to develop solid manipulative control while also becoming adept at moving in their environment. Learning manipulative skills (including the critical elements in the space, effort, and relationships concept areas) will help students become successful movers and skillful games players. The following activities address each of the manipulative skills listed on the Flip 'n' Fold. As you introduce each manipulative skill to learners, keep in mind their developmental stage and use appropriate extensions to the activities, as needed. Chapter 11, Educational Games, has additional activities that address manipulative skills.

## ACTIVITY 48

## Self-Toss

### Topic: Manipulative (throw, catch)

Many of the games children play involve throwing and catching. Prior to this activity, children who are at the initial or early elementary stage of development may benefit from throwing an object and catching it in their own self-space. They can then progress toward throwing an object higher than they can reach. You can make this into a game-like activity that includes math skills by asking children to count the number of times they are able to throw and catch the object within a given amount of time.

### Equipment

Balls, beanbags, or movement education beach balls (one for each child)

### Instructions

1. In your own space, gently toss your ball or beanbag higher than you can reach.
2. See if you can catch it every time. Can you throw it a little higher each time?

MMSD Elementary School Physical Education Curriculum Committee, A Guide to Curriculum Planning in Elementary School Physical Education, 1986, updated 1991 (Madison, WI: Madison Metropolitan School District).

## ACTIVITY 49

## Stretch and Catch

### Topic: Manipulative (throw, catch)

This is an extension of activity 48. In this activity, each child needs a hula hoop and an object to throw and catch. You are looking for children who are able to reach or stretch to catch the object. You are also looking for children to be able stay in their own self-space as they throw and catch.

### Equipment

- Hula hoops (one for each child)
- Objects to toss (yarn or fleece balls, soft gator skin balls, beanbags; one for each child)

### Instructions

1. Staying in your own space, toss your yarn ball [or object] in such a way that you have to stretch to catch it.
2. Stand inside your hoop so you can keep your own self-space.
3. Can you step with one foot outside of your hoop to catch the object? Try to keep the other foot inside the hoop.

MMSD Elementary School Physical Education Curriculum Committee, A Guide to Curriculum Planning in Elementary School Physical Education, 1986, updated 1991 (Madison, WI: Madison Metropolitan School District).

## ACTIVITY 50

# Throw and Go

### Topic: Manipulative (throw, catch)

Moving from a static to a dynamic pattern is a bit more challenging. Children need to be able to maintain control of the object as they travel.

### Equipment

Yarn or fleece balls, soft gator skin balls, or beanbags

### Instructions

1. This time, throw and catch your object as you move or travel around the general space.
2. When you hear the stop signal, quickly stop and hold on to your object.
3. Remember to stay in your self-space as you move or travel, throw, and catch.
4. You may choose how slowly or how quickly you travel as you throw and catch the object by yourself.
5. Show me how many times you can throw and catch your object by yourself as you travel.

MMSD Elementary School Physical Education Curriculum Committee, A Guide to Curriculum Planning in Elementary School Physical Education, 1986, updated 1991 (Madison, WI: Madison Metropolitan School District).

## ACTIVITY 51

# Scoop It Up

### Topic: Manipulative (throw, catch)

A variation of the preceding activities involves the use of a scoop. Using a yarn ball and a scoop, children practice their throwing skills.

### Equipment

- Yarn balls (one for each child)
- Scoops (one for each child)

### Instructions

1. Working in your own space, practice throwing and catching your yarn ball in and out of the scoop by yourself. Try to catch it each time.
2. Can you send it to different levels?

## ACTIVITY 52

# Beanbag Body Part Catch

### Topic: Manipulative (throw, catch)

The cues for catching are introduced in this activity, although catching is in the subcategory of gaining control. This activity provides a variation on the preceding activities.

### Equipment

Beanbags (one for each child)

### Instructions

1. As you practice throwing and catching your beanbag, can you find different body parts (e.g., elbow, head, knee, and so on) with which to catch?
2. As you catch it, think about "giving" with your body part(s) to catch.

MMSD Elementary School Physical Education Curriculum Committee, A Guide to Curriculum Planning in Elementary School Physical Education, 1986, updated 1991 (Madison, WI: Madison Metropolitan School District).

## ACTIVITY 53

# Crash, Pow!

### Topic: Manipulative (throw)

Sending an object away (throwing) occurs in many game activities. Cues for throwing are provided in this activity as well.

### Equipment

Soft gator skin or foam balls

### Instructions

1. Each of you will have your own self-space near the wall.
2. Show me how you can crash (send with great force) the ball into the wall so that it comes back to you.
3. Remember to step with the opposite foot from the hand you are using to throw.
4. Think about our other cues for throwing: arm back, trunk rotation, follow through in the direction you want to send the object.
5. If you choose to stand close to the wall, how much force should you put on the ball? [Let students respond.]

6. If you choose to move farther back or take a step back after each throw, what happens to the amount of force you put on the ball?

7. I am looking for good throws. You need to stay in your own self-space. Remember, your self-space is that space around you that is yours to do the activity.

MMSD Elementary School Physical Education Curriculum Committee, A Guide to Curriculum Planning in Elementary School Physical Education, 1986, updated 1991 (Madison, WI: Madison Metropolitan School District).

## ACTIVITY 54

## Ball Rolling

### Topic: Manipulative (ball rolling)

Helping children to throw underhand or roll an object toward a target will relate to later bowling activities, as well as underhand throwing activities. Providing children at an early elementary stage with cues, one at a time, will help them to be successful.

### Equipment

- Bowling pins (one for each pair)
- Soft coated foam balls (one for each pair)

### Instructions

1. You and your partner have a bowling pin and a soft coated foam ball.
2. You and your partner find your own self-space.
3. Choose who will be the first roller. The other partner sets up the pin after it has been knocked down.
4. Choose a comfortable distance to stand away from your pin.
5. Think about bringing your arm back, stepping with your opposite foot (from your throwing hand), and releasing the ball at a medium level.
6. Now, send the ball toward the pin and try to knock it down.
7. Take five turns as the roller, and then trade places with your partner.

## ACTIVITY 55

## Balloon Strike

### Topic: Manipulative (strike)

Students at the early elementary stage enjoy balloons. In this activity, each child has a balloon and a foam paddle. They can begin in their own self-space. Variations of this activity might include traveling slowly and then more quickly, still striking the balloon in an upward direction.

### Equipment

- Balloons (one for each child)
- Foam paddles (one for each child)

### Instructions

1. For this activity, you will need a balloon and a paddle. Find your own self-space.
2. When you hear the signal, show me how you can strike the balloon with the paddle in an upward direction.
3. How many times can you keep the balloon going at one time? Can you keep it going five times in a row? Can you keep it going ten times?
4. Think about keeping your wrist tight and your paddle flat.

## ACTIVITY 56

## Hockey Pathways

### Topic: Manipulative (strike)

As you introduce this activity, you may want to discuss the various pathways in the space concept (i.e., straight, curved, zigzag). The purpose of this activity is to introduce children to striking with long-handled implements. Younger children should be working with long-handled implements that are appropriate for their developmental level. This may be noodles or soft hockey sticks (e.g., Pillo Polo sticks).

### Equipment

- Noodles or soft hockey sticks (one for each child)
- Beanbags or small foam balls (one for each child)

## Instructions

1. Choose a noodle [or a soft hockey stick]. You will also need one object to strike.
2. In your own self-space, can you strike (dribble) the object back and forth, keeping two hands on the stick?
3. Remember to keep your favorite hand lower on the stick and your less favorite hand (the one you don't write with) on the top, or higher on the stick.
4. Now, see if you can strike (dribble) the object in a straight pathway.

## ACTIVITY 57

### Kicking Fun
#### Topic: Manipulative (kick)

Many children love to kick a ball. This activity allows them to kick very hard! Use appropriate equipment for your space and location. Soft coated foam balls are good for inside.

### Equipment

Soft coated foam balls (one for each child)

### Instructions

1. You will all need a ball and your own self-space. Right now, we are doing this activity inside, but we could also do this outside.
2. I want to see if you can kick the ball very hard toward the wall, using the instep of your foot, or your shoelaces.
3. See if you can kick the ball in a straight line [direct].
4. Now see if you can kick the ball a little harder. What do you need to do to kick the ball harder? Where does your nonkicking foot go?

## ACTIVITY 58

### Kicking to a Partner
#### Topic: Manipulative (kick)

This activity is an extension of activity 57. Following partner work, you may choose to place children in groups of three. Older children at the upper elementary stage may be able to create a kicking game that includes traveling. See what your students can create!

### Equipment

Gator skin balls of various sizes (one for each pair or group of three)

### Instructions

1. This time you and a partner will work together. Find a partner with whom you can work well.
2. Place your nonkicking foot beside the ball and swing your kicking leg really fast as you kick the ball.
3. You will each have five turns to kick the ball to your partner. Then, you will switch roles.
4. I am looking for good kicks. Can you show me a big step as you place your supporting leg? Can you swing your kicking leg hard to make a good, strong kick toward your partner?
5. When you and your partner are ready, take a step back from each other and continue kicking.
6. While you are working, see if you can watch your partner's kick. Is your partner really stepping beside the ball? Is your partner using the shoelaces? Where is your partner contacting the ball?

## ACTIVITY 59

### Self-Volley
#### Topic: Manipulative (volley)

Young children enjoy volleying to themselves. Having children at an early elementary stage of development volley balloons or beach balls is a great way to introduce this manipulative skill.

### Equipment

Balloons or movement education beach balls (one for each child)

### Instructions

1. Find your own self-space. When I see you are ready, I will give you each a balloon to volley.
2. Think about using your fingertips to volley the balloon in an upward direction.
3. See if you can volley the balloon to a medium level. How about a high level?
4. How many times in a row can you volley the balloon?

## ACTIVITY 60

# Partner Volley

### Topic: Manipulative (volley)

This activity extends individual volleying to partner volleying. Once you have introduced partner volleying, you can have the children volley over ropes attached to cones, or set up badminton nets at a low height.

### Equipment

- Balloons (one for each pair)
- Rope (one for each pair)
- Cones (two for each pair)
- Badminton net(s), if desired

### Instructions

1. Find a partner with whom you think you can work well.
2. When I say "Go," volley your balloon back and forth with your partner.
3. Can you send the balloon to a medium level as you volley? How about a high level?
4. Can you keep the balloon going?

## ACTIVITY 61

# Step Back

### Topic: Manipulative (catch)

As children become more proficient with their catching skills, encourage them to take one step back each time they have a successful catch. Ensure that they stay in their own self-space.

### Equipment

- Soft tennis balls, yarn balls, or beanbags (one for each pair of children)
- Scoops (one for each child)

### Instructions

1. This activity is called Step Back.
2. As you are throwing and catching your object with the scoop, take a step back each time you catch the object.
3. As you step back, what happens to the amount of force you need to use? [Children may not have been introduced to force yet. Consider asking them how hard or soft they

have to throw for their partner to catch the object.]
4. I am looking for good catches as you work with your partner.

## ACTIVITY 62

# Trap It for Me

### Topic: Manipulative (trap)

The skill of trapping later translates into gym hockey or soccer. Trapping an object involves gaining control of it to then redirect it to a partner or teammate.

### Equipment

Soccer or gator skin ball (one for each pair)

### Instructions

1. Please find a partner with whom you can work well.
2. You and your partner need one ball and your own self-space.
3. When you are ready, I am looking for one partner to send the ball to the other using dribbling with the feet. See if the first partner can send it directly to the other partner.
4. We are working on trapping, so as you receive the force of the pass, move your body in a sideways, forward, or backward direction to be ready for the ball. You can trap the ball with your feet or use another body part.
5. Let's start out using the feet to trap. As you trap the ball, think about using a soft amount of force so you can gain control and redirect the ball back to your partner. Let's work on that for a few minutes.
6. When you are ready, you and your partner can begin to count the number of successful passes and traps.

## ACTIVITY 63

## Dribble Away

### Topic: Manipulative (dribble)

The manipulative skill of dribbling can be done with either the feet (as in soccer) or the hands (as in basketball). Children at different stages of motor development will be successful at different dribbling activities. In this activity, children need to be thinking about moving to the empty spaces.

### Equipment

Soccer or gator skin balls (one for each child)

### Instructions

1. You will need a ball you can dribble.
2. Find your self-space in which to begin.
3. When you hear the start signal, begin to dribble your ball with your feet in all the general space. Show me how you can move into empty spaces.
4. Think about pushing the ball forward with either the inside or outside of your foot, using a gentle amount of force.

### Variation

As children become adept at dribbling, you can then combine dribbling with passing and shooting skills. Children must be able to demonstrate controlled dribbling and the ability to move into open spaces to receive a pass.

## ACTIVITY 64

## Dribble Some More

### Topic: Manipulative (dribble)

This is a continuation of activity 63. You are looking for children who can show you controlled dribbling.

### Equipment

Soccer or gator skin balls (one for each child)

### Instructions

1. Still using your feet, can you think of other parts of your feet with which you can dribble or make the ball move? Which parts of your feet work best?
2. As you move, stay in your own self-space while using all the general space.

3. You can decide when to increase your speed.
4. Remember, I am looking for controlled dribbling.

## ACTIVITY 65

## Carry On

### Topic: Manipulative (carry)

Carrying activities occur when a player is running with the ball, as in American football or lacrosse.

### Equipment

The equipment listed here are options from which children may choose.

- Foam footballs in varying sizes
- Soft gator skin balls
- Stuffed animals

### Instructions

1. Choose an object and find your own self-space to begin.
2. When you hear the signal, carry your object as you move throughout our general space.
3. When you move, show me how you can change directions and pathways quickly. Think about the dodging skill we talked about in a previous activity. I should see quick direction changes.

## ACTIVITY 66

## Carry Flag Tag

### Topic: Manipulative (carry)

This activity involves both carrying and dodging skills. You are looking for children who can change direction quickly while maintaining control of their objects. Each group of four will need an object and four flags.

### Equipment

- Foam footballs (one for each group of four)
- Flag belts and flags (one for each child)

### Instructions

1. You will be working in groups of four. See if you can create a group of four people with whom you can work well and find a working space.

2. In our game of Carry Flag Tag, one person carries the object, using good dodging skills. The other three try to take that person's flag.

3. Show me how well you can keep control of the ball and not get your flag pulled. If your flag is pulled, another group member gets the object.

# Space Activities

The categories outlined in chapter 2 for the concept of space are location, direction, level, pathway, plane, and extension. Combined, these categories focus on the space available for movement as well as the spatial characteristics (elements) of movement. Children are taught to think about spatial awareness and orientation as they move their bodies.

As noted in chapter 7, you are working with children on building a movement vocabulary that can be used in their everyday physical education programming and activities. You want to increase that vocabulary from the beginning so you can later concentrate on using each movement element in a game, gymnastics task, or educational dance movement. Children should understand that "Space is the medium of movement" (Gilliom, p. 53) and outlines where the body moves. All movement takes place in space.

In educational games, children focus on using all of the available space, constantly changing direction and pathways to avoid contact with other objects or people. The space concept is also used as children learn to lead teammates by sending objects into open space. Objects may be sent away (e.g., throwing) from either a stationary (static) or a moving (dynamic) position. Children learn to manipulate a variety of objects while using the space around them as they change direction, levels, and pathways. The use of planes terminology can simplify giving cues in game situations

(e.g., increasing a child's awareness of space by explaining that she changed her striking pattern from a chopping motion in the sagittal plane to a more effective twisting motion in the transverse plane).

In educational dance, children use space in creative ways. They change direction, move along various pathways on the floor or in the air as well as at different levels, and they vary the range of their movement by extending from, or moving toward, the center of their bodies.

Children involved in educational gymnastics define and work within their own self-space as they develop a variety of nonlocomotor movements. They may also travel through general space as they learn and practice locomotor skills, as well as move at, in, or through various levels and pathways. They also learn how to vary their range of movement by extending from, or flexing toward, the center of their bodies.

## Introduction to Activities

This section provides a sampling of activities you can use to teach the movement concept, categories, and elements of space awareness. The focal point should be on the elements, so that children can learn to define and apply them. You can teach the elements either individually or in combination. Information within the activities provides additional information. Using pocket chart cards or the movement word wall helps children focus on the elements and their definitions, and apply them to other content areas such as reading and language arts.

# Building a Word Bank: Location

Location is the category title given to self- and general space, suggesting where the movement takes place. Self-space comprises each child's individual working space, and general space is the total space you are providing the child for movement.

## Self-Space

Self-space is that area immediately surrounding the body. Self-space goes with you as you travel. General space is the area surrounding self-space, the space that is available for movement. Children should be able to demonstrate moving into all the space available for movement while still working in their own space.

Teaching the element of self-space early helps children work independently without moving into other children's space. Begin by selecting the element cards of self-space and general space and placing them in the pocket chart or pointing to them on the word wall. Children need to know that their own self-space is not only the space that surrounds them and moves with them, but also the space in which they perform whatever additional movements they are learning.

The following activities use carpet squares or hula hoops to introduce the element of self-space. Older children may not need these props to understand this element. As children work with partners or in small groups, they should understand that their self-space is important for solving the movement problems posed to them. You may choose to tell children that their self-space may also be called their working or personal space. For example, when children are

working with a partner or in small groups, they still have self-space. This self-space is that space surrounding the children as they work or move. You may also use hula hoops, poly spots, or jellyfish floor discs to teach self-space and general space. Hula hoops can travel with children as they learn about general space (see appendix B for example sources). You may be more comfortable with the term *bubble*, asking children to stay inside their bubbles as they move through the general space. Be sure to provide children with start and stop signals.

## ACTIVITY 1

## Me and My Hoop

### Topic: Location

Using elements learned in the body concept area, see how many creative ways children can find to solve this movement problem.

### Equipment

Hula hoops or jellyfish floor discs (one for each child)

### Instructions

1. On the signal, put both hands on the floor inside your hoop and see how many ways you can move your body around your hands.
2. Can you make your body small and curled as you move it around your hands?
3. Can you make your body long and stretched as you move it around your hands?

## ACTIVITY 2

## Object Control

### Topic: Location

This activity adds another variation to working in self-space. Encourage children to begin to think about their self-space as the area in space where they do their movement work (working space).

### Equipment

- Objects to delineate self-space (hula hoops, carpet squares, or jellyfish floor discs; one for each child)
- Objects to use in self-space (yarn balls, beanbags, soft coated foam balls; one for each child)

## Instructions

1. Now, we are going to combine objects with our self-space element. On the signal, choose an object and find your self-space.

2. See how many different things you can do with your object while standing in your own self-space. I am looking for you to control your object. That means you tell the object where to go rather than the object telling you where to go. [You want to encourage bouncing, tossing, catching, and rolling the object.]

3. Let's specifically work on throwing and catching your object while staying in your own self-space. Remember, I want to see how well you can control your object. [You are working on children staying in their own self-space while undertaking a variety of movements as well as working on start and stop signals.]

## General Space

Begin your introduction of the element general space by holding up the element card or pointing to it on the word wall. An understanding of general space allows children to move freely around all the space open for movement. This may be in the gym or in a classroom. If you are teaching this element in the classroom, you may have limited space for movement; encourage the children to move all around the available space. In a physical education environment, children should move into all the empty spaces. Teaching self-space and general space will help not only in movement element acquisition but also in class management.

## ACTIVITY 3

## Take It With You
### Topic: Location

Once children have an understanding of working in their self-space (static), they are ready to learn how to take that self-space with them as they move.

### Equipment

None required. You may choose to identify all the space in which children have to move (general space).

### Instructions

1. We have been working on moving in our own space while on a carpet square [or in a hula hoop]. I want you to think about taking this self-space with you as you move.

2. We are not going to take our carpet squares with us, but we are going to think about staying in our own self-space while we move.

3. Remember our definition of self-space? Right, it is the space that is right around us.

4. When I say "Go," I would like you to move all around our general space while staying in your own self-space. See if you can do this without bumping into anyone else. Ready, go.

### Variation

If children are having trouble staying in their own space and not running into other children as they move around the general space, have them take their self-space with them by carrying a hula hoop around them. You will need to decide what works best for your children and their developmental stage(s). The game Road Trip in activity 9 on page 151 teaches the combination of self-space and general space.

## ACTIVITY 4

## Where Is My General Space?
### Topic: Location

Encouraging children to move into all the empty spaces is the focus of this activity. Give positive feedback to children who are able to stop and start while moving into all the empty spaces. You may choose to have cones or other objects to help children identify all the general space in which they have to move. In addition, you may also choose to have music not only as your start signal, but also for children to listen to as they move (www.shopstationpe.com).

### Equipment

- Cones to identify the general space, if desired
- Music for a start signal and for traveling, if desired

### Instructions

1. This time, when you move, make sure you are exploring all the possible space in the gym. I want to see you moving all around our space, moving into empty spaces where no one else is moving.

2. Each time you hear the stop signal, I want you to freeze in your self-space and be ready

to move again as soon as you hear the start signal. Can you use all the empty spaces in the gym?

3. When you hear the stop signal and freeze, look around to see if there are empty spaces. Then, when you start again, try to move into all the empty spaces until you hear the stop signal again.

## ACTIVITY 5

## Locomotor General Space

### Topic: Location

Once children have explored their self-space and general space, you can add various locomotor movements. See how many locomotor movements they can show you as they move into all the empty spaces while staying in their own self-space.

### Equipment

As in activity 4, cones and music (e.g., www .shopstationpe.com) would help children enjoy this activity.

### Instructions

1. Now, think about moving in lots of different ways. Sometimes, I want you to skip, run, slide, gallop, and walk. I am looking for you to use all the space but show me different ways to move.

2. Listen for the start signal. I am also going to give you a stop signal. When you hear that signal, I want you to freeze as quickly as you can with control. That means to stay on your feet. I am going to be tricky, so listen for all the stop signals!

3. As you move into all the empty spaces, remember to stay in your own self-space.

You should make the general space smaller as the lesson progresses. This will encourage children to focus on using all the general space, while maintaining their self-space. With each stop signal, check to make sure children are using all the general space and not bumping into or touching each other as they move or when they stop. They should also stop on their feet unless told otherwise. Encourage them to think of lots of different ways to move as you make the general space smaller.

## Combining Self-Space and General Space

These activities help children work within their self-space as they continue to travel around the general space.

## ACTIVITY 6

## General Space Locomotion

### Topics: Location

This activity is an extension of activity 5. You are looking for children who can travel around all the general space, while maintaining their own self-space as they combine locomotor movements.

### Equipment

As in activities 4 (on page 149) and 5, both cones and music would add to this activity.

### Instructions

1. On the signal, move slowly into the general space. I want to see how well you can travel around using a variety of locomotor movements. Can you hop and jump? Show me how you can do this while staying in your self-space. How about skipping and leaping?

2. Can you combine two locomotor movements while moving into all the empty spaces? Can you change the combination of locomotor movements?

Encourage children to come up with a variety of combinations of locomotor movements; however, your focus is on watching for children who are staying in their own space while using all the general space.

## ACTIVITY 7

## Here and There

### Topics: Location

In this activity children practice moving with an object, keeping that object under control when traveling around the general space, and staying in their own self-space.

## Equipment

Yarn balls, soft tennis balls, soft coated foam balls, stuffed animals, beanbags (one object for each child)

## Instructions

1. On the signal, find an object from the ones provided. We have yarn balls, soft tennis balls, and soft coated foam balls, as well as stuffed animals and beanbags.
2. When I say "Go," start moving around the general space, while controlling your object. You can throw and catch the object as you move here and there.
3. Start out moving slowly. When you are ready and can demonstrate control, you may move a little faster.

MMSD Elementary School Physical Education Curriculum Committee, A Guide to Curriculum Planning in Elementary School Physical Education, 1986, updated 1991 (Madison, WI: Madison Metropolitan School District).

## ACTIVITY 8

# More Here, There, and Everywhere

### Topics: Location

This activity challenges students to think of many ways to move into all the empty spaces while controlling their objects. Again, allow students to change objects to add variety to the activity.

## Equipment

Objects used in activity 7 may be used, with children having the option to trade their equipment choices.

## Instructions

Can you move, with your object, into all our empty spaces while staying in your own self-space as you travel?

## ACTIVITY 9

# Road Trip

### Topics: Location

Most children love this activity. Younger children enjoy the imagination involved. For older children (at the upper elementary stage), change the activity

to Race Trip. Although older children may move faster, focus on their maintaining their self-space while using all the general space. Instead of shaking hands, older children can high five and say, "On your way." If tagged, they must go to the pit stop area and have their tires fixed, while doing a designated activity.

## Equipment

- Hula hoops or jellyfish floor discs (one for each child)
- Two jerseys for crazy drivers

## Instructions

1. We are going to play a game called Road Trip. You will each have a hula hoop. Two people will be the crazy drivers and will wear jerseys to identify them. Your hula hoop is your car, and the general space is the road.
2. When I say "Go," move around the general space (road) in your car (self-space) attempting to avoid all the other traffic (other students).
3. If you collide with another car (student), both students have to stop, put their cars on the floor, step out of their cars, do 10 jumping jacks [or exercise of your choice], shake hands with the other driver, and say, "I am sorry, please drive safely." Then, they may get back in their cars and drive away.
4. If you are tagged by a crazy driver, you should step out of your car, do the jumping jacks, and then continue driving.
5. Crazy drivers do not have to do jumping jacks; they can keep driving crazy!

## Variations

Change crazy drivers often. Remind crazy drivers that they should not use force when bumping into other drivers. You can use the following commands to control students' speed and provide variety in the game:

- Green light—begin walking
- Yellow light —jog
- Red light—stop
- School zone—skip
- Highway—run
- Tunnel—walk at a medium level
- Pasture—gallop
- Over bridge—walk on tiptoes at a high level

- Under bridge—walk at a low level
- Ice—slide
- Pot holes—leap
- Speed bump—jump
- Road dots—hop

You may add others as well. Your emphasis is on the children moving in self-space as they travel throughout all the general space.

Cristina Welch contributed to the development of this activity.

# Building a Word Bank: Direction

In these activities, children learn to move in a variety of ways in each direction. They work on developing control of their bodies while doing manipulative skills as well as locomotor and non-locomotor skills.

## Forward, Backward, Sideways, Up, and Down

The category of directions includes the elements forward, backward, sideways, up, and down. Many children will be familiar with these terms. Place these cards in the pocket chart or point to them on the word wall, and discuss their definitions. Explain that our bodies can move in these directions, but that we can also move objects through space in these directions. Children work on developing control of their locomotor and manipulative movements so they can change directions quickly and efficiently as they move into the realm of games playing. Remind them about your start and stop signals.

## ACTIVITY 10

### Traveling Show 1

#### Topic: Direction

Direction elements are words that most children know. However, they may be unfamiliar with these words as they are applied in a movement setting.

#### Equipment

- Music or drumbeat for a start signal or to signal a change of direction
- Directions movement set cone caps

### Instructions

1. Today we are going to think about moving in lots of different directions. Who can think of some directions? Right, we put up our cards of forward and backward. [Children may provide other directions, too.]
2. When you hear our start signal, show me how you can move in all the general space in either a forward or backward direction.
3. When you are moving backward, what do you have to really think about?

## ACTIVITY 11

### Traveling Show 2

#### Topic: Direction

Children should be able to show you many ways they can move in a sideways direction. This activity will particularly help younger children with remembering the difference between right and left.

#### Equipment

- Music or drumbeat
- Directions movement set cone caps

### Instructions

1. Now, let's add another direction. As you move, show me traveling in sideways directions also.
2. Think about moving right and left.
3. When you pass by a cone cap, use a sideways movement to travel in the direction of the arrow on the cone cap.
4. You might have to move more slowly so you stay in your own self-space.

## ACTIVITY 12

### Traveling Show 3

#### Topic: Direction

Adding in up and down can be fun for children. Challenge them to think about how they can do various locomotor movements in an up direction. Can they do these in a down direction?

#### Equipment

- Music that helps children with up and down movements (e.g., www.shopstationpe.com)

- Locomotor cone cap set
- Directions (up and down) cone caps

### Instructions

1. This time, as you move around the general space, show me how you can move either up or down.
2. Also, can you make a body part lead the movement? How about your head or back? Can this body part lead the movement?
3. When you come to a cone cap, show me the locomotor skill and direction (up or down) on the cone cap.
4. I am still looking to see if you are using all our general space.
5. Remember, as you move, you need to stay in your own self-space.

## Clockwise and Counterclockwise

Some children may be familiar with the terms *clockwise* and *counterclockwise*. Place each of these elements in the pocket chart or point to them on the word wall, and ask children if they know their definitions. Ask a student to demonstrate moving in a clockwise and then a counterclockwise direction.

### ACTIVITY 13
## Tick, Tock, Around the Clock
#### Topic: Direction

Clockwise and counterclockwise are often difficult directions for children to learn. A big clock may help and will add a bit of fun to this activity. See how many ways children can think of to move clockwise and then counterclockwise.

### Equipment

- Big clock so children can see how learning these elements relates to telling time
- Music or drumbeat

### Instructions

1. We have been working on moving in various directions. This time, I want you all to find your own self-space throughout our general space. I should not see any empty spaces.
2. When I say "Go," show me how you can move in a clockwise direction. Go.

3. Freeze. Now, show me how you can move in a counterclockwise direction.
4. Now find your own space again. When I say "Go," I want you to think of different ways to move, sometimes in a clockwise direction and sometimes in a counterclockwise direction. You choose when to change directions.

## Building a Word Bank: Level

The words associated with levels will most likely be familiar to children; however, how they relate to a movement setting may not be. For example, when teaching dribbling to children, you may discuss dribbling at a low or medium level as opposed to a high level. The activities in this category address these elements as related to movement.

Although children may most likely be familiar with the elements low, medium, and high, using these elements in relation to movement may be foreign to them. Place these cards in the pocket chart or point to them on the word wall, reminding students that the category of levels is an area of space in relation to the body when standing. Depending on the developmental stage of the students with whom you are working, you may choose to ask them to provide examples of how they might make a shape at a low level, medium level, and high level before you ask them to undertake tasks. Remind children of your start and stop signals.

### ACTIVITY 14
## High for Me
#### Topic: Level

In this activity children demonstrate an understanding of a high level. This activity is most appropriate for children at an early elementary stage.

## Equipment

Hula hoops, jellyfish floor disks, or carpet squares for self-space

## Instructions

1. I want you all to find your self-space. When you hear our start signal, show me how you can spin at a high level. What do your arms need to do? Do your arms raise really high?
2. Use all your self-space that is at a high level and all the space above your shoulders as well.
3. Remember to stay on your feet. I am looking for movements at a high level.

## ACTIVITY 15

### Medium Shapes

#### Topic: Level

This activity encourages children to think about ways to move at a medium level.

## Equipment

Music or drumbeat for a start signal. If needed, you may choose to use a drumbeat so children will know when to change their shape at the medium level.

## Instructions

1. Your medium level is the working space between your shoulders and knees when you are standing, right?
2. Show me (on the start signal), how big your self-space is at a medium level.
3. Can you make different shapes at a medium level? Show me three different shapes at a medium level.
4. Think of new ways to make shapes at a medium level.

## ACTIVITY 16

### Feelin' Low

#### Topic: Level

The final element is the low level. See how many different ways children can think of to move at a low level.

## Equipment

None required. Music may be used.

## Instructions

1. The rest of your self-space is at a low level. How many different ways can you move at a low level?
2. This time, you may move out of your self-space throughout all our general space.

## ACTIVITY 17

### Level It Out

#### Topic: Level

This activity encourages children to think of many different ways to move at different levels. As they make their shapes, encourage them to really make each level distinct.

## Equipment

Drum

## Instructions

1. When you hear our start signal, I want you to travel all around the general space.
2. When you hear a drumbeat, I want you to freeze and make a shape at either a low, medium, or high level.
3. Make your body shapes really distinct each time and vary the level you choose.

## ACTIVITY 18

### Level Changes

#### Topic: Level

Now that children have demonstrated their understanding of levels, let them show you how they can move with objects at various levels.

## Equipment

Yarn balls or other objects (one for each child)

## Instructions

1. On the signal, get a yarn ball [or object] and see how many ways you can throw and catch the ball with control at different levels.
2. Can you throw the ball at different levels?
3. When you hear the signal, change the level at which you are throwing and catching the ball.

4. Now, find a ball that you can dribble with your hands. Can you dribble this ball at various levels?

5. Can you dribble in your own self-space at a low, medium, or high level?

6. Can you dribble at a low, medium, or high level while traveling around the general space?

MMSD Elementary School Physical Education Curriculum Committee, A Guide to Curriculum Planning in Elementary School Physical Education, 1986, updated 1991 (Madison, WI: Madison Metropolitan School District).

## ACTIVITY 19

### Partner Levels

#### Topic: Level

In this activity children demonstrate levels with partners. Have them show you various levels and then tell you why they liked a particular level best.

### Equipment

Objects from which children can choose such as yarn balls, stuffed animals, beanbags, and soft coated foam balls (one for each child)

### Instructions

1. You are going to work with a partner. I want to see how many ways you and your partner can make the ball [or other object] move back and forth at different levels.

2. Can you move the ball back and forth by tossing it at a high level? How about a low level? Medium level?

3. What do you have to think about when you move the ball back and forth at different levels?

## ACTIVITY 20

### Choose Your Level

#### Topic: Level

Asking children to move smoothly from one level to the next as they travel allows them to demonstrate a sound understanding of this category. See if children can demonstrate level changes on their own as they travel. They should be demonstrating a variety of locomotor skills as well as staying in their own self-space while using all the general space.

### Equipment

Music as children travel and change levels

### Instructions

1. Can you move smoothly from one level to the next? Try this as you travel around the room.

2. I will ask for different levels first and you decide what movement you want to make to demonstrate that level.

3. Now, you decide when to change levels.

## Building a Word Bank: Pathway

In this section, children are introduced to the elements straight, curved, and zigzag. Children may be familiar with these terms, but not necessarily in relation to movements. Place these cards in the pocket chart and discuss the definitions of each. Explain that as we move, we make floor or air pathways with our bodies. These are either straight or curved lines. Depending on the developmental stage of the students with whom you are working, you may ask them to provide examples of traveling or moving in a straight, curved, or zigzag pathway.

## ACTIVITY 21

### Air Brush

#### Topic: Pathway

In addition to drawing pathways in the air with various body parts, children can also draw letters and numbers that have pathways in them.

### Equipment

None

### Instructions

1. We are going to draw pathways in the air again. First, find your own self-space.

2. Show me how you can trace a straight, curved, or zigzag pathway in the air with your finger.

3. Can you use other body parts to make pathways in the air? Think of all the body parts you can use to make different pathways in the air.

4. Can you think of letters that use curved pathways? Can you think of numbers that use curved pathways? How about straight pathways? Zigzag pathways?

5. When you hear our start signal, move into all the general space and see how many ways you can make a curved pathway on the floor. See if you can make big curved pathways and small curved pathways. Can you make high curved pathways and low curved pathways? How about high and low straight pathways? Zigzag pathways?

## ACTIVITY 22

### Pac-Man

#### Topic: Pathways

This game includes elements from various categories in the space concept. Explain to the children that you are looking for good use of self-space and general space as well as various directions, pathways, and levels.

#### Equipment

- Cones
- Jerseys (for ghosts)

#### Instructions

1. We are going to play a game called Pac-Man. You may have seen this on a video game. The Pac-Men move quickly in different directions. We are going to add pathways and levels to our game as well.
2. All of you Pac-Men are going to move around the general space in different directions. Our general space is limited by the cones.
3. Two people will be ghosts. If a ghost comes near you, see how quickly you can change direction.
4. You decide how you want to travel (such as walk, hop, skip).
5. We will all travel safely.
6. If a ghost reaches out and touches you, freeze like a statue and then change places with the ghost.

#### Variations

Add in level changes and pathway changes during the game. Ensure that all children have a turn to be a ghost as well as a Pac-Man. After playing a few rounds, ask children to help alter the rules. You are working on levels, directions, and pathways. What else might they add to the game?

Frank Arthurs contributed to the development of this activity.

## Building a Word Bank: Plane

It is likely that children will not be at all familiar with the planes terms. Explain to them that our self-space can be described with even more detail than what they have already learned and that these words help us to know more about how we move in our self-space. Children who are ready to receive feedback on fundamental motor skills are ready to begin exploring the ideas and movements of the planes. You might use a little word play to help make these ideas a bit easier to learn and a lot more fun. While the movement term *plane* is a geometry term, the term *airplane* is one that children are very familiar with and that they enjoy mimicking! Here are descriptions of the planes that you might use with children using a play on words to help them build their planes word bank.

If an airplane flew right through someone going from their head to their toes so that one wing was sticking out in front of the body and the other was sticking out behind the body, the plane would divide them into a right and left side (sagittal plane). Figure 8.1 shows a typical sagittal plane movement.

If an airplane flew right through someone going from their head to their toes with one wing sticking out to the right side of the body and the

**Figure 8.1**   Example of a sagittal plane movement.

other sticking out to the left side of the body, the plane would cut them into a front part and a back part (frontal plane). Figure 8.2 is a typical frontal plane movement.

If an airplane flew directly into a person with the nose leading into their belly and with the wings sticking out to the right and the left (parallel to the ground), it would divide them into top and bottom parts (transverse plane). Figure 8.3 is a typical transverse plane movement.

**Figure 8.2**   Example of a frontal plane movement.

**Figure 8.3**   Example of a transverse plane movement.

## ACTIVITY 23

# Paper Air "Planes"
### Topic: Plane (spatial)

This is a fun activity to help children experience that planes are used to divide the body. The use of the paper airplanes will make the ideas more concrete and less abstract.

### Equipment

1 sheet of colored construction paper per child

### Instructions

1. Get a piece of construction paper and sit in your own self-space. [You might provide the names of each plane by putting a pocket chart card for each up in the pocket chart (sagittal, frontal, transverse).]

2. Let's make a simple paper airplane together. [Use any type of folding; just make sure that the wings can represent the flat surface of the plane. Help the children visualize the areas of movement created by the division of the plane. Make sure you prepare them with a very simple definition or example of what a plane is (e.g., use a stiff piece of paper) and help them make the connection between this and the wings of the paper airplane.]

3. Take your airplane and fly it through your own self-space. How many ways can you find to divide your self-space with your plane? Can you fly the plane so that it divides your body into two parts?

4. You may have discovered that there are three different ways that you can divide your space using your plane. If you haven't found all three, try again. [Let the children experiment for a little bit, trying to move in all kinds of ways within their self-space before you give them any clues.]

5. Can you share your discoveries of your self-space with a partner? [Be on the lookout for children who have discovered a plane or an idea about the planes and encourage them to help discover another plane (e.g., you might refer them to these terms as they are working on their problem-solving activity).]

6. Let's review your methods and solutions.

## ACTIVITY 24

# Using "Plane" English
### Topic: Plane (spatial)

If children can perform the movements for each plane, then they are ready to apply the technical movement terminology to those movements (e.g., sagittal plane: curl = flexion, stretch = extension; frontal plane: sideways = abduction, adduction; transverse plane: twist = rotation to the right or left). Use the first word of these pairs from the movement education framework to teach the technical terms initially. Return to this lesson when children are confident with the MEF terms and are ready for the more advanced anatomical terms (e.g., flexion).

### Equipment

None required.

### Instructions

1. Demonstrate, in your own self-space, some of the movements you have discovered for each plane. [Children should demonstrate all three parts (sagittal, frontal, transverse) that they discovered in activity 23 on page 157. Give them an example of a movement in each plane if they are having trouble remembering.]

2. In groups of three, one of you will be the performer and the other two will work together to solve the movement problem. The performer should demonstrate one of the movements you did earlier and the others will work together to describe the main movement action (i.e., curl, stretch, twist, sideways). Change roles until you have applied all four terms and demonstrated all of their movements.

3. Observe a skill that has been analyzed for planes in a previous lesson and determine the plane (sagittal) and the movement term (e.g., curl). Work together to create a clever feedback statement (e.g., rhyming feedback, metaphor feedback, silly saying feedback; see table 2.2 on page 18 for examples) that will remind the performer which plane will give the most effective or efficient performance of the movement.

4. In small groups, practice giving your feedback statements to another group who is performing the movement for which the statement was designed.

# Building a Word Bank: Extension (Range or Size)

In this section children are introduced to the elements large (far) and small (near). Children may be familiar with these terms, but not necessarily in relation to movements. Place these cards in the pocket chart or point to them on the word wall. Movements within this category refer to the size of the movement and where it is executed. Some movements may be executed near to the body (e.g., a golf putt), and some may be executed far away from the body (e.g., a golf swing or drive). Some children might be familiar with holding a tennis racket. Do they hold the racket near to their body or far away from it? Depending on the developmental stage of the students with whom you are working, you may ask them to provide examples of other types of movements that are performed far or near in relation to the body.

## ACTIVITY 25

# Dribbling Close to Me
### Topic: Extension

In this activity children explore whether it is more effective to keep an object near them or farther away when striking, or dribbling, in a game situation.

### Equipment

Objects for dribbling with the feet (one for each child). You may want to provide a variety of objects from which children may choose.

### Instructions

1. This time, I want you to strike the object with your feet. As you do so, sometimes keep the ball close to your body and sometimes farther away.

2. Move all around the general space. I am looking for "near the body" and "farther away from the body."

3. When you play soccer, which do you think is more effective and why? [You may want to use this question in a discussion.]

## ACTIVITY 26

# Near to My Partner
### Topic: Extension

Students may have worked on throwing and catching with partners previously. In this activity, you are asking them to think about particular elements. When they throw the beanbag near to their partner, is it easier or harder for their partner to catch?

## Equipment

Beanbags (one for every two children)

## Instructions

1. When you hear the "Go" signal, find a partner with whom you think you can do great work today.
2. Now, one partner from each pair selects a beanbag.
3. Toss the beanbag so it is near your partner, so he or she can catch it easily. Remember, you are working with your partner, not trying to make her miss.

Helping children learn how to choose and work with a partner is included in the Critical Elements section on page 28 of chapter 2. Teaching children how to select a partner with whom they can work well will foster greater use of activity time and independence.

## ACTIVITY 27

# Far From My Partner
### Topic: Extension

This is an extension of activity 26. Once children are comfortable with tossing (throwing) the object near to their partners, you can ask them to work on throwing it far from their partners. They need to be able to tell you the difference in how the object is delivered.

## Equipment

One beanbag for every two children. You may choose to use other objects for children to throw and catch.

## Instructions

1. Now, we are going to work on throwing the beanbag so your partner has to reach to catch it. They will have to move to catch it because it is farther away from them.
2. Throw the beanbag so your partner has to reach forward, sideways, or upward. We are working on reaching catches. I want to see how well you and your partner can work together.
3. What do you have to think about to send the beanbag near your partner and then farther away from your partner?

# Effort Activities

The effort concept addresses how the body moves in space and the quality of that movement as a progression of intensity. There are nine basic effort qualities in the movement education framework (see elements E1-E9 in appendix A). To help clarify this, we provide you with some examples in each of the three core content areas. When children play a chasing, fleeing, and dodging game (often known as Tag), they need to think about how they move. Are they going to move quickly (fast), slowly, or change speed (acceleration)? Will the movements be in a direct line (focused energy), or will they be more scattered (wavy, or expanded, energy)? The same types of questions are raised in the core content areas of educational gymnastics and dance. In gymnastics, one can turn a rock into a roll by accelerating the movement. In dance, a feeling or idea may be created by using the category of time or weight. Moving one's body in a light or fine manner conveys a certain idea, whereas moving in a strong, firm, or heavy manner conveys a different type of idea.

The categories within the effort concept, outlined in chapter 2, are time, force, flow, and focus. Children are taught to think about the rate of their movement (time), the amount of tension in their movement (force), the fluidity of their movement (flow), and the effort they use as

they move throughout space (focus). All of the elements in the effort concept are introduced in this chapter and applied more fully in chapters 11 through 13.

## Introduction to Activities

This chapter provides a sampling of activities you may use to teach the movement concept, categories, and elements of effort awareness. It is important to emphasize the elements, providing children with appropriate definitions and showing them how the elements are applied. You may teach the elements either individually or in combination. Using pocket chart cards helps children focus on the elements and their definitions, and apply them to other content areas such as reading and language arts. Some applications to reading and language arts are provided in this chapter.

## Building a Word Bank: Time

Place the time category card in the pocket chart, followed by the elements of fast, slow, and accelerating. Ask the children if they can think of movements that are fast and slow and those that might require a change in speed. Answers might include running, walking, going from a walk to a jog or run, or rolling fast or slow.

## ACTIVITY 1

# Speed Match

### Topic: Time

You are looking for children to show you slow, fast, and acceleration. See how creative they can be with their movements.

### Equipment

Drum. However, you may choose to substitute changes in music or other musical instruments for the drumbeat.

### Instructions

1. Find your own self-space on the gym floor. Remember to use all our general space. I should not see any open spaces.
2. Let's try demonstrating moving slowly and quickly while staying in your own self-space. How slowly can you move your whole body while staying in your own self-space?
3. I am going to strike this drum. As you hear the drumbeat, move your whole body slowly if the beat is slow, and more quickly if the beat is faster. When you move faster, you are working on changing your speed, or acceleration. Listen carefully to the beat so you will know when to change the speed of your movement.
4. When you move slowly, I want you to think about keeping your movement continuous.
5. Fast movements can also be sudden movements.
6. When the drum beats faster, think about moving quickly or suddenly, and when it beats more slowly, make your movements reflect a slow and sustained movement.

## ACTIVITY 2

# Slow It Down

### Topic: Time

In this activity you want to see children who can demonstrate slow and sustained movements. Help them understand that *sustained* means "prolonged" or "ongoing." See how many of their locomotor skills they can use as they demonstrate the element slow.

### Equipment

Drum. However, you may choose to substitute changes in music or other musical instruments for the drumbeat.

### Instructions

1. This time you are going to move around the general space while staying in your own self-space.
2. When you hear the start signal, show me how you can move around the room slowly.
3. OK, now change the way you are moving. Maybe you walked before; now see if you can jump (two feet to two feet) or hop (one foot to the same foot).
4. I bet you can think of lots of ways to move slowly all around our space. Can you use all the locomotor skills we have learned?

## ACTIVITY 3

# As Fast as I Can

### Topic: Time

Encourage children to demonstrate quick speed. How fast can they move and still maintain self-space while using all the general space?

### Equipment

Music or musical instruments that encourage children to show you quick speed

### Instructions

1. Now, see if you can move quickly. What kind of animal might move quickly? [Allow students to say the names of animals they think might move quickly.]
2. Show me how you can move very quickly all around our general space. As you move, you want to remember to move in your own personal space. [Encourage children to focus on the element of fast, or quick, rather than the animal. However, younger children may want to think about becoming the animal as they move.]

## ACTIVITY 4

# Dash About

### Topic: Time

Children love to demonstrate quick, explosive movements.

### Equipment

Music or musical instruments that encourage children to show you quick, explosive movements

### Instructions

1. Let's see if you can find a starting spot.
2. When you hear the "Go" signal, see if you can start very quickly.
3. For good starts, I want to see your body leaning forward with most of your weight on your forward foot.

Students should have their weight in a forward stride position, about shoulder-width apart. The level of the body should be slightly lower, perhaps at a medium level. The feet should be pointing forward in the direction of the desired movement.

### Variations

Have children practice explosive starts, followed by quick traveling around the general space. Ask them to gradually change their speed, slowing down and coming to a stop on cue (acceleration is a change in speed, either slowing down or speeding up). You should see quick starts and traveling throughout the general space while staying in their self-space. When children travel around the general space, they may choose how to travel, or you can provide options (e.g., "When you travel, you can jog or walk, skip or jump").

MMSD Elementary School Physical Education Curriculum Committee, A Guide to Curriculum Planning in Elementary School Physical Education, 1986, updated 1991 (Madison, WI: Madison Metropolitan School District).

## ACTIVITY 5

# Acceleration

### Topic: Time

In this activity children show changes in speed as they travel. Remind them to stay in their own self-space as they travel and to use all the general space.

### Equipment

Music with changes in tempo encourages children to demonstrate changes in speed.

### Instructions

1. This time, I want you to show me if you can alternate, or change, your speed. Sometimes go fast and sometimes go slowly. Ready, go.
2. Think of different ways to move slowly and quickly. I want to see clear changes in your speed as you travel.

## ACTIVITY 6

# Rush Hour

### Topic: Time

Most children have driven with their parents or caregivers in rush hour. Ask them to describe to you what it is like during rush hour. You are looking for answers that reflect changes in speed (alternating).

### Equipment

Depending on the developmental stage of the children with whom you are working, you may choose to use hula hoops to encourage them to stay in their own self-space. Music would be fun also.

### Instructions

1. Have you ever ridden with your parents during rush hour? Do your parents drive very slowly and then speed up a bit in rush hour traffic?
2. This time, as you move, show me how you would move in rush hour traffic. Sometimes you will move slowly (like in bumper-to-bumper traffic), and sometimes you will move very quickly.
3. We always stay in our own self-space.

## ACTIVITY 7

# Road Trip II

### Topic: Time

The game Road Trip was introduced in chapter 8. It is repeated here with the emphasis on moving slowly and quickly.

## Equipment

Hula hoops, jerseys, and cones to denote general space in which children may travel. Music would be fun as well.

## Instructions

1. We are going to play a game called Road Trip. You will each have a hula hoop. Two people will be the crazy drivers and will wear jerseys to identify them. Your hula hoop is your car, and the general space is the road.

2. When I say "Go," move around the general space (road) in your car (self-space) attempting to avoid all the other traffic (other students).

3. If you collide with another car (student), both students have to stop, put their cars on the floor, step out of their cars, do 10 jumping jacks [or exercise of your choice], shake hands with the other driver, and say, "I am sorry, please drive safely." Then, they may get back in their cars and drive away.

4. If you are tagged by a crazy driver, you should step out of your car, do the jumping jacks, and then continue driving.

5. Crazy drivers do not have to do jumping jacks; they can keep driving crazy!

Alter the commands to address the elements of fast, slow, and acceleration. Here are some examples:

- Green light—begin walking slowly
- Yellow light—jog
- Red light—stop
- School zone—skip
- School zone after hours—skip quickly
- Highway—run
- Tunnel—jog quickly
- Pasture—gallop slowly
- Over bridge—walk on tiptoes slowly
- Ice—slide with smooth motion at a medium speed
- Pot holes—leap
- Speed bump—jump quickly
- Road dots—hop slowly and then quickly

You may add others as well. Your emphasis is on the children demonstrating their understanding of the elements of fast and slow while still staying in their self-space as they travel.

## ACTIVITY 8

# Slow, Fast, and In Between
### Topic: Time

This activity is for children operating at the upper elementary or mature stage. See if children can demonstrate both slow and quick speed as they also show you direction and pathway changes.

## Equipment

Noodles, yarn balls, Pillo Polo sticks, or hockey sticks and plastic pucks depending on the developmental stage of the children (one noodle or stick and one ball or puck for each child)

## Instructions

1. This time, propel your object around the room while you sometimes move slowly and sometimes move more quickly.

2. I also want to see direction changes and good control.

3. Can you also change your pathways as you propel your object around the general space?

# Building a Word Bank: Force

Place the force category card at the top of the pocket chart followed by the cards for the elements you are focusing on in a particular lesson (e.g., hard and soft). Students likely understand the terms *hard* and *soft,* but not necessarily in relation to movement. They should understand that the amount of force used is produced by muscle tension. The range of muscle tension is from strong and powerful (hard) to light and weightless (soft).

Explain to your students how they can vary the amount of force they produce and when it is useful to use a strong, hard force and when it is useful to use a soft, light force. Ask them what definitions they would give for the words *hard* and *soft* or *strong* and *light.* See if they can think of types of movements that might be soft or hard. Perhaps they have thrown a ball very hard or very softly. Their answers might include throwing a ball with varying amounts of force, striking a hockey puck or ball with varying amounts of force, or moving (traveling) in a strong, or light, manner.

Younger children may relate more to animals that move in a hard (strong) or soft (light) way than to manipulative skills. Ask them to suggest animals that move forcefully (or who are strong) and animals that move softly or lightly. They might identify an elephant, lion, or bear as moving forcefully or being strong, and mouse, cat, or small dog as moving softly or lightly.

## ACTIVITY 9

# Hard and Soft
### Topic: Force

This activity helps children differentiate between a strong, tense, tight muscle and one that is soft.

### Equipment

None required; however, you may choose to have pictures of children or characters demonstrating strong, powerful muscles.

### Instructions

1. Find and touch a muscle. While you are touching that muscle, can you make it very strong? Can you feel the muscle getting stronger while you are touching it?
2. Now relax the muscle and let it become limp. How does it feel now?
3. Can you tell the difference between when it is strong and when it is soft? [You want children to understand that they can control the amount of force they create.]
4. Now, show me how you can make a strong body shape and make both your arms and legs very strong and powerful.
5. Can you change that body shape to make it limp and soft?

## ACTIVITY 10

# Light as a Feather
### Topic: Force

This additional activity will help children differentiate between soft and hard force.

### Equipment

None

### Instructions

1. This time, pick up a pretend feather in your self-space.
2. Can you toss it gently in the air?

3. When you are throwing a feather lightly or softly, what happens to your muscles? How are they different from when you are throwing an object with a lot of force?
4. Can you feel the difference in your muscle tension?

## ACTIVITY 11

# Strong Shape
### Topic: Force

Demonstrating strong and light (or hard and soft) is the focus of this activity.

### Equipment

None required. If you are working with children who have difficulty staying in their own space, you may have them use hula hoops, carpet squares, or poly spots to denote their self-spaces.

### Instructions

1. In your own space, show me a strong shape. [You are looking for children to show an increase in muscle tension.]
2. Can you hold that strong shape for a count of 3? [Younger children will respond well to counting cherries or bananas—for example, "one cherry, two cherries, three cherries").
3. Now, show me a soft, or light, shape. [You are looking for children to show a decrease in muscle tension.] Think of three strong shapes and three light, or soft, shapes. Hold each for a count of 3.
4. Can you make shapes at different levels? Can you make some shapes at a low level and some at a medium or high level?

## ACTIVITY 12

# Power Up
### Topic: Force

Children love to move in strong, powerful ways. In this activity ask them to think about showing you strong muscle tension.

### Equipment

None required. Music that encourages children to show you strong, powerful movements would be a great addition.

## Instructions

1. When you hear the start signal, move into all our general space using strong, forceful movements.
2. Can you find different ways to move very strongly?
3. How can you move forcefully in different directions?
4. How about in a backward direction?

## ACTIVITY 13

## Soft Feet

### Topic: Force

In this activity children explore the difference between hard and soft movements. This will help in later activities, such as those that involve jumping and landing with soft landings.

### Equipment

As in activity 12, music that encourages both hard and soft movements would help children be successful.

### Instructions

1. Can you move very strongly (hard) and make a lot of noise with your feet?
2. Now, can you do this without making any noise with your feet?
3. Show me how you can make big, fast movements.
4. How about slow, quiet movements?

## ACTIVITY 14

## May the Force Be With You

### Topic: Force

For this activity and the one that follows, you can use dancing ribbons, scarves, or even crepe paper. Have the children use their props to show you the difference between strong, powerful movements and soft, light movements. Relating hard (strong) and soft (light) to the core content areas of educational games, educational gymnastics, and educational dance is important as well. These ideas will be more fully presented in the lessons in chapters 11, 12, and 13.

### Equipment

* Dancing ribbons, streamers, scarves, or crepe paper
* Music that inspires strong, powerful movements and light, airy movements

### Instructions

1. Everyone will have a scarf [or ribbon or strip of crepe paper] to use in these activities. See if you can use the scarf to make sudden, strong movements in the space around you.
2. Now, see if you can change from strong to fine, or light, and sustained movements. When I talk about sustained movements, I mean movements that are ongoing and continuous. See if you can make your movements with the scarf light, airy, and continuous.
3. Show me distinct changes in hard, or strong, movements and soft, light, and sustained movements with the scarf.
4. Now, see if you can travel and use your scarf to make strong, sudden movements. Can you change directions as you use your scarf?

## ACTIVITY 15

## Partner Creation

### Topic: Force

In this activity, you want to see if children can create three separate movements that combine the elements of hard and soft. You have not introduced the element of movement sequence yet (it is addressed in the relationships concept in chapter

10), so for now, ask the children to make three separate and distinct movements so everyone would be able to tell which is the hard one and which is the soft one. Relating hard (strong) and soft (light) to the core content areas of educational games, educational gymnastics, and educational dance is important as well. These ideas will be more fully presented in the lessons in chapters 11, 12, and 13.

## Equipment

Children may choose to use the equipment listed or no equipment. Provide music or musical instruments that inspire both hard, or strong, and soft, or light, movements.

- Dancing ribbons, streamers, scarves, or crepe paper
- Music that inspires strong, powerful movements and light, airy movements

## Instructions

1. Place your ribbon on the floor.
2. Choose a partner with whom you can work well.
3. You and your partner will create three movements together. They should be a combination of hard (strong) and soft (light) movements. You decide the order. Practice these movements so I can see three distinct movements.
4. Find your self-space.
5. Be ready to show your movements.

## ACTIVITY 16

# Muscle Fun

### Topic: Force

As children show you tight and loose muscles, you may choose to introduce the muscle names. The focus of this activity, however, is for children to demonstrate tensed and relaxed muscles.

## Equipment

None required. If you choose, you may provide pictures identifying muscle names.

## Instructions

1. Find a space on the floor and lie down.
2. Show me how you can tighten all your muscles. Can you become as stiff as a board?

3. Now, become very relaxed and let your entire body relax.
4. I am going to call out body parts, and I want you to tighten the muscles in them. [Call out a variety of body parts. As you move around the general space, check to see whether children are using strong muscle tension to tighten body parts.]

## ACTIVITY 17

# Contrasting Light and Strong

### Topic: Force

As children move around the general space, you are looking for a contrast between strong, powerful movements and light, soft movements.

## Equipment

Aerobic steps, benches, or folding foam exercise mats in their closed position for children to jump down from in order to demonstrate soft landings.

## Instructions

1. I have placed some benches (or other pieces of equipment as noted above) around the general space. When you hear the start signal, I want to see if you can travel around the general space.
2. You should show a contrast between strong, forceful movements and light, airy movements.
3. When you come to a bench, I want you to mount the bench and practice taking off and landing softly on the floor. [Make it clear that a soft landing is the intent of this, not the jump.]
4. See if you can land without making any sound!

## ACTIVITY 18

# Balloon Fun

### Topic: Force

In this activity, children work on the use of equipment and the elements of soft and hard strikes. Being able to demonstrate a contrast between these types of movements will be helpful in later educational game activities.

### Equipment

Balloons (one for each child; however, it is a good idea to have more than you need because balloons often pop) or movement education beach balls

### Instructions

1. Staying in your own space, keep your balloon going by gently striking it with different body parts. Hitting the balloon softly will keep it close to you.

2. Now, travel and strike the balloon softly. This time I want you to use a variety of body parts to strike the balloon. Think about alternating soft and hard, or forceful, hits. Start in a stationary position in your own self-space, and then begin to travel when you are ready.

3. Use all the general space when you travel, yet remain in your self-space.

4. Can you control the balloon by using only the amount of force you need to keep it in the air? Is that soft or hard force? Does it vary? Do light taps keep the balloon in the air?

5. See if you can make your balloon go very high. Do you need more force to keep your balloon going high?

MMSD Elementary School Physical Education Curriculum Committee, A Guide to Curriculum Planning in Elementary School Physical Education, 1986, updated 1991 (Madison, WI: Madison Metropolitan School District).

## ACTIVITY 19

# Partner Tap

### Topic: Force

In this activity, children work on the use of equipment and the elements of soft and hard strikes. Taking the individual work to partner work is an appropriate next step. See if children can keep the balloon going as they strike back and forth, showing you a contrast between soft and more forceful hits.

### Equipment

Balloons, movement beach balls, or regular beach balls (one for every two children)

### Instructions

1. I want you to work with a partner. Remember, we choose partners with whom we think we can work well.

2. You and your partner will need one balloon [or movement beach ball; see more details on these beach balls in appendix B]. You are going to tap the balloon back and forth, keeping the balloon going as much as you can.

3. Do you want to tap the balloon softly or with more force?

4. As you work, slowly back away from your partner. Do you need more force to keep the balloon going now?

## ACTIVITY 20

# Make a Force Game

### Topic: Force

In this activity, children work on the use of equipment and the elements of soft and hard strikes. This is an opportunity for children to design a game that shows you soft and hard amounts of force.

### Equipment

- Balloons or movement beach balls (one for every three children)
- Short jump rope (one for every three children)
- Cones to denote working space for groups, if desired

### Instructions

1. Now, I want you and your partner to find two other people with whom you think you can work well. Stand beside those two people.

2. In your group of four, you will need one balloon [or movement beach ball] and one short rope. Decide who will get the equipment and show me when you are ready by sitting down with all the equipment.

3. Now that you are ready, your group is going to make up a game with two people holding the rope and the other two sending the balloon back and forth over the rope.

4. After a few minutes, switch places so everyone gets a chance to send the balloon back and forth. We are working on creating force (or using soft and hard amounts of force). I will be looking for children who are working on force.

5. Remember to stay in your own working space.

## Variations

Variations of this activity might include the following:

1. Can you hit the balloon two times softly and one time hard over the net?
2. Can you hit the balloon one time hard and two times softly over the net?
3. How about one time softly and two times hard?

# Building a Word Bank: Flow

Place the flow card in the pocket chart, followed by the element cards for bound and free. Because the element terms *bound* and *free* may not be familiar to children, particularly at the younger ages and developmental stages, provide the definition of each, along with a visual example. For instance, *bound* suggests movements that are not continuous. They are "stoppable," such as moving and stopping, emphasizing a freeze position or one of alert stillness, and then moving again. You could demonstrate the slow and stiff movements of a giant dinosaur as an example of a bound movement. *Free* suggests a movement that is ongoing, or continuous, such as traveling in a continuous manner without stopping. To demonstrate the free flow idea, you could pretend to be a bumble bee in flight as a contrast to a bound dinosaur.

Let the children know they will be practicing bound and free movements. What you are looking for in the tasks is whether they can show you the difference between moving continuously and stopping their movements. In educational games, movement flow is combined with the acquisition of basic manipulative skills as well as the use of space and effort. Keeping the game or action alive is also part of the category of flow in a game situation. Encouraging students to keep play continuous, once they can successfully demonstrate the skills of a game or gamelike situation, will add to their enjoyment. However, as we note in chapter 11, Teaching Educational Games, children should not be placed in a game or gamelike situation in which they are not equipped to be successful.

## Energizer Bunny
### Topic: Flow

See if children can show you movement that is ongoing and continuous. You have used the word *sustained* previously. Free flow is comparable to sustained movements.

### Equipment

Music that assists children in demonstrating free flow

### Instructions

1. Travel throughout the room, moving continuously until I ask you to stop.
2. Remember, as you move, you need to stay in your own working space, even as you travel throughout all the general space.
3. I am looking to see if you can keep moving all the time. This is known as free flow.

## Moving Freely
### Topic: Flow

This activity adds equipment to the free flow element.

### Equipment

- Yarn balls, beanbags, or other objects (one for each child)
- Music that encourages free flow, if desired

## Instructions

1. When I ask your group of three to do so, please get a yarn ball or beanbag and return to your spot. [A movement education–themed beanbag can be used to reinforce these ideas or to extend to other ideas; see appendix B.)

2. When you hear the "Go" signal, throw and catch your ball or beanbag as you travel continuously around the room.

3. Be prepared to stop, but do not do so until you hear the freeze signal.

MMSD Elementary School Physical Education Curriculum Committee, A Guide to Curriculum Planning in Elementary School Physical Education, 1986, updated 1991 (Madison, WI: Madison Metropolitan School District).

## ACTIVITY 23

### Smooth Moves

#### Topic: Flow

In this activity, children work on continuous and ongoing running or skipping (locomotor) movements.

## Equipment

None required. A drumbeat, music, or other musical instrument would be a good addition.

## Instructions

1. Run or skip freely, smoothly, and continuously.

2. When you are ready [or when you hear the stop signal], stop.

MMSD Elementary School Physical Education Curriculum Committee, A Guide to Curriculum Planning in Elementary School Physical Education, 1986, updated 1991 (Madison, WI: Madison Metropolitan School District).

## ACTIVITY 24

### Alert

#### Topic: Flow

In this activity children work on demonstrating quick stops. As they move, initially provide them with a stop signal. This is wonderful for working on the bound aspect of flow.

## Equipment

None

## Instructions

1. I want to see if you can travel throughout the general space emphasizing bound movements.

2. Show me if you can make each bound position important by holding it while you count to 3.

3. The first time we practice this, I will give you a special signal so you can know when to show me how you emphasize the stopping action of the movement. After that, I want to see if you can do this without my signal.

4. Ready, go.

## ACTIVITY 25

### Dribble Start and Dribble Stop

#### Topic: Flow

This activity includes equipment and is most appropriate for children at a higher developmental stage. You are working on the category of Flow, specifically bound flow. Can children move with an object (dribble) and start and stop on signal?

## Equipment

Objects for dribbling with the hands (one for each child)

## Instructions

1. I want you to hand dribble the ball throughout the general space. You may choose which hand you use.

2. As you dribble, think about starting and stopping.

3. The first time, I will give you a stop signal. When you hear it, quickly come to a stop, pause, and then continue dribbling.

4. I am not looking for good dribbling skills, but to see if you can start and stop.

5. What type of flow is it when we start and stop?

6. This time, when you hear our start signal, can you show me how you can dribble and create your own starts and stops?

7. Can you dribble without stopping? [Free flow]

## ACTIVITY 26

# Partner Flow Control

### Topic: Flow

This activity includes equipment and is most appropriate for children at a higher developmental stage. It focuses on keeping the object going (free flow).

### Equipment

Objects for children to send back and forth (free flow; one for every two children)

### Instructions

1. You are going to be working with a partner in this activity. You and your partner will send the object back and forth.
2. I want to see if you can keep it going as well as keep it under control using a variety of body parts.
3. See if you can find ways to change the level of the ball without stopping it.

MMSD Elementary School Physical Education Curriculum Committee, A Guide to Curriculum Planning in Elementary School Physical Education, 1986, updated 1991 (Madison, WI: Madison Metropolitan School District).

## ACTIVITY 27

# Group Free Flow Catching

### Topic: Flow

This activity includes equipment and is most appropriate for children at a higher developmental stage. Children at the upper elementary developmental stage enjoy working on developing games. In this activity they work on continuous throwing and catching (or free flow).

### Equipment

Yarn balls, stuffed animals, beanbags, or soft coated foam balls (one for every three or four children)

### Instructions

1. You are going to be working in a group of three or four. Find a small group with whom you can work very well.
2. You are going to be playing a catching game in which the object and all of the players are continuously traveling in their self-space.

3. Your group can move all throughout the general space, but you must stay in your own self-space.
4. I want you to work on throwing and catching the object continuously. If you are not ready to travel as you throw and catch, you may choose to stay stationary.

Depending on the developmental stage of the children, you may want to have them all begin in a stationary position.

MMSD Elementary School Physical Education Curriculum Committee, A Guide to Curriculum Planning in Elementary School Physical Education, 1986, updated 1991 (Madison, WI: Madison Metropolitan School District).

# Building a Word Bank: Focus

Place the focus category card in the pocket chart, followed by the elements of direct and indirect. The intent of this category is to help learners understand that effort can be channeled in space. Although space primarily describes where a movement occurs, manipulating what we do in space involves effort. Depending on whether one compresses or expands the space in which one moves, the effort either increases (compresses) or decreases (expands). In the category of focus, movement is typically described as being relative to space in either a direct or indirect way.

- Movements that are direct channel energy in a straight, penetrating, compressed, or threadlike way. Jumping straight up in the air in a direct line with all one's energy (perhaps off of a vaulting box or springboard) is an example of a direct movement.
- Indirect movements are wavier, more like a curved pathway, and may be more expansive. An example of this is moving through an obstacle course in a curvy pathway with twisting actions.

Although children may be familiar with the terms *direct* and *indirect,* they are unlikely to be able to relate them to movement. Begin by asking them how they might move from one point to another in a straight line. Younger learners may be able to identify the element of a straight pathway. Having already introduced pathways (straight, curved, and zigzag) will aid in the understanding of these new elements. The following activities will help children understand the difference between expanding their energy in the space (indirect) as well as constricting their energy in the space (direct).

## ACTIVITY 28

### Direct Focus

#### Topic: Focus

You want to see children showing you a very direct and focused energy release.

#### Equipment

None required. You may choose to use music to encourage direct movements.

#### Instructions

1. Find your own self-space on the gym floor.
2. When you hear the start signal, show me how you can travel in a direct line, or straight pathway, across the floor.
3. Think about putting all your energy into this direct movement.

MMSD Elementary School Physical Education Curriculum Committee, A Guide to Curriculum Planning in Elementary School Physical Education, 1986, updated 1991 (Madison, WI: Madison Metropolitan School District).

## ACTIVITY 29

### Space Knives

#### Topic: Focus

In this activity children work on demonstrating a variety of locomotor movements as they think about moving in a direct, or pointed, line.

#### Equipment

None required. You may choose to use music to encourage direct movements.

#### Instructions

1. This time, as you move, think about moving in different directions.
2. Move as if you are cutting through the space, separating it into two halves.

MMSD Elementary School Physical Education Curriculum Committee, A Guide to Curriculum Planning in Elementary School Physical Education, 1986, updated 1991 (Madison, WI: Madison Metropolitan School District).

## ACTIVITY 30

### Greedy Goblins

#### Topic: Focus

The indirect movements children demonstrate should show you a use of curved pathways and expanded energy.

#### Equipment

None required. You may choose to use music to encourage indirect movements.

#### Instructions

1. Now we are going to work on indirect movements. See if you can move in curved pathways, rising and sinking as you move.
2. Think about taking up as much space as possible and using your energy in a flexible way.

MMSD Elementary School Physical Education Curriculum Committee, A Guide to Curriculum Planning in Elementary School Physical Education, 1986, updated 1991 (Madison, WI: Madison Metropolitan School District).

We have been talking about direct and indirect movements. In activity 31, children are working on these elements with fun effort words, such as slash, float, and glide. For additional information on effort words, see Laban and Ullmann (1971). If children are not familiar with these words, use pictures to help them understand. You may also use the characters on the direct and indirect pocket chart cards. Have children add sounds to the movements. Creating their own fun effort words may encourage the application to direct and indirect movements as well. Classroom teachers and art teachers may be able to incorporate the effort words into their lessons. What type of drawing might a child do to show *thrust?* What about *float?*

## ACTIVITY 31

# Moving Words

### Topic: Focus

Bringing the elements of direct and indirect into a discussion of effort words can be lots of fun. See what you and the children can create together. You don't need gym space to do this activity. Push aside the desks and begin moving!

## Equipment

Music to inspire the use of effort words

## Instructions

1. When you hear the word *float,* do you think of using your energy in a straight, piercing way or a wavy and loose way? [Wavy or indirect] What about the word *slash?* [Piercing or straight]

2. Now, see if you can show me how you would move in each of these ways. I will call out the word, and I want you to show me the action. I am looking for movements that are direct or indirect. Some of the words are the same as I just mentioned. I will also add some additional words.

3. You can move in all the general space while staying in your own self-space as you move. [You want to see children showing you direct and indirect movements. Direct movements are done in a straight line. Indirect movements are wavy.]

| | |
|---|---|
| Thrusting | Floating |
| Slashing | Gliding |
| Wringing | Pressing |
| Flicking | Dabbing |

## ACTIVITY 32

# A Direct Hit

### Topic: Focus

This activity gives children an additional opportunity to use striking skills and apply the element of direct focus. This gives them another chance to explore this element with equipment.

## Equipment

A variety of rackets and objects for children to strike (one of each, for each child). The objects you choose will partially depend on the developmental stage of the children with whom you are working.

## Instructions

1. Today we are working on striking with a racket. You will all have your own racket and ball.

2. Find your own space so you can hit your ball against the wall.

3. I want you to concentrate on moving your racket in a direct line.

MMSD Elementary School Physical Education Curriculum Committee, A Guide to Curriculum Planning in Elementary School Physical Education, 1986, updated 1991 (Madison, WI: Madison Metropolitan School District).

# Relationships Activities

The fourth movement concept, relationships, focuses on relationships that may occur as the body moves. All movement takes place in connection, or relation, to the environment, to other people, or to objects or apparatus. The relationships concept "brings ideas together in a unified whole and acts as a major source for making experiences increasingly challenging in all parts of the physical education program" (Logsdon et al., 1984, p. 137).

People can have a variety of relationships in movement situations. Some of the most frequent and important are relationships with other people in partner formations and in small groups of three, four, or five. Formations such as the triangle, circle, and square are used in games, and the spokes of a wheel formation occurs most often in gymnastics and dance.

Positional, or spatial, relationships occur in relation to body parts or other people. In relation to other people, spatial relationships occur between individuals, between an individual and a group, and between groups. For example, body parts may be above or below one another, a child may be over or under a piece of equipment or apparatus, or a child may partially or wholly support the weight of another child. These types of relationships occur in all three core content areas.

- In educational dance, a child may move in relation to the beat of a drum, or two children

may work together in a question-and-answer timing pattern. Children may also be given the task of meeting and parting, circling, or going around one another.

- In educational gymnastics, children might be asked to show their understanding of leading and following when displaying the skills of rolling, weight transfer, or jumping and landing. Children may also show their understanding of relationships that require interdependency by exploring lifting and being lifted, or supporting and being supported in partner work.

- In educational games, relationships can be both basic and complex. A basic relationship may be between a person and an object or target. Is the target stationary or moving? Is the object stationary or moving? People as well, can be either stationary or moving. Throughout a game, children must become familiar with where they are in relation not only to the object being manipulated, but also to others in their environment. In all types of games, whether net, invasion, or wall games, the connection to others on the team is critical.

Players must relate to boundaries as well. They establish positions and vary their positions throughout the game situation. Complex relationships occur as strategy becomes involved (e.g.,

Where am I in relation to my teammate? How can I create an open space into which my teammate can pass the object? Where do I need to position myself so my teammate can pass the object in front of or ahead of me?). We teach learners to pass objects ahead of (in front of), behind, or even with teammates or opponents.

Following are the categories in the relationships concept:

- People (organization of)
- Position (spatial relationships)
- Timing (of the action)
- Goal (of the activity)
- Environment (nature of)

All of the elements within these categories are introduced in this chapter and applied in greater detail in the core content area chapters.

This chapter provides a sampling of activities you may use to teach the movement concept, categories, and elements of relationship awareness. As with the previous concept chapters, it is important to focus on the elements, providing children with appropriate definitions and showing them how the elements are applied. This can be done through use of the pocket chart cards or movement word wall. You may teach the elements individually or in combination according to the developmental stage of your students. As they become familiar with the elements, individual introductions may not be necessary. Using pocket chart cards or the movement word wall helps children focus on the elements and their definitions and apply them to other content areas such as reading and language arts.

Children should understand that the various ways people, objects, and the environment connect with one another are the bases for relationships. You can help them grasp the concept of the various types of connections with other people by asking the question, Move with whom? To help children understand the various types of connections with objects we manipulate or maneuver in the environment, you could ask the question, Move with what? In the relationships concept, unlike the other concepts, younger learners may have difficulty understanding category terms. For this reason you might want to focus on the elements themselves rather than the category terms.

As with the other concepts, building a word bank in the relationships concept provides chil-

dren with knowledge and language to support their movement. For example, in the category of people, children need to be able to demonstrate an understanding of how to work solo, alone in a mass, with a partner, and with a small group. Once children have learned these introductory elements, you can then move on to other elements that most prudently reflect the lesson: even group(s), uneven group(s), individual to group, group to group, triangle, circle, square, scattered, spokes of a wheel, and X.

## Building a Word Bank: People

The first category in the relationships concept is people. We opted to place this as the first category for your benefit as well as that of your students. Every lesson you teach requires that you ponder how to organize your students. Is it most beneficial to have students working solo (alone)? Will they need to be working alone, but within the scope of the entire class (alone in a mass)? Perhaps partner work is most useful within a portion of the lesson. In educational dance, you may place your students in a formation such as the spokes of a wheel or an X. One student may relate to an entire group, or groups may relate to each other as in educational games lessons.

Teaching children how to choose partners and relate with them early in the year can help you improve class organization or socialization. Similarly, teaching children how to work in even and uneven groups or to choose their own groups of four or five can teach them responsibility and how to make choices.

When teaching about partners, place the partners element card in the pocket chart or point to it on the movement word wall. Ask the children what is important about choosing a partner and working with a partner. You can pose similar questions for each of the elements in this category because they all involve an organizational arrangement of some kind. Answers might include getting along with your partner, not criticizing your partner's skills, working in your own self-space, and developing team goals or strategies. Younger learners can demonstrate their understanding of geometric shapes such as a triangle, square, or circle. Ask children to form small groups (e.g., of three or four students) or you can place them in groups. Children can form triangles, squares, or circles with their bodies.

In addition to teaching children the definitions of the elements, a central purpose of the people category is to maximize activity time by training children to form partnerships and small groups quickly. Forming partnerships or small groups are two of the critical elements (see list in chapter 2, page 28). You may wish to work with children on forming and working with partners or in small groups early in the presentation of the movement education framework (MEF) so as to maximize activity time during later lessons.

Forming partners may be initiated by you or the children. Allowing children to form their own partnerships teaches responsibility and gives them a sense of control. The developmental stage(s) of your students will determine their readiness to form partnerships on their own. Children's ability to work with partners and in small groups is critical to the success of MEF lessons and many activities in all three core content areas.

The activities in this section help children both understand and apply the elements. The first two activities involve children working by themselves (solo). Although children would rarely work solo, they may do so when demonstrating their understanding of a movement element or task. We suggest that you not have children demonstrate a movement element in front of the class or group unless they choose to do so. Most often, children work alone in a mass as they move in their self-space throughout the general space.

## ACTIVITY 1

### Solo Home
#### Topic: People

This activity gives children an opportunity to demonstrate movement elements.

### Equipment

Music would add a great deal to the demonstration as well as the fun for all the activities.

### Instructions

1. We have previously worked on the locomotor movements of running, leaping, hopping, and jumping today. Who would like to show us the difference between a hop and a jump? [This demonstration should be short because you want all the children to be active during as much of the class period as possible. As the child demonstrates, comment on the hop and the jump, and also note that the child who is demonstrating is working solo, or by herself.]

2. Does anyone remember the word *solo*? Can you tell us what it means?

## ACTIVITY 2

### Moving Within the Group
#### Topic: People

Children often work independently within the scope of the entire group. Remind them that this is similar to working in their own self-space within the context of all the general space.

### Equipment

Music would add to the demonstration as well as the fun.

### Instructions

1. As we work today, I want you to focus on moving in your own self-space throughout the general space.

2. Sometimes this is called working alone in a mass. You are working by yourself, but the whole class or your group is also working. [Point out students who are working well in their self-space as they move throughout the general space.]

## ACTIVITY 3

### Find a Friend
#### Topic: People

In this activity children focus on successfully finding partners. This is an important procedure to practice.

### Equipment

Music would add to the demonstration as well as the fun.

### Instructions

1. When I say "Go," I want you to find one other person with whom you can work well. Working well with a partner means that you help your partner to do his very best work; you cooperate.

2. Sometimes in our partner work, I will ask you to find a partner with whom you think you can work well. Sometimes, I will ask you to find a partner who is of similar height or weight. Sometimes, I may assign you to a partner.

3. If someone asks you to be her partner, say, "Yes, thank you."

4. If our class is uneven, we will have a partner location spot and I will help make groups of three.

5. We always give compliments to our partners and thank them for being our partners.

6. I will give you to the count of 3 to find a partner. Go.

7. Now, you and your partner find a working or self-space.

Although this is part of the relationships concept, you may use this as a teaching moment for partner and small-group formation.

MMSD Elementary School Physical Education Curriculum Committee, A Guide to Curriculum Planning in Elementary School Physical Education, 1986, updated 1991 (Madison, WI: Madison Metropolitan School District).

## ACTIVITY 4

# Partner Shape and Copy
### Topic: People

Copying body shapes provides an additional opportunity for partner work. Again, the focus is on partner work, rather than on specific body shapes.

### Equipment

Small cones to designate specific working spaces for partners, if desired

### Instructions

1. This time, I want you and your partner to copy each other's shapes.

2. Decide who will be the first leader. The leader has three turns to make a shape for the follower to copy. I want to see you working together, so you will need to make shapes your partner can copy.

3. After three turns, trade roles.

4. Make the best shapes you can make.

## ACTIVITY 5

# Chute It Up, Partner
### Topic: People

Challenge partners to show you how well they can work together. Children at both the younger and older developmental stage can benefit from this activity.

### Equipment

- Towel, panel chute (like a parachute only rectangular rather than round), or large scarf (one for every two children)
- Objects to toss and catch (one for every two children)

### Instructions

1. You and your partner will hold a towel [or panel chute or scarf] at each end.

2. Working together, toss and catch your object back and forth.

3. See if you can count the number of times you can keep it going without dropping it.

4. Remember, you are working together with your partner.

Once children are comfortable choosing and working with a partner, or if their developmental stage is appropriate, they can move on to working in small groups. As group size increases, so does the complexity of the relationships.

## ACTIVITY 6

# Group Shape It Up
### Topic: People

Other formations that are an important part of the People category are scattered and X. Scattered formations may be used when you want children to find work in their self-space throughout the general space. This is an organizational tool that may be very helpful for children to learn early in the year. The X formation may be used when working on symmetrical shapes (Body Shapes B6).

## Equipment

None

## Instructions

1. When I say "Go," see if you can move to your own self-space within the general space. I want to see how quickly you can move to that space and freeze when you get there.

2. This is a scattered formation. See how much space you have in which to work? Now that you are in this scattered formation, I am going to say "Go" one more time. I want to see if you can move quickly to another scattered formation.

3. Great job! You moved quickly to make a scattered formation.

## ACTIVITY 7

## Group Toss

### Topic: People

See how well even groups of six can work together in this activity. You can add in the elements of even and uneven groups, if you like. Discussing even and uneven numbers will enhance children's classroom learning as well.

## Equipment

- Towels, panel chutes, or large scarves (one for every two children)
- Objects to throw and catch (one for every six children)

## Instructions

1. You will need to form a small even group of six. Within that group of six, you will have a partner. Each partner set should have a towel [or panel chute or scarf]. There will be one object for the entire group to toss and catch.

2. In your self-space, throw and catch your object so each set of partners can catch it. See how many times you can throw and catch your object.

3. You may vary your distance as you are ready, and you may change your object as you are ready.

## ACTIVITY 8

## Geometric Grouping

### Topic: People

Geometric shapes can be found in all aspects of the movement curriculum. Students are often asked to form circles or squares. Encouraging students to form a variety of geometric shapes is a great way to incorporate math into a lesson. Alter the shapes students are creating according to their age and developmental stage. This fun activity can be used in both the gym and the classroom. The focus here is on geometric formations.

## Equipment

None

## Instructions

1. Find an even working group of four. You should be able to work very well with all the members.

2. I am going to call out some geometric formations and let's see how quickly your group can move.

3. Show me a triangle, circle, square, rectangle, scattered, X.

4. When you get into each shape, stand very still. Make your shape very clear. Can you become a statue at a low level in your shape? Can some people stand at a high level and some at a low level in your shape?

## Variation

Depending on the developmental stage of the students, have them demonstrate various geometric formations they have learned in math.

## ACTIVITY 9

## Spokes of a Wheel

### Topic: People

Dances done in the formation of spokes of a wheel are varied and numerous. Contra dances, Sicilian dances, and trio dances, as well as some country dances, are often done in this formation. Variations in dance formations give children opportunities to expand their shape vocabulary.

## Equipment

Music and steps for Cotton-Eyed Joe (or other dance in this formation)

## Instructions

The dance we are going to learn today is called Cotton-Eyed Joe. In some states, this is a very popular dance. It is done in a formation known as spokes of a wheel. Provide a demonstration of this formation prior to teaching the dance. There are many variations to the dance. This is probably the easiest version of this dance and fun to learn and do. Enjoy!

1. Counts 1-2: Stick out your right foot and tap the ground with the bottom of the heel twice.
2. Counts 3-4: Put your right foot behind you and tap the ground with your toe twice.
3. Counts 5-6: Put your right foot forward and tap the ground once with the bottom of the heel.
4. Counts 7-8: Put your right foot back and tap the ground once with the toe of the foot.
5. Counts 1-2: Put your right foot forward and tap the ground once with the bottom of the heel.
6. Counts 3-4: Tap the ground to the side of you with your right foot once.
7. Count 5: Raise your right foot up to the left thigh behind you and touch the foot with the left hand.
8. Count 6: Return to side position.
9. Count 7: Raise your right foot up to the left thigh in front of you and touch the foot with the left hand.
10. Count 8: Return foot to normal position.
11. Counts 1-4: Move 3 steps to the right and then clap the hands on beat 4.
12. Counts 5-8: Move 3 steps to the left and then clap the hands on beat 8.
13. Counts 1-4: Move 3 steps back and then clap the hands on beat 4.
14. Counts 5-8: Move 3 steps forward and then clap the hands on beat 8.
15. Counts 1-8: Turn around in a circle for 6 beats. Then put your right foot back and tap the ground once with the toe of the foot on 7, 8.
16. Repeat steps 1-15 until the end of the song.

Adapted from http://www.wikihow.com/Do-the-Cotton-Eyed-Joe-Dance.

# Building a Word Bank: Position

Positional relationships refer to the relationship a child has with a body part, teammate, partner, or the equipment they are manipulating. For example, a child can place one body part above or below another body part. Children can pass an object over their head or under their legs to a teammate. It is this connection to each other or to the equpiment in space that sets this category apart from the Space concept.

## ACTIVITY 10

# Way Above, Way Below

### Topic: Position

Showing above and below can be done with body parts or the entire body. Allow children to problem solve this activity.

## Equipment

None

## Instructions

1. When I say "Go," I want you to find your own self-space. We are going to think about elements of above and below in this activity.
2. Can you stay in your own self-space and show me how you can place one body part above another? Maybe you will place your arm above your head. That is an easy one. See if you can think of two different ways you can place a body part above another body part.
3. Now change levels and show me how you can place one body part above another body part.
4. Can you place a body part below another body part? Can you do this at different levels?
5. Now find a partner with whom you can work well.
6. See if you and your partner can show me how one of you can be above the other person. Can you do this at a low level?
7. Find two ways you and your partner can show above and below.

## ACTIVITY 11

# Upside Down

### Topic: Position

Children enjoy performing a variety of inverted, or upside-down, shapes. See how much fun they can have!

### Equipment

Mats (one for each child or for two or three children to share)

### Instructions

1. We are going to try something really fun. I want you to start in a standing position.
2. Now, transfer weight onto your hands and one foot. Put one foot in front of the other and bend your knee to lean out over the lead foot. See if you can stretch your arms out and reach down to the mat.
3. Transfer your weight onto your hands and one foot and kick the other leg up to a medium level. See if you can come back to the same starting position. How high can you kick your back leg?
4. Practice this for a couple of minutes on your part of the mat. Your head should be below the leg you are taking to a medium level. This is an inverted position.

## ACTIVITY 12

# Upside-Down Balances

### Topic: Position

This activity is a continuation of the element inverted. However, children are working on balancing which was previously learned in combination with the element inverted. Allow children to problem solve and see how succcessful they can be with their upside-down balancing.

### Equipment

Mats (one for each child or for two or three children to share)

### Instructions

1. We are going to make a five-part balance in an inverted position, where five parts of your body (head, arms, and legs) are braced on the mat while you balance in a position.
2. Place your head on the mat with your hands on the mat on either side of your head, raise your hips, and make your legs straight. See if you can balance on your head, toes, and hands.
3. If you want, you can try to raise one arm off the mat, creating a four-part balance.
4. You may want to challenge yourself by raising both arms and making this a three-part balance (with head and both feet staying on the mat).

## ACTIVITY 13

# Mount Up

### Topic: Position

In this activity children work on mounting and dismounting. Encourage them to think of many ways to mount and dismount the equipment.

### Equipment

Aerobics steps, boxes, benches, balance beams, balance tracks. If you do not have some of these pieces of equipment, you can use stacked mats or benches.

### Instructions

1. We have aerobics steps, boxes, benches, and balance beams around the general space.
2. You and your partner are going to see if you can mount the same piece of apparatus and create a shape.
3. Now show me how you can dismount the piece of equipment.
4. Can you think of different ways to mount and dismount different pieces of equipment?

## ACTIVITY 14

# Obstacle Course Fun

### Topic: Position

There are a variety of ways to show over and under. Have children show you the various positional relationships as they move through the obstacle course.

## Equipment

Objects for children to go over, to go under, to mount and dismount, to go through, and to go around. Examples include cones, hoops, benches, boxes, mats (stacked), rope attached to chairs (under the rope), small hurdles, and a stop sign. Be creative.

## Instructions

1. As you move through the obstacle course, focus on moving over and under the apparatus, mounting and dismounting the boxes, moving through the cones, and moving around the hoop.

2. When you come to a stop sign, make a balanced shape and hold that shape for three seconds. Count one cherry, two cherries, three cherries, and then move on.

3. We are working on over and under, mount and dismount, through, and around in this activity.

## ACTIVITY 15

### Lift Off

#### Topic: Position

Only children who are at a developmental stage appropriate for work with other children and whose skill level supports these types of tasks should undertake relationships that require interdependency. Elements of counterbalance and countertension (from the actions of the whole body category in the body concept), as well as support and supported and lift and lifted, require children to be responsible for the safety of others.

## Equipment

Mats (one for each child or for two or three children to share)

## Instructions

1. We are going to work on some partner balances. Our focus elements are support/supported and lift/lifted.

2. When we support our partner's weight, what do we have to think about? [Strong muscle tension]

3. We have already learned about counterbalance and countertension. These are important elements in our balances.

4. With your partner, stand back to back and lock elbows. Bend your knees and come to a medium level. You are using counterbalance and supporting each other's weight.

5. See if you and your partner can walk a short distance in one direction. Decide which direction you want to go first.

6. Can you move at different speeds?

## ACTIVITY 16

### Surround It

#### Topic: Position

Younger children may have difficulty surrounding an imaginary object. A hula hoop or small parachute may be helpful.

## Equipment

Parachute or hula hoop, if desired

## Instructions

1. You are going to be working in a small group of three people.

2. Think about surrounding an imaginary shape to keep it from flying away.

3. Start apart from each other and move together in a sustained (ongoing) way until the group gets to the imaginary shape.

4. On a signal, move apart suddenly as if the shape shocked you.

5. Come together again to surround the shape.

## ACTIVITY 17

### Near Me

#### Topic: Position

Using the element of near to encourages children to keep the object close to them. This teaches control of an object in a gamelike situation.

## Equipment

- Paddles or rackets (size should be appropriate for the developmental stage of the children; one for each child)
- Yarn balls or other object to strike (one for each child)

## Instructions

1. I want to see if you can strike your yarn ball, keeping it close to, or near to, you as you move slowly around the general space.
2. Keep the yarn ball under control and close to you by using short, little taps.
3. If you come to another person as you are moving, find a different pathway.
4. Go! What would happen if you kept the object far from you? Try this and tell me what is different.

## ACTIVITY 18

## Meet My Friend

### Topic: Position

Meet My Friend is a fun, exciting game. As children are traveling around the general space, play music. Stop the music and ask them to quickly meet and part with a friend. See how quickly they can then begin to travel and repeat the process.

### Equipment

Music for traveling

### Instructions

1. With a partner, start a short distance away.
2. Move very slowly toward one another.
3. As you are about to touch, jump and move quickly back to where you started. This is working on meeting and parting.
4. When we are on a team, we might meet and part with other teammates. We have to know where they are in relation to where we are and how to work with them.

## Building a Word Bank: Timing

The elements in the timing category of relationships are mirroring, matching, contrast, unison, taking turns, movement sequence, canon, question/answer, act/react, and lead/follow. These elements all involve actions that occur simultaneously, alternately, or one after the other in a flowing fashion (i.e., successive). Activities are provided from all three core content areas.

## ACTIVITY 19

## Mirror Me

### Topic: Timing

This activity emphasizes the element of mirroring. Children enjoy creating shapes their partners can mirror.

### Equipment

None required. You may choose to have music playing while the children create their mirroring shapes.

### Instructions

1. Find a partner with whom you can work well. We have practiced finding partners.
2. Face your partner as if you were standing in front of a mirror.
3. Decide who will be the first leader. Using one body part at a time, move slowly so that your partner can move with you to mirror your actions.
4. Use different body parts to mirror with your partner. Can you use more than one body part at a time? Can you change levels and speeds?
5. Now, move in different directions slowly and see if your partner can mirror your actions. Take turns being the leader.

## ACTIVITY 20

## Match Me

### Topic: Timing

Similar to mirroring is matching. Help partners think of various ways to match each other.

## Equipment

None required. You may choose to have music playing while the children create their matching shapes.

## Instructions

1. With the same partner, face the same direction now.
2. We are going to work on matching. Matching means you are facing the same direction and moving at the same time. You are attempting to make your movements identical.
3. In your own working space, you and your partner think of three ways to move.
4. Start with a shape, then add a locomotor movement, and then make another shape.

MMSD Elementary School Physical Education Curriculum Committee, A Guide to Curriculum Planning in Elementary School Physical Education, 1986, updated 1991 (Madison, WI: Madison Metropolitan School District).

## ACTIVITY 21

# Match and Roll

## Topic: Timing

This activity provides an additional way to emphasize matching. Although the focus is on the matching element, you want to ensure that children are safe and creating rolls that both partners can do.

## Equipment

Mats (one for every two children)

## Instructions

1. With your partner, find a space on a mat.
2. Select rolling and traveling movements both you and your partner can do.
3. See if you and your partner can show me two matching gymnastics rolls with one travel in between.

MMSD Elementary School Physical Education Curriculum Committee, A Guide to Curriculum Planning in Elementary School Physical Education, 1986, updated 1991 (Madison, WI: Madison Metropolitan School District).

## ACTIVITY 22

# Different From Me

## Topic: Timing

This can be a fun game that children of varying developmental stages can play. The focus is on movements that are contrasting, or different from one another. Bring in elements you have previously taught such as high, medium, and low levels, various pathways, or various speeds.

## Equipment

None

## Instructions

1. Contrasting movements are ones that are intended to be very different from each other.
2. You and your partner are going to think of contrasting movements. For example, one may do a movement at a high level. What would the other one do? [Low or medium level]
3. Think of three movements and show me how they are contrasting.
4. I am going to come around and see your partner work.

## ACTIVITY 23

# One and the Same

## Topic: Timing

Movements in unison are to be done at exactly the same time. Again, you can bring in elements previously acquired.

## Equipment

None

## Instructions

1. Sit in your self-space and move your hands in the air so their pathways are just alike.
2. Try two other body parts such as knees or elbows. Can you make these body parts move in unison?
3. Now, find your good working partner. See if you and your partner can move a body part in unison. Can you move two body parts in unison? How about three?

4. Can you travel in unison with your partner?

5. Can you change directions or pathways as you move in unison?

## ACTIVITY 24

# My Turn and Your Turn

### Topic: Timing

Alternating, or taking turns, can be thought of in terms of body parts or people. This activity helps children think of ways to work together as they learn to alternate movements they have created.

### Equipment

Mats (one for each group of three). If your class size prohibits making small groups of three, adjust to an appropriate size for you. It is helpful to keep the working groups as small as possible.

### Instructions

1. When body parts or people move one right after the other, we think of them, or the movements, as being successive. However, when body parts or people use a slower action, almost like taking turns, we think of this as alternating.

2. Find a group of three. In your small group, we are going to work on alternating, or taking turns.

3. To show alternating, you have to think about the timing and the pathway of your movement.

4. Think of a roll that you can do well. Each of you will start from a different place on the mat.

5. Show me how you can demonstrate alternating rolls starting from different places on the mat.

## ACTIVITY 25

# Movement Sequence

### Topic: Timing

Refining a movement sequence entails helping children to learn to remember movements in an order and to show a definite beginning and ending, as in a sentence. Words used in presenting movement sequences should include a beginning and

ending as you would do when writing a sentence. Movement sequences may be developed from a variety of movement elements. Although the element term *movement sequence* is listed under the relationships concept, the compilation of elements in the sequence should consist of movement elements already acquired in the students' movement word bank.

Movement sequences require children to create smooth, flowing orders of movements that can be repeated. Successive movements are one right after the other. The movements do not necessarily need to be exactly the same. However, a canon-style movement is a form of copying performed by more than two people, who, one at a time, repeat a movement sequence with the exact dynamics initiated by the first person. In this activity place the following in the pocket chart or point to it on the word wall: Start at a high level, travel in different directions, finish at a low level.

### Equipment

None

### Instructions

Show me a movement sequence that starts at a high level, then travels in different directions, and finishes at a low level. Can you make your movement smooth and free-flowing?

## ACTIVITY 26

# Smooth Sequence

### Topic: Timing

As you continue with movement sequences, encourage children to show you how smooth and free flowing their movement sequences can be.

### Equipment

None

### Instructions

1. Find your self-space and sit down.

2. Show me how you can stand up, turn around, and make a low balance. This is called a movement sequence because you had a beginning and an ending.

3. Can you tell me what the beginning and ending of your movement sequence is?

4. Let's try this again and see how smoothly you can make the sequence.

## Variations

Once students grasp the idea of creating a smooth, or free-flowing, movement sequence, you encourage them to create their own movement sequence. The amount of latitude will depend on the developmental stage of your students. You may choose to provide parameters (e.g., twisted shape balance, pencil roll, walk, wide balance) or you may be able to allow students to create their own (e.g., mount, travel, turn, dismount).

## ACTIVITY 27

# How Movement Is Like Language
### Topic: Timing

Children operating at an early elementary developmental stage may need to have pictorial representations of shapes and traveling (such as pathways, directions, and locomotor skills) to help them create their movement phrases. Children operating at a mature developmental stage can use word cards.

### Equipment

- Enough locomotor, pathway, direction, and shape cards to provide all students with one of each type
- Music is a good addition to this activity.

### Instructions

1. Choose at least three movement cards (one from each set) to form a movement sequence. [Example: general space, forward, low level]
2. Place the cards you picked in order on the floor to show a movement sequence.
3. Now, create a sequence of movements that show this sequence.
4. Can you make a longer movement sequence?
5. Make sure you can show me a definite beginning, middle, and ending for your sequence.
6. Creating a movement sequence is just like writing a sentence. Each part of the movement sequence should link with the one before it and the one after it in a smooth and free-flowing motion.
7. Think about getting your body ready to move. This is working on your movement order (preparation). Action is making the movements, and recovery is finishing your sequence on balance.

8. Now, I want you to think of making your own movement phrase. Start with a beginning shape at a low level. Travel using your locomotor skill and make an ending shape at a high level. See how smooth you can make your movement sequence.
9. Change the speed of your sequence. First try it slowly, and then try it more quickly. Can you still keep it smooth and free flowing?

## ACTIVITY 28

# Creating a Movement Story
### Topic: Timing

Children of both elementary and mature developmental stages can create movement stories. You should direct them at first, and then students can direct themselves.

Movement stories can be created from a variety of movement elements. Students need to understand that a movement story has a definite beginning, middle, and ending, much like sentences that make up a story they might read in their classroom or like the movement sequences they make in physical education. Classroom teachers may also use this approach to provide a movement focus to their language arts or reading lessons. You can place the elements within the movement story on the pocket chart as a whole or in part, and then have the students demonstrate them in class. You may also choose to point out the movement elements on the word wall.

### Equipment

Music to help children create movements. Movement stories such as this one:

Picture yourself in a tropical jungle. You are suddenly stuck in quicksand, and you slowly start to sink. Try to pull yourself out in several different ways.

The following movement concepts, categories, and elements are used in this movement story:

- Self-space (S1); sideways (R5), up (R6), down (R7), clockwise (R8), counterclockwise (R9); levels (low, medium, high)
- Slow (E2), fast (E1); strong (E4), light (E5); bound (E6)
- Narrow (B2), wide (B3), round (B4), twisted (B5)

Place these concepts in the pocket chart or point to them on the word wall for students to review prior to demonstrating their understanding. Helping students to differentiate between mimicking movements and moving their bodies like the movement elements is important. This will be discussed further in the educational dance chapter.

## Instructions

1. You are going to work in small groups. Can you find a small group in which you can work well?

2. I'm going to read a movement story [see the example in the Equipment section]. As I do, I will place movement words on pocket chart cards in the pocket chart in the order they occur in the movement story. [Read the story.]

3. Now, I want you to combine these movement words into a story through your actions. Show me the movement words in the order they occurred in the story.

4. There is no right way to do the movements.

MMSD Elementary School Physical Education Curriculum Committee, A Guide to Curriculum Planning in Elementary School Physical Education, 1986, updated 1991 (Madison, WI: Madison Metropolitan School District).

## ACTIVITY 29

## Dynamic Canon

### Topic: Timing

Canon movements are fun. Now that children have learned mirroring, matching, and movement sequence, you can add the canon relationship. The focus of this activity is duplicating movements with the same effort dynamics. For example, if a child rolls slowly, the other children copy this roll with the same slow dynamics.

### Equipment

None

### Instructions

1. When we do canon movements, one person performs a movement and everyone else, moving one at a time, copies the movement in the same way (Logsdon et al., 1984).

2. As you work with your group of three or four, see if you can demonstrate a canon-style relationship.

3. Can you copy the dynamics of the first person? For example, if that person's movements were quick, slow, quick, can you make your movements the same?

## ACTIVITY 30

## Lead and Follow

### Topic: Timing

### Equipment

None

### Instructions

1. Work with a partner. Decide who is to lead first.

2. The leader makes a short movement pathway.

3. The leader should clearly stop when done.

4. The follower then copies the leader's movement as closely as possible.

### Variation

Activity 30 can be done in self-space using one body part at a time. Body parts can then be added as well as traveling (as in the above example). You are looking for students to demonstrate the relationships element of lead/follow.

## Building a Word Bank: Goal

Cooperation, collaboration, and competition are three types of relationships that require groups to function together to make the activity, task, or game work. As groups or teams are relating together, they are seeking to either work together (cooperate), outwit an opponent (collaborate), or win an event (competition). The goal for the situation may vary yet the focus is on how the individuals are relating to each other and the outcome they are seeking.

- In cooperative relationships, people or groups work together to help each other perform better. This can occur with a partner or in a small or large group. Examples include two people playing catch, someone rebounding for someone shooting baskets, someone spotting someone who is performing a gymnastic stunt, and dancing with others. Cooperative relationships generally result in more successful performances.

- Collaborative relationships involve a strategic approach. For example, teams create strategies to help them achieve their goals. Playing offense and defense and taking turns playing in a game are examples of collaboration to achieve the ultimate goal of winning. When children are collaborating, they are working together to achieve a goal, as in cooperation. However, when children are collaborating, they are not only working together but developing a strategy or plan to outwit the opponent. This suggests a problem-solving approach to the activity.

- In competitive relationships, winning is the primary goal rather than creating a strategy to work together, as in collaboration. The competitive relationship is about working to win or be better than another person or team.

## ACTIVITY 31

# Cooperation With Self
### Topic: Goal

Explain to children that they can cooperate with themselves, with a partner, with a small group, or with a larger group. Children can cooperate with themselves by working independently to complete a task (e.g., throwing and catching an object).

### Equipment

A variety of objects to throw and catch (e.g., beanbags, stuffed animals, yarn balls, and soft coated foam balls)

### Instructions

1. When you hear the start signal, choose an object to throw and catch.
2. You may change your object when you want to.
3. When you are ready to begin, throw and catch your object in your own self-space.
4. Can you catch your object five times in a row? How about ten times?

## ACTIVITY 32

# Cooperation With a Partner
### Topic: Goal

Cooperating with a partner entails two children working together to achieve a goal (e.g., throwing and catching an object).

### Equipment

- Towels, panel chutes, or large scarves
- A variety of objects to throw and catch (e.g., beanbags, stuffed animals, yarn balls, and soft coated foam balls)

### Instructions

1. Choose a partner with whom you can work well. With your partner, choose one object to throw and catch.
2. Now, each of you will hold either end of a towel [or panel chute or scarf].
3. When you are ready, throw your object into the air from the towel and then catch it on the towel. [See www.reg8.net/docs/2-P.pdf for more information on panel chute activities.]
4. You will have to work together to catch the object on your towel.
5. See how many times you can throw and catch the object on your towel.
6. Can you move and still throw and catch it?
7. You may change objects whenever you like.

## ACTIVITY 33

# Cooperation With a Small Group
### Topic: Cooperative

In this activity you can provide multiple options and allow the children to choose as well as to alter the object they are using. The focus is on cooperation with the group. Cooperating with a small group encourages larger groups of children to work together. In this example, four children are working together to achieve a goal.

### Equipment

A variety of objects to throw and catch (e.g., beanbags, stuffed animals, yarn balls, and soft coated foam balls)

## Instructions

1. With your partner, find another set of partners with whom you can work.
2. Each set of partners will throw and catch an object back and forth. Start with one object. When you are ready to begin, you may start.
3. See if you and your partner can throw or toss the object to the other set of partners so they can catch it. See how many times in a row you can do this. Change objects whenever you like.
4. If you believe you are ready, you may add a second object.
5. Can you think of different ways to cooperate with your partner or small group using the towel and one or two objects?

Encourage students to add an additional set of partners so there are six children working together if they are ready and want to do so. They may also choose to continue to work just with their own partner as well.

## ACTIVITY 34

# Capture the Critter

### Topic: Collaborative

This activity is for children at the upper elementary or mature developmental stage. Begin by creating two teams of six, eight, or ten players, depending on the number of children you have in a class and their ability to work together.

## Equipment

- Jerseys (pinnies), wristbands, or scarves to denote teams
- Critters (animals) to be captured (one for each team)
- Cones to denote working space

## Instructions

1. I am going to divide the class into two teams. Children on each team need to wear either the same color of pinnies or wristbands identifying them as teammates.
2. Each team will begin the game on their own side of the gym [or playing space].
3. Each team has a critter on the end line of the other team's space.
4. Your team's job is to capture the other team's critter without getting tagged.
5. Team members who are tagged must return to their own side of the gym.

## Variations

To make this game collaborative, encourage the teams to strategize about how to capture the critter. They may choose to block for a particular team member who has been designated as the one to capture the critter. They may choose to sacrifice themselves by being tagged to assist the team member who has been designated as the one to capture the critter.

You may want to have several games going at one time to maximize space and minimize wait time. If space is limited, have several timed rounds, so children are not standing around waiting too long. Children waiting their turns may be playing a different type of chasing, fleeing, and dodging game. Another idea is to have teams create their strategies as they await their turns.

## ACTIVITY 35

# Voyage Across the River

### Topic: Goal

This game may be played with children from the upper elementary to the mature or even transitional stage of development. To be successful, children should be able to work in a small group, communicate with each other, and be considerate of their teammates. Ask children to divide themselves into teams of their choosing. You may decide to have teams of five, six, or more. This will depend on the size of your class and the equipment and space available. Each team should select the same amount and type of equipment.

### Equipment

Examples of equipment:

- Mat (one for each team)
- Jump rope (one for each team)
- Scooter (one for each team)
- Poly spots or arrows (four to six for each team)

You will also need to place cones to designate a start and end location. Vary this distance depending on the developmental stage of the children.

### Instructions

1. You are going to cooperate with your teammates to get each team member across the river (the gym floor) without any body part touching the floor.
2. You may sit on the mat, use the scooter, or stand on the poly spots.
3. All team members must cross from point A (the starting cone) to point B (the end cone) without any body part touching the floor.
4. Take a few minutes to discuss your cooperative plan with your teammates. Remember, you must work together to achieve your goal.
5. Can you now go from start to end and back to start?
6. This time, when you go from start to end and back to start, collect all your equipment. All the equipment should be back with you at the starting line.

### Variations

Options for this game:

- As a cooperative activity, the focus is on how the teams work together. There is not a winner.
- As a collaborative activity, the focus is on how the teams work together. A winner is declared.
- As a group cooperative activity, see how much time it takes for the entire class to complete the activity.

- As a team competitive activity, see how much time it takes for each team to complete the activity and compare times.
- As a team competitive activity, see how much time it takes for each team to complete the activity over several rounds.
- Change team members as you feel necessary, or allow children to change team members depending on your focus.

MMSD Elementary School Physical Education Curriculum Committee, A Guide to Curriculum Planning in Elementary School Physical Education, 1986, updated 1991 (Madison, WI: Madison Metropolitan School District).

# Building a Word Bank: Environment

The environment in which children move may be either static or dynamic. A static environment is one in which the object or equipment is stationary, or stable. A dynamic environment is one in which the object or equipment is not fixed, but moving. A dynamic environment is certainly a more difficult one in which to be successful.

### ACTIVITY 36

## Static Target Throw
### Topic: Environment

Children, particularly those at the early elementary stage of development, should work in a static, or stationary, mode. Give them choices of targets and even objects.

### Equipment

- Targets on the wall such as a large circle with smaller circles drawn inside (one per child); seasonal pictures such as pumpkins in October, turkeys in November, and snowmen in December would be fun.
- Objects for children to throw at the stationary target such as soft coated foam balls, yarn balls, or beanbags (one for each child)

### Instructions

1. Find a comfortable starting line for you.
2. As you can see, there are several targets on the wall. Choose the one you want to throw at.
3. When you are ready, throw your object against the target on the wall.

## ACTIVITY 37

### Static Striking

#### Topic: Environment

In striking, it is important to remember that children at an early elementary stage will be more successful striking off a tee (static activity) rather than at a moving object (dynamic activity).

#### Equipment

- Batting tees (one for every two or three children)
- Plastic bats (one for every two or three children)
- Plastic balls (one for every two or three children)

#### Instructions

1. Choose a partner with whom you can work well.
2. When you are ready, see if you can strike the ball off the batting tee.
3. Take three turns and let your partner work on this task.
4. Each time, bring the ball back to the tee before striking.

## ACTIVITY 38

### Dynamic Striking

#### Topic: Environment

This is an additional example of a dynamic task. Children are working in partners, throwing a ball underhand to their partner who will strike it with a bat. The moving target (ball) makes this a dynamic activity.

#### Equipment

- Plastic bats of various sizes (one per pair)
- Plastic balls (one per pair)

#### Instructions

1. You will be working with a partner in this activity. Show me how quickly you can find a partner with whom you can work well.
2. You and your partner will need one bat and one Wiffle ball (or other soft foam ball) to strike.
3. Find a self-space in which to work. One partner will throw (pitch) underhand to the receiving partner who will strike the ball with the bat.
4. The partner who threw the ball will retrieve the ball.
5. Take two turns and switch places.
6. This is a dynamic activity because the ball is moving toward you to hit.
7. You and your partner decide the distance for throwing. Think about the amount of force the thrower will put on the ball. Remember, I want to see the batter being successful in striking the object.

# Building a Word Bank: Review Activities for Chapters 7–10

## REVIEW ACTIVITY 1

### Matching Fun

Matching activities are a fun way to build a word bank and see what the children have learned. In this activity, children match words to definitions. It can easily be done in conjunction with classroom teachers. You may choose any of the elements from chapters 7 through 10 upon which to focus. The example provided is for the concept Space and categories of Directions, Pathways, and Levels. This review activity can be done individually, in partners, or in small groups. Using this as a lesson closure is a great way to see what children have learned.

#### Equipment

None

#### Instructions

1. Each of the categories for space have been placed in the top left of the pocket chart and each of the definitions have been placed in the right. They are not in the right order. Can you match the definitions to the words? [For students operating at lower deveopmental stages or whose first language is not English, you can read the word and definitions or ask students to work together. You might also place photos of children moving in a variety of directions,

pathways, and levels in the pocket chart. You may also use the characters on the cards.]

2. Can you tell me which elements best fit each picture?

## REVIEW ACTIVITY 2

### Drawing What I Know

Often younger children enjoy drawing their thoughts after a movement lesson. After teaching elements of springlike actions, see if children can draw their understanding of the differences between various movements. This activity can be done in the gym or the classroom.

#### Equipment

- Paper
- Crayons and markers

#### Instructions

We have been learning about the elements of springlike actions. Can you draw the differences between a leap, a hop, and a jump?

## REVIEW ACTIVITY 3

### Creating a Cooperative, Collaborative, or Competitive Game

Children at the upper elementary and mature stages of development will enjoy creating activities that demonstrate their understanding of cooperative, collaborative, and competitive games. Choose additional elements to help them focus, such as manipulative skills of kicking, striking, or throwing and catching.

#### Equipment

Provide children with choices of equipment (e.g., gator skin balls, paddles, soft yarn balls, scoops, bases, flags, and jerseys)

#### Instructions

1. Working in small groups, create a cooperative game that involves throwing and catching. [Children may decide whether or not to include scoring, but you are looking for a game that is clearly cooperative.]

2. When you are finished creating your game, explain it to the rest of the class. We will be playing these games in later classes.

# Part II

# CORE CONTENT AREA LESSONS

The core content areas in the movement education framework (MEF) are divided into educational games, educational gymnastics, and educational dance. Lessons presented in this book reflect only a partial application of what you might do in each of these content areas. It was our desire to create appealing lessons that apply in a variety of situations. The key is to be able to take the MEF elements presented in chapters 7 through 10 and apply them to a variety of games, gymnastics, and dance situations. Our lessons are consistent with the national standards (NASPE, 2004), and objectives for lessons cover all three learning domains, respect learners' individuality, and apply MEF elements.

Chapters 7 through 10 present activities for each of the concept areas (body, space, effort, and relationships). Chapters 11 through 13 provide specific lessons in each of the core content areas (educational games, educational gymnastics, and educational dance). In each of these chapters, we address a variety of developmental stages and apply the MEF language. As in the concept chapters, you will find that each activity includes a list of suggested equipment.

## Planning for Teaching

An MEF approach to physical education can be blended with many of the activities and games you have already been doing or might choose to do in the future. Basic movement is the foundation of physical education, as discussed in chapter 2. The MEF approach allows for children to take control of their movement choices, be successful, and build a knowledge base and a movement vocabulary for a lifetime of activity. The lessons presented in this text are merely examples of what you can do with your own curriculum.

To be successful with the MEF approach, you must do the following:

- Help children build a movement vocabulary (e.g., through the use of pocket chart cards and poster sets).
- Respect individual differences in learning.
- Use guided discovery and problem solving to encourage children to be successful movers.

Using this approach with your own style of teaching will help you provide a quality movement education program.

## Motor Learning Applications to Movement Education Lessons

The purpose of this section is to provide you with specific applications of several practice procedures that will help you create increasingly challenging experiences for your learners. These progression procedures deal with the structure of practice repetition (e.g., from blocked to random), the variability of repetition (e.g., from less variable to more variable), and the degree of task practice fragmentation (e.g., from practicing a single part or parts of a task to practicing the whole task). The methods presented include contextual interference (blocked and random), variability (from schema theory), and part/whole practice (fractionalization and segmentation). We have provided specific applications of these methods to lessons in chapters 11 through 13. For more detail on these methods, please see chapter 3. The importance of being able to apply these practice methods is to help you create more effective and efficient lessons by giving you logical tools to create a progression from one lesson to another. These practice methods will help you meet the individual needs of all students in your classes more easily.

## Using Pedometers in Movement Education Lessons

Teachers can provide children with pedometers at the beginning of each lesson. Pedometers may be numbered so each child can use the same pedometer each class period. Teachers can have the pedometers in a box so children can select their pedometer as they enter class. At a minimum, have the children discuss or record the number of steps or physical activity time (PAT) in a journal. Be sure to consider privacy of data for the children when you select your methods.

A variety of data analysis options are available. In the Station Hockey activity (see page 206), students can record how many steps they take during each station of practice and discuss the differences during the lesson closure. You may also have children compare the number of steps they are taking while performing their movement sequences where they incorporate traveling versus sequences where they are only doing rocking and rolling (lesson 3 on page 218). You might have them compare their physical activity time or number of steps among the various parts of the Umbrella dance (e.g., chapter 13) or maybe compare to a different dance (e.g., Cotton-Eyed Joe on page 180).

## Content

The lessons presented in chapters 11 through 13 apply a number of movement elements in various combinations. Some lessons or parts of lessons ask children to demonstrate a variety of responses, which allows them to be successful. Some lessons encourage children to solve movement problems, whereas others are more directed. However, it is important to note that as children move through the developmental sequences, they should be able to apply movement elements to a variety of applications. Lesson objectives may focus on combinations of cognitive, affective, and psychomotor domains. Tasks may and often should be repeated from one lesson to the next. In addition, movement elements learned in previous lessons or those learned early in the developmental sequence can and should be built on in future lessons.

You do not need to reteach basic movement elements in lessons for older children; rather, focus on the application of these elements at a higher developmental stage, as noted in chapter 3. Using problem-solving methods to present tasks allows children to discover their own movement solutions. While you are guiding them with element definitions, you want them to create a variety of movement solutions. Lessons may also include matching activities, small-group activities using movement elements, or a variety of assessment tools, as noted in chapter 5.

Preservice teachers will enjoy the direct word-for-word phrasing these chapters provide. More experienced teachers may choose to take portions of the activities with the needed movement elements and make them their own (i.e., apply their own style to the tasks).

As discussed in chapter 2, the MEF not only fosters the acquisition of movement knowledge, but also supports literacy efforts. Some suggestions for activities that go beyond traditional physical education activities are discussed in chapter 4.

## Lesson Organization

Each lesson provides warm-up activities from which you can choose. We have also provided you with cognitive, motor, and affective objectives based upon a movement education perspective. Affective objectives also include a social and emotional component (e.g., follows directions, respects skill differences). You will see these presented in a progressive manner. Elements that have been presented in prior lessons are a lighter shade. This indicates elements previously presented. Those elements that are central to the lesson being presented are in darker font.

Your introduction to the lesson should include a focus on the use of MEF elements. You can discuss these using the pocket chart cards and chart or the movement word wall. As you present elements during your introduction to each lesson, think about what your students already know and that which needs additional emphasis. If you feel students need a refresher on previously presented elements, time should be spent on those to ensure students' success in both content and movement knowledge.

You should present objectives at the beginning of each lesson—MEF objectives as well as cognitive, motor, social, and affective objectives. Cognitive objectives should focus on children being able to provide definitions of elements in the lesson. These elements may include motor skills as presented in the manipulative category. Social objectives refer to interpersonal skills; for example, as children learn to work with partners or in small groups, they are also learning to respect the skill levels of others. When combined with MEF objectives students should be able to demonstrate an application of these movement elements in the movement setting. To focus on more or fewer elements, add or subtract these as needed.

Introductions to lessons should be brief, yet include a focus on movement elements important for children to be successful. As the children progress through the developmental stages, they should be familiar with basic MEF elements and focus on those needed for being successful in the tasks of the lesson. Observing through an MEF lens may take some practice, but in the end it will help your students succeed.

# 11

# Teaching Educational Games

The term *educational games* has been used to describe games that foster skill acquisition and help children become skillful games players. Barrett (1984) suggests that physical educators should help all children reach their full potential, not just the athletically gifted. The same philosophy applies to all teachers of physical education. Using the developmental approach outlined in chapter 3 can foster student success. Far too often children are placed in game situations for which they are not ready; as a result, only a few are successful.

As noted in chapters 1 and 2, the movement education approach emphasizes contribution, activity, and success for all children. This may require altering the rules, equipment, or player combinations. To approach games play from a movement perspective, you must examine what you want your students to be able to do in a game or gamelike experience and include these movement elements in the lesson.

## Motor Learning Applications to Teaching Educational Games

This chapter uses a progression of the contextual interference motor learning method (blocked and random) which is laid out in table 11.1 on page

198. The first three lessons use the blocked practice method, focusing only on one skill (striking) for the entire lesson. The blocked method helps the learner get early success through repetition. It also helps the learner to understand the basic idea of what to do because things are kept simple. Once children have the basic idea, it is good to add variability to the practice repetitions of the skill.

For example, in lesson 1 on page 199, children first strike a yarn ball with a Pillo Polo stick in self-space. This task is then made slightly more difficult by asking the children to strike the yarn ball in general space. This is made even more difficult by challenging the children to attempt to move in different pathways through the general space. Lesson 2, Hockey Freeway (page 201), emphasizes the variability of the practice repetition method through the need to avoid collisions by changing pathways on the freeway and integrating abrupt stops at the toll booths. Moving Mania (lesson 3 on page 202) increases variability by incorporating a greater number of parameters (e.g., changes in speed, pathways, planes, equipment, and the use of partners).

A false sense of competency can occur when using blocked methods. Children can often perform well in a blocked practice situation because the activity is limited to simple tasks. Therefore, the amount of real motor learning is limited when

**Table 11.1**  Motor Learning Application to the Teaching of Educational Games

| Practice method | Lesson | | | | | |
|---|---|---|---|---|---|---|
| | 1—Striking in Self- and General Space | 2—Hockey Freeway | 3—Moving Mania | 4—Hockey Shoot-a-Round | 5—Station Hockey | 6—Mini Hockey |
| | Progression → | | | | | |
| Blocked method examples | Striking | Striking | Striking | None | None | None |
| Emphasis of blocked method | High | High | High | None | None | None |
| Random method examples | None | None | Dribble | Dribble, pass, trap | Dribble, pass, trap, shoot | Dribble, pass, trap, shoot |
| Emphasis of random method | None | None | Minimal | Low | Medium | High |
| Variable method examples | Self- and general space, stopping and starting, slight pathway changes | Freeway pathways, abrupt stops at hockey toll booths | Changes in speed, pathway, planes, equipment, use of partners | With a partner | In groups of three | In groups of six to eight |
| Emphasis of variable method | Low | Medium | Heavy | Low | Medium | Heavy |

using blocked practice. In order to avoid this false sense of security from blocked practice, it is important to continue to increase the challenge in subsequent lessons. As the teacher, you want to change the method from blocked to random practice in order to increase this challenge. You will see this in the continuing analysis for lessons 4, 5, and 6. Table 11.1 shows an increase in the use of the random practice method, increasing the number of motor skills. Increasing this difficulty results in more performance errors by the children, but, with quality feedback to assist them and encouragement to motivate them, that difficulty is exactly what will result in better learning and ultimately better performance!

With the addition of the random skills in lesson 4, there is an abrupt change in heavy variability to low variability. This decrease is helpful to the child by decreasing the difficulty level and

allowing a bit of success prior to the increase in challenge again in lesson 5. Without this decrease in variability from lesson 3 to 4, the tasks would likely become overwhelming and the child would do poorly. The variability then gradually increases through lesson 5 to hit a high level in lesson 6 by doubling the number of participants. Of course, you will want to adjust any of these choices to fit the actual needs of your specific children.

# Educational Games Lessons

In the six lessons presented, we focus on striking an object with a noodle, Pillo Polo stick, or a hockey stick. Lessons presented are progressive in nature, both within and between lessons. The developmental stages presented are only a general guide. A better way to match a lesson topic to a group of children would be to use a developmental analysis to determine their actual stage (see table 3.1 on page 33). Review the lessons and adapt them as needed according to the developmental stages of your students. You will see each lesson opened with MEF objectives, divided into cognitive, motor, and affective. Cognitive objectives focus on asking children to articulate definitions of MEF elements, whereas motor objectives focus on those elements which are directly related to motor skills. The affective objectives have an emotional and social focus. Each lesson has all movement elements contained in that lesson; however, elements which have already been covered are presented in a lighter shading while those that are more pertinent to the lesson are presented in a darker shading. In addition to the MEF affective objectives that directly relate to the movement framework, you will see objectives included that have a social focus but are not directly MEF objectives. We felt it important to include objectives such as "follows directions of teacher" and "respects skill differences" in lessons as these may contribute to the overall success of lessons.

## LESSON 1

# Striking in Self- and General Space
## Initial or Elementary Stages; Grade K

### Cognitive and Motor Objectives
- Strike (tap)
- Self-space
- General space
- Straight, curved, zigzag pathways
- Soft force
- Near to

### Affective and Social Objectives
- Working in self-space; keeping hands, feet, and objects to yourself
- Working in general space
- Following directions
- Respecting skill differences and skill levels of peers

### Equipment
- Hula hoops (one for each child)
- Pillo Polo sticks or noodles (one for each child)

- Cones (15-20)
- Soft yarn balls (one for each child)
- Soft foam balls (one for each child)
- Pedometers (one for each child, if desired)
- Music and player, if desired

### Warm-Up

You may choose to adapt these warm-up activities. The purpose is to ensure that students have an understanding of self- and general space and pathways before receiving equipment.

1. Each student stands inside a hoop with the hoop on the floor. Tell them this is their self-space. See if they can move all around in their self-space. Can they reach up high while staying in their self-space? Can they make a very small shape while in their self-space? They should not touch the sides of the hoop.

2. Students pick up their hoops and hold them around their waists. Ask them to walk all around the gym. Tell them they are moving in general space and taking their self-space with them. See if they can walk a bit faster and avoid collisions.

3. Collect the hoops. Ask students to move in general space, using a variety of locomotor movements. See if they can move without any collisions.

4. Ask students to travel in different pathways while still using all the open spaces. Encourage them to move to the open spaces and avoid collisions.

### Striking in Self-Space and General Space

This portion of the lesson focuses on the manipulative skill of striking as students stay in their own self-space. Once they have demonstrated an understanding of striking in self-space, they can move to striking in general space.

1. When I say "Go," I want you all to find your own self-space on the floor. Walk there and sit down quietly. Go.

2. I am going to give each of you a yarn ball and a Pillo Polo stick [or a noodle]. It is like a hockey stick, but it has a soft top. When you get your stick, stand with it and hold it.

3. Some of our safety rules are that we keep our sticks to ourselves and we keep our sticks at

our waist or below. I also want you to hold your stick using two hands.

4. Put the hand you eat with [or hold your fork with] lower on the stick and the other hand higher on the stick. This is how I want you to always hold your stick.

5. When I say "Go," put your yarn ball on the ground and softly strike or tap your ball with your stick. See if you can stay in your own self-space and gently tap the yarn ball.

6. Listen for the start and stop signals. Can you start tapping when I say "Go"? Can you stop tapping when I say "Freeze"? Can you use both sides of your stick while you are tapping?

You are looking for children who are holding the Pillo Polo stick or noodle as suggested and using soft taps to keep it in their own self-space.

7. Now, we are going to move around in the general space. Remember, as we move, our self-space, or working space, goes with us.

8. When I say "Go," I want to see if you can strike, or dribble, your yarn ball, keeping it close to you as you move slowly around the general space. I want to see you keep the yarn ball under control by using short, little taps and keeping it near to you.

9. If you come to another person as you are moving, find a different pathway. Go.

Give children a few minutes to practice this skill. You are looking for short, soft taps as they move around the general space. Remind them to stay in their own space as they move.

Reprinted, by permission, from Debbie Rhea.

## Striking and Frozen Statue

In this activity, called Frozen Statue, children are asked to maintain body and object control as they dribble and then freeze.

1. Everyone, freeze in your own space. Put your stick and yarn ball on the floor between your feet.

2. This time we are going to practice dribbling and starting and stopping on signal. Our game is called Frozen Statue. Listen for the music as our start signal. When you hear me say "Go," you may travel around the general space, dribbling your yarn ball with the Pillo Polo stick.

3. When you hear me say "Freeze," see if you can stop right away and freeze like a statue!

I am looking for quick stops when you hear the music stop. I want to see you freeze like a statue.

4. What do you have to think about when you want to stop quickly and still keep the yarn ball under control? What do you have to do with the stick?

You are looking for children who are staying in their own self-space as they travel and who can stop quickly when the music stops. Continue to give cues to students so they can work on starting and stopping when you give the signals. Point out a student who is stopping with the yarn ball under control. Have the students analyze how one does this successfully. Ask students to think about what they have to do with the stick to stop the ball.

MMSD Elementary School Physical Education Curriculum Committee, A Guide to Curriculum Planning in Elementary School Physical Education, 1986, updated 1991 (Madison, WI: Madison Metropolitan School District).

## Striking and Changing Pathways (Individual)

You want to see how well children strike the ball when they add in pathway changes. Allowing all children to be active at once and bringing in the elements of pathways adds to the activity level during this lesson.

1. I want you all to freeze and sit in your own space for a minute so you can listen. You did great! I saw some really quick stops and frozen statues!

2. We are going to work on changing pathways and keeping the yarn ball under control. When I say "Go," I want you to travel and strike your yarn ball. Keep it close to you by using soft taps.

3. Think about changing your pathway now as you move all around the general space. I am looking for straight, curved, and zigzag pathways. Go.

As children travel, continue to remind them to keep the yarn ball close to them so they can keep it under control. You are looking for changes in pathways.

I have put cones all around the gym. I want you to change your pathway when you come to a cone. I want to see

1. light, soft taps;

2. changes in pathways; and

3. keeping the ball near you.

You are looking for children who are keeping the yarn ball under control as they dribble (strike) all around the general space. You also want to see them using all the general space while staying in their self-space. This will demonstrate an understanding of self- and general space.

## LESSON 2

# Hockey Freeway
### Initial or Elementary Stages; Grade 1

## Cognitive and Motor Objectives
- Strike (tap)
- Self-space
- General space
- Soft force
- Straight, curved, zigzag pathways
- Near to
- Around

## Affective and Social Objectives
- Working in self-space; keeping hands, feet, and objects to yourself
- Respecting general space
- Following directions
- Respecting skill differences and skill levels of peers

## Equipment
- Hula hoops (one for each child)
- Pillo Polo sticks or noodles (one for each child)
- Soft yarn balls (one for each child)
- Soft foam balls (one for each child)
- Pedometers (one for each child, if desired)

## Warm-Up
You may choose to adapt these activities. The purpose is to ensure that students have an understanding of self- and general space and pathways before receiving equipment.

1. Each student stands inside a hoop with the hoop on the floor. Tell them this is their self-space. See if they can move all around in their self-space. Can they reach up high while staying in their self-space? Can they make a very small shape while in their self-space? They should not touch the sides of the hoop.

2. Students pick up their hoops and hold them around their waists. Ask them to walk all around the gym. Tell them they are moving in general space and taking their self-space with them. See if they can walk a bit faster and avoid collisions.

3. Collect the hoops. Ask students to move in general space using various locomotor movements. See if they can move without any collisions.

4. Ask students to travel in different pathways while still using all the open spaces. Encourage them to move to the open spaces and avoid collisions.

## Striking in Self-Space and General Space
Children should be able to focus on the manipulative skill of striking as they stay in their own space and move throughout the general space.

1. When I say "Go," I want you to find your self-space on the floor. Walk there and sit down quietly. Go.

2. I am going to give each of you a Pillo Polo stick [or noodle] and a yarn ball. When you get your stick, you may stand with it and hold it.

3. Some of our safety rules are to keep your stick to yourself and keep it at your waist or below. I also want you to hold your stick using two hands.

4. Put the hand you write with lower on the stick and the other hand higher on the stick. This is how I want you to always hold your stick.

5. When I say "Go," put your yarn ball on the ground and softly strike it with the stick.

6. See if you can stay in your own self-space and gently tap the yarn ball with the stick. Use both sides of the stick.

7. If you come to someone else as you are traveling with your stick, find another pathway. Go.

You are looking for children who are holding the stick as requested and using soft taps to keep it in their own self-space.

1. Now, we are going to move around in the general space. Remember, as we move, our self-space goes with us.

2. When I say "Go," I want to see if you can strike your yarn ball, keeping it near you as you move slowly around the general space.

3. I want to see you keep the yarn ball under control by using soft taps and keeping it near you. Go.

Give children a few minutes to practice this skill. You are looking for soft taps as children move around the general space. Remind them to stay in their own space as they move and avoid collisions.

## Hockey Freeway

A fun game for children that can be adapted to a variety of developmental stages, Hockey Freeway, brings together elements of self- and general space, as well as pathways.

1. We are going to play a game called Hockey Freeway. When we play this game, you will be using your short, soft taps.
2. When I say "Go," find your self-space and start your engines. That means that you tap your object back and forth in your own self-space. Do this about 10 times.
3. When you have done this, you can then begin moving slowly around the general space.
4. Can you show me how you can move in different pathways? What are our pathways? I am looking for curved, straight, and zigzag pathways.
5. When you come to someone else, go around them. I don't want to see collisions.

After the children have played this for a few minutes, add the following activities. You want to encourage problem solving and provide as much activity as possible. Keep looking for children who are moving in different pathways and avoiding collisions. You should also remind them to use soft taps and to keep control of their objects. Asking questions such as Who can show me a pathway you chose? and Can you think of different pathways in which you can move? may encourage creativity and problem solving. Allowing children to change objects also encourages them to think about which object they are better able to control.

## Hockey Toll Booths

Demonstrating control of the hockey object is the focus of Hockey Toll Booths. Children at an early elementary stage of development may choose to walk while traveling. Older children may be comfortable and able to demonstrate the ability to freeze from a jog as they control the hockey object.

Everyone freeze. This part of our freeway has toll booths. You have to stop and pay a toll when I say "Toll booth!" To do this, I want you to freeze in your self-space and dribble your object back and forth for a count of 10. Then you can travel again. Go.

You are looking for children to demonstrate alert stops and starts. Ask them what they have to do to be able to stop when you say "Toll booth." Do they have to keep control of their object? How are they able to do this?

## LESSON 3

# Moving Mania
### Elementary and Mature Stages; Grade 2

### Cognitive and Motor Objectives

- Strike (tap)
- Near to
- Around
- Soft
- Hard
- Trap
- Sagittal
- Frontal
- Fast
- Slow
- Acceleration
- Partners
- In front of

### Affective and Social Objectives

- Working within self-space; keeping hands, feet, and objects to yourself
- Respecting general space
- Following directions
- Respecting skill differences and skill levels of peers

### Equipment

- Hula hoops (5-10)
- Poly spots (5-10)
- Cones (5-10)
- Noodle, Pillo Polo, or hockey sticks (one for each child)
- Soft yarn balls (one for each child)
- Plastic pucks
- Plastic Wiffle balls
- Pedometers (one for each child, if desired)

### Warm-Up

1. Students move through the general space while staying in self-space using a variety of locomotor movements.
2. As students move through general space, make the general space smaller so they can really work on moving without collisions.

3. Add moving in different pathways all around the general space.

4. As students move around the general space, they start and stop on your signal.

5. Students move at various speeds as they travel (using a variety of locomotor skills) all around the general space.

6. Students could pretend they have a hockey stick or Pillo Polo stick as they travel.

## Striking in General Space

Children should be able to focus on the manipulative skill of striking as they move throughout all the general space. Although you do not directly focus on self-space, you should expect to see children working (striking) and staying in their own space as they travel.

1. When I say "Go," I want you to find your own self-space on the floor. Walk there and sit down quietly. Go.

2. You will each have a Pillo Polo stick [or noodle or hockey stick] and an object you are going to dribble or strike. When you get your stick, you may stand with it and hold it.

3. Remember our safety rules for using this equipment: Keep the stick at your waist or below and keep two hands on the hockey stick.

4. When I say "Go," show me how you can move around in the general space. Remember, as we move, our self-space goes with us.

5. When I say "Go," I want to see if you can strike your object, keeping it near you as you move slowly around the general space. I want to see you keep the object under control by using short, little taps and keeping it close to you. Go.

Give children a few minutes to practice this skill. You are looking for short, soft taps as children move around the general space. Remind them to stay in their own space as they move. Encourage them to think about moving in different directions and pathways as they dribble.

## Moving Mania

This activity combines the categories of time, pathway, and plane. You want to see if children can use all the general space as they alter their speed and pathway. Planes knowledge can be used by children to make movement decisions such as

how to change their movement mechanics to avoid a defender.

1. Now you are going to travel a little faster, but still keep control as you dribble. When you hear me say "Go," you may start. When you hear the freeze signal, see if you can stop right away. Keep dribbling in your self-space and wait for the "Go" signal to start again.

After children have practiced this for a few minutes, let them choose their speed and pathway.

2. This time when you hear the "Go" signal, decide how you are going to propel your object. Will you go slowly or more quickly? I want you to also think about moving in different pathways and planes. You will hear the "Freeze" signal to stop.

3. Now, let's vary the speed on purpose. As you propel your object, can you show me changes in speed? So, sometimes you will go slowly and sometimes more quickly. Still vary your pathway as well. I am looking for controlled dribbling.

4. Can you discover in which plane your arms will primarily be working to increase or decrease dribbling speed? [Answer: sagittal plane; flexion and extension movements] Can you identify in which plane your arms will typically be moving to dribble sideways for several steps to the left or right? [Answer: frontal plane; abduction and adduction]

You should see children varying speed, pathways, and planes while maintaining control of their objects. You may ask children to change objects.

## Pathway and Object Obstacle Course

Set up hoops, poly spots, and cones around the general space for this activity. Choose equipment you think will be fun! Some of the equipment described in chapter 5 might be fun here! You can set up several courses and divide children into working groups.

1. We have lots of objects set up around the gym. We are all going to dribble our objects around equipment.

2. When you come to a cone, dribble all the way around it and continue on. When you come to a hoop, dribble all the way around it and continue. When you come to a poly spot, stop and dribble in your self-space back and forth five times and continue.

3. Find ways to dribble so you can avoid other people. Remember, no collisions. You will have to think about changing pathways as you move. Go.

After children have demonstrated successful dribbles, changes in pathways, and staying in their own self-space, add the following.

4. Now see if you can think of different ways to move around the equipment. We are working on controlled dribbles using different speeds and different pathways. Go.

## Partner Passing

Decide what type of implement you wish students to use for this game. If you are comfortable with students using Pillo Polo sticks or hockey sticks, this may appropriate. You may also continue to have children use noodles. Children can make decisions about how far apart to stand and how much force to use.

1. Find a partner with whom you can work well and stand beside the partner with your stick and object still. Go.

2. You will only need one object, so decide which object to keep. Please put the other object in the bucket.

3. You and your partner will pass the object back and forth. When we pass, we send an object to a partner or teammate. To do this, will you need light force or medium force? What does it depend on? [The force will vary depending on the distance between partners.]

4. I am looking for successful passes. A successful pass is when your partner sends the object to you and you are able to stop it or collect it to send it back to your partner.

5. At first, when your partner sends you the object, see if you can stop or trap it, dribble two times in your own space, and then send it back to your partner. So, we will have a pass, trap, dribble, and send.

6. Remember all our safety rules about using the stick.

You are looking for successful passes and controlled dribbling. Once children have worked on choosing the amount of force to use, move them so they are both facing the same direction and passing diagonally in front of their partners. If they are having difficulty, have one partner hand roll the object to the receiving partner, who stops, or traps, it.

Reprinted, by permission, from Debbie Rhea.

## LESSON 4

# Hockey Shoot-a-Round
### Elementary or Mature Stages; Grade 3

## Cognitive and Motor Objectives

- Strike (tap)
- Trap
- Fast
- Slow
- Hard
- Soft
- Straight
- Curved
- Zigzag
- Partners
- Near to
- Around
- In front of
- Apply force
- Receive force or weight
- Forward direction
- Acceleration

## Affective and Social Objectives

- Working in self-space
- Respecting general space
- Following directions
- Respecting skill differences and skill levels of peers
- Working with a partner

## Equipment

- Cones (one for each child)
- Pillo Polo or hockey sticks (one for each child)
- Soft yarn balls (one for each child)
- Plastic pucks
- Plastic Wiffle balls
- Pedometers (one for each child, if desired)
- Music and player, if desired

## Warm-Up

1. Students move through the general space while staying in self-space. They should use a variety of locomotor movements.

2. As students move through the general space, make the space smaller so they can really work on moving without collisions.

3. Add moving in different pathways all around the general space.

4. As students move around the general space, they start and stop on your signal.

5. Students move at different speeds as they travel (using a variety of locomotor skills) all around the general space.

6. Students could pretend they have hockey sticks or Pillo Polo sticks as they travel.

## Striking in General Space

You want to see how well children can dribble in general space while maintaining control of the object.

1. When I say "Go," I want you to find your own self-space on the floor. Walk there and sit down quietly. Go.

2. Each of you will get a Pillo Polo stick [or hockey stick] and an object to dribble. When you hear the music begin, show me how you can dribble the object in the general space, changing pathways and speed as you dribble.

3. Keep your object under control and use both sides of your stick.

4. Remember all our safety rules as you travel.

## Partner Passing and Trapping

You may choose to have two children demonstrate this partner task. The movement element this task focuses on is sending the object ahead of, or in front of, the partner. You are looking for successful passes. If it is not possible to set up children facing a wall, they may be scattered throughout the general space. Each pair will have its own working space. Emphasize this working space to the children.

1. Find a partner with whom you can work well and stand beside that person facing the same direction (looking at a wall) with your stick and object still. Go.

2. You will pass the object in front of your partner. Your partner will trap (stop) the object and then send it in front of you.

3. I am looking for successful passes. A successful pass is when you send the object in front of your partner and your partner traps it and sends it back to you.

4. When your partner sends you the object, see if you can stop it, or trap it, dribble two times in your own space, and then send it back to your partner. So, we will have a pass, trap, dribble, and send.

5. Now, you and your partner will get two cones. These will serve as your goal.

6. I want you to repeat the task, passing in front of your partner. But this time, the partner who receives the pass dribbles twice in self-space and then shoots for the goal. Take turns so both of you get to shoot for the goal.

7. What do you have to do to send the object away? What are you thinking about? How about when you receive the object?

8. If you find you are too close to your partner, move back a little bit. If you move back, what else do you have to consider when passing?

Reprinted, by permission, from Debbie Rhea.

## Hockey Shoot-a-Round

Have two partners demonstrate. As children dribble around the general space, watch for good passing (sending away) and collecting (receiving force from the object). If children are moving too fast and not being successful, remind them of what you want to see and ask them to think about what they need to do to adjust their work.

1. We are going to work more on shooting. You and your partner each need a hockey stick [or Pillo Polo stick] and one object.

2. You and your partner will travel around the general space. One partner will dribble three or four times and then pass to the other partner. The partner receiving the pass will trap, dribble three times, and send the object back to the other partner.

3. After each partner has dribbled and passed, the first partner then shoots toward an empty space on the wall, collects the ball, and dribbles and passes again. The second partner will then have an opportunity to shoot the object toward an empty space on the wall.

4. So, we should have: partner 1—dribble, pass to partner 2; partner 2—dribble, pass to partner 1; partner 1—shoot for the wall, collect, dribble, and send to partner 2; partner 2—dribble and pass to partner 1 and then take a turn shooting for the wall and collecting the object. This may be repeated as many times as you feel is necessary for children to be successful.

5. I want to see good dribbling, trapping, and passing and shooting. You may decide how slowly or how quickly to travel. If you travel too fast and cannot control your passing, think about what you might need to do to have better control. Go.

Reprinted, by permission, from Debbie Rhea.

## LESSON 5

# Station Hockey
## Elementary or Mature Stages; Grade 4

### Cognitive and Motor Objectives

- Receive force or weight
- Strike (tap)
- Trap
- Low
- Forward
- Straight
- Curved
- Zigzag
- Sagittal
- Frontal
- Fast
- Slow
- Hard
- Soft
- Acceleration
- Partners
- Near to
- In front of
- Apply force
- Direct
- Individual to group
- Cooperation
- Competition

### Affective and Social Objectives

- Working in self-space
- Respecting general space
- Following directions
- Working with a partner
- Respecting skill differences and skill levels of peers
- Working cooperatively and competitively with a small group

### Equipment

- Hockey sticks (one for each child)
- Soft yarn balls (one for each child)
- Plastic pucks
- Plastic Wiffle balls
- Pedometers (one for each child, if desired)

### Warm-Up

1. Students move through the general space while staying in self-space. They should use a variety of locomotor movements.
2. Add moving in different pathways all around the general space.
3. Students move at various speeds as they travel (using a variety of locomotor skills) all around the general space. Ask them to show you acceleration (change of speed). See if they can show you this both on request and on their own.
4. Students may be given Pillo Polo sticks or hockey sticks to use in the warm-up.

### Instructions

1. We are going to set up three stations in the gym today:
   - Partner passing and trapping
   - Passing and shooting
   - Interception
2. We will rotate from one station to the next. After that you will be allowed to choose the station at which you want to work.

### Station 1: Partner Passing and Trapping

Discuss how to pass on a diagonal (ahead of, or in front of) to the partner in a direct line. A demonstration may be needed. As children dribble around the general space, watch for effective passing (sending away ahead of the receiver) and collecting of the object to redirect it. If children are moving too fast and not being successful, suggest that they slow down and focus on where to direct the pass.

1. At this station you and a partner are going to travel around the general space allotted for this station. One partner will dribble three or four times and then send your pass in a direct line in front of the other partner.
2. The other partner receiving the pass will trap, dribble three times, and send the object back to the other partner.
3. I want to see effective dribbling, trapping, and passing. We are working on sending the object in front of, or ahead of, our partners in a direct line.
4. You may decide how slowly or how quickly to travel. If you travel too fast and cannot control your passing, think about what you might need to do to have better control. Go.

Reprinted, by permission, from Debbie Rhea.

### Station 2: Passing and Shooting

Discuss the differences between passing and shooting. When children are working on passing, they are sending the object in a direct line in front of a teammate. Shooting also uses the direct element, but children are trying to score a goal. As children are working on their two types of passes, you are watching for effective passing. You should see children showing you that they can control the amount of force they place on the object, using more force for longer distances in the drive pass and less force with a quick movement and no backswing on the push pass.

1. At this station you are going to work on types of passes. These same cues can be used when shooting for a goal. Think about using different amounts of force depending on where your partner is located.

2. We are going to practice two types of passes—the drive pass and the push pass.

3. You may choose the object to use—either a plastic puck or a yarn [or fleece] ball.

4. These are the performance cues I want you to think about for each shot:
   - Drive pass: Uses more force and is used for longer distances between partners and for goal shots.
     - Keep your hands together.
     - Don't lift the stick higher than your waist in either direction.
     - Drive passes can be straight, left, or right.
     - Drive passes should be in a direct, penetrating line.
   - Push pass: Used for shorter, more accurate passes.
     - Execute the pass quickly off the dribble; movement is very quick.
     - There should be no backswing.
     - Keep your right hand lower on the stick than your left (the opposite if you are left-handed).
     - Push or sweep the ball along the ground so it is at a low level.

5. At the station, you and your partner need the following: three cones, two yarn [or fleece] balls, and a place near the wall where you can set up your station. You will be practicing the two types of passes, or shots.

6. Find a spot on the wall and set up two cones as the goal. Use the third cone for a starting spot.

7. Take turns facing the wall and practicing the drive shot between the cones from a stationary position (10 shots each).

8. Next, practice the push pass between you from a stationary position (10 passes each).

9. Once you have practiced a bit, we will count the number of passes of both types you can make in 30 seconds.

10. What elements are we working on at this station? I am looking for successful passes and shots. Trap the ball first to redirect it appropriately.

Encourage students to tell you the MEF elements they are focusing on at this station. Responses should include passes executed in a direct line or passes executed quickly at a low level.

## Station 3: Interception

At this station you want to see good teamwork (e.g., partner passing). At station 3, you will be working in a group of three. When you are working at this station, show me how quickly you can form a working group of three. The third person will act as a defender to play against the partners. The defense, or opponent, is a competitor who is trying to collect the object in order to redirect it. However, the intent is for all children in the group to experience both offense and defense (or cooperation and competition) as well as to focus on their passing skills. Encourage children to think about passing in front of their partners and receiving the object to shoot for a goal as well as the amount of force needed for passing successfully. The defensive person should think about watching the hips of the offensive player and the direction of the object being sent. Defensive and offensive movements can be improved with an insightful application of planes. One example of an insightful defensive application includes maximizing the ability to intercept a pass by positioning

their body so that they present themselves with the greatest amount of frontal plane perspective (make yourself wide). This will help to physically block pathways and open spaces. Alternatively, positioning themselves to use sagittal plane movements can help them get more quickly to the open space (e.g., running well is done mostly in the sagittal plane).

1. At this station you will work in groups of three. You will be passing as you did at station 1, but this time one person will try to intercept the puck [or ball] and shoot for a goal.

2. Set up your area with two cones as your goal (for three people in your group). We are working on passing ahead of, or in front of, our partners, and on playing defense. I want to see effective passing and shooting and quick defense. Trade roles so each person has a chance to be the defender. Partners are working on passing ahead, and defenders are working on interception. If you intercept the object, return it to the offense.

Reprinted, by permission, from Debbie Rhea.

## LESSON 6

# Mini Hockey

### Elementary, Mature, or Transitional Stages; Grade 5

### Cognitive and Motor Objectives

- Apply force
- Receive force or weight
- Strike (tap)
- Trap
- Hard
- Soft
- Fast
- Slow
- Acceleration
- Collaboration

- Direct
- Partners
- Individual to group
- Group to group
- Even groups
- Uneven groups
- Cooperation
- Competition
- Indirect

### Affective and Social Objectives

- Working in self-space
- Respecting general space
- Following directions
- Working with a partner
- Repecting skill differences and skill levels of peers
- Working cooperatively, competitively, and collaboratively with a small group
- Working cooperatively and competitively with a small group

### Equipment

- Hockey sticks (one for each child)
- Soft yarn balls (one for each child)
- Plastic pucks
- Plastic Wiffle balls
- Pedometers (one for each child, if desired)

### Warm-Up

1. Students move through the general space while staying in self-space. They should use a variety of locomotor movements.

2. Add moving in different pathways all around the general space.

3. Students move at various speeds as they travel (using a variety of locomotor skills) all around the general space. Ask them to show you acceleration (change of speed). See if they can show you this both on request and on their own.

4. Students may be given hockey sticks to use in the warm-up.

### Passing and Shooting

Bringing in the elements of light and strong force is important when teaching passing and shooting. This activity focuses on these two elements.

1. We are going to work on passing and shooting techniques first. When we pass, we send an object away using medium, light, or strong force depending on where our teammate is.

2. We are going to practice two types of shots, the drive pass and the push pass.

3. For this activity, we will start off using yarn [or fleece] balls, and then we will change to plastic pucks.

4. Before we change to plastic pucks, I want you to think about the amount of force you are using, sending the object in a direct line, and sending the object in front of (ahead of) your partner so your partner can receive the pass.

5. Here are some cues I want you to think about for each shot:

- Drive shot: Uses more force and is used for longer distances between teammates and for goal shots.
  - Keep your hands together.
  - Swing the stick backward and forward in a manner similar to a golf swing.
  - Do not lift the stick higher than your waist in either direction.
  - Drive shots can be straight, left, or right.
  - Drive shots should be in a direct, penetrating line.
- Push pass: Used for shorter, more accurate passes.
  - Execute this pass quick off the dribble; movement is very quick.
  - There should be no backswing.
  - Keep your right hand lower on the stick than your left (the opposite if you are left-handed).
  - Push or sweep the ball along the ground so it is at a low level.

6. Select a partner. You and your partner need two cones, two yarn [or fleece] balls, and a place near the wall where you can set up your station. You will be practicing the two types of shots.

7. Find a spot on the wall and set up your cones as the goal.

8. Take turns facing the wall and practicing the drive pass between the cones (10 shots each).

9. Then practice the push pass between you (10 of each type of pass).

10. Once you have practiced a bit, we will count the number of both types of passes you can make in 30 seconds.

11. I am looking for successful passes. If you need to trap the ball first, do so, in order to redirect it appropriately.

You are looking for children who are using good shooting techniques, adequate force, and direct lines. You may substitute plastic pucks for soft balls when the children are ready.

Reprinted, by permission, from Debbie Rhea.

## Keep Away

Students at the mature and transitional stages (and the older elementary stage) enjoy Keep Away. In this game they need to problem solve what to do to be successful in sending a pass away, receiving a pass, and blocking or intercepting a pass.

1. You will be working in a group of three to play Keep Away. Each group member needs one hockey stick and your group needs one object to strike and two cones. You may choose from the yarn or fleece balls or the plastic pucks.

2. Take turns being the defender. The two partners who are on offense will see if they can complete three successful passes. How can you move to open spaces to receive a pass?

3. Set up cones as if they are a goal but remember, you are only working on passes. Your team will score a point for completion of three successful, unblocked passes, not goals scored.

4. After each attempt of three passes, switch places so there is a new defender.

5. Think about what you have to do to receive the pass from your teammate. Think about what you have to do as the defender to block or intercept the pass.

6. As you are working, your group needs to stay in their own working space.

You are looking for students who are focused on leading the receiver. After students have practiced this, add a goalie to create a group of four and allow children to shoot for a goal. Once they have worked with a goalie for a few minutes, allow them to make up games using these skills. Ask them to identify the MEF elements of their games.

## Ultimate Mini Passing Hockey

Students work in groups of six or eight, depending on the number of students in your class, the working space available, and your thoughts on students' readiness for larger group activity. In this gamelike experience, students are on teams. Each team consists of either two or three people, with one additional person on each team as a goalie (to make teams of three or four). To score points, students must have successful passes. Teams get 1 point for each successful pass and 2 points for each goal scored. Ask students to think about passing ahead of, or in front of, their teammate. Questions to students might include the following:

- Where should your teammate stand so you can successfully pass to him (or her)?
- Should you pass the puck in a direct or indirect line? Which would be most beneficial?

- How much force do you need to put on the puck to send it away to your teammate?
- What if your teammate is far away from you as opposed to near you?

If teams must wait their turns, have students play five-minute rounds and switch teams. Use as much of the general space as possible. Designate working spaces for groups. Students should work in even groups. If the number of students in your class is not even, allow students to work in uneven groups. Make sure you rotate the goalie position so everyone has a chance to be both a player and a goalie.

This game focuses on the elements of in front of and direct; the students are already familiar with passing to a partner and including a defensive person. Allow the activity to flow continuously, but provide feedback as needed to ensure that students are focused on the MEF elements.

Following this activity, you may have students create their own version of Ultimate Hockey. Provide them with MEF elements such as those listed at the beginning of this lesson, and encourage them to create games that includes striking; using force; and passing, trapping, and shooting.

Reprinted, by permission, from Debbie Rhea.

# Teaching Educational Gymnastics

Movement education is about developing the full potential of each child and providing success, enjoyment, and activity in movement. Because we want each child to love physical activity, we promote a perspective that fosters accomplishment by all children. Where does educational gymnastics fit it? How does it differ from traditional gymnastics?

Educational gymnastics originated in England (Logsdon, 1984). The distinction between educational gymnastics and formal gymnastics is that the latter involves stunts, complex routines, and the use of a great deal of apparatus. Morrison (1969) asserted that an important purpose of educational gymnastics is to develop children's movement powers as far as possible. Morrison described educational gymnastics as functional movement, whereas educational dance was described by Morrison as an expressive movement. We focus on educational dance in chapter 13. Functional movement refers to movement that has an external focus and deals with objects and physical tasks. Educational gymnastics emphasizes activities that all children can master such as the following:

- Body shapes
- Balancing tasks
- Tumbling tasks
- Understanding bases of support
- Weight transfer

Although development of movement sequences, movement sentences, and movement routines may be a part of educational gymnastics, children are invited to solve problems and incorporate tasks that are appropriate for their developmental stages. Because children can solve gymnastics movement problems in a variety of ways, all can be successful.

## Motor Learning Applications to Teaching Educational Gymnastics

The contextual interference (blocked and random), variability (schema theory), and part/ whole practice methods of motor learning are used throughout the six lessons in this sample unit. This is a particularly interesting motor learning analysis because it demonstrates the combined use of both part/whole practice and contextual interference methods (see table 12.1).

The segmentation part practice method is used in the first two lessons through a progression of movements that begins with one body part and adds a new body part to each successive activity.

This is helpful to the child because it reduces the number of body parts to concentrate upon in the early activities, making it a safe activity and helping to increase children's confidence and reduce fear. Because of the difficulty of doing inverted balances, lessons 5 and 6 appropriately employ the use of the fractionalization part practice. The first two tasks in lesson 5a help the child adjust to being upside down. The last activity helps the

**Table 12.1**  Motor Learning Application to the Teaching of Educational Gymnastics

| Practice method | Lesson | | | | | | | | |
|---|---|---|---|---|---|---|---|---|---|
| | 1—Body Part Balancing | 2—Rockin' Body Part Balancing | 3—Rock and Roll | 4a—Just Plane Rolling | 4b—Weight Transfer | 5a—Inverted Balances | 5b—Individual and Partner Balances | 6a—Partner Activities | 6b—Balancing on Beam and Benches |
| | Progression → | | | | | | | | |
| Part method | Segmentation | Segmentation | None | None | None | Fractionalization | | Fractionalization | |
| Blocked method examples | Balancing | Balancing | Rocking | None | Roll and travel; steplike | None | | None | |
| Blocked method emphasis | High | High | Low (at the beginning of the lesson) | None | Medium | None | | None | |
| Random method examples | None | None | Different types of body rolling | Different types of body rolling | None | None | | None | |
| Random method emphasis | None | None | Low (last in lesson) | Medium (throughout lesson) | None | None | | None | |
| Variable method examples | Change of base of support and levels | Change of base of support and levels | Different body parts, directions, and speeds | Changes in tension, directions, speeds, extensions, levels, and planes | Changes in speed, extensions, levels, and free leg movements | None | | None | |
| Variable method emphasis | Low | Low | Medium | High | High | None | | None | |

child focus on separate parts of the body: head, hip, and knee. In activity 6, inverted balances are continued, working on a wide range of separate pieces of balancing tasks.

There is a simultaneous use of contextual interference and part practice in lessons 1 and 2. Both lessons 1 and 2 have a high emphasis on balance (blocked practice) and add a low emphasis on variable practice by asking students to change their base of support and levels. Lesson 3 begins with blocked and variable practice (rocking on different body parts in different directions and at different speeds) and then at the very end of the lesson moves to random practice (different types of body rolls). Lesson 4 continues the progression of using different types of body rolling (random) and advances to variable practice by adding tension and changes in directions, speeds, extensions, and levels.

# Educational Gymnastics Lessons

Educational gymnastics may be an area in which teachers do not feel confident or comfortable. You might be saying, "I was not a gymnast; I can't do all of these skills, stunts, and tricks." Relax. Using the critical movement elements your children have already learned and adding such elements as weight transfer, receiving force or weight, applying force in actions of body parts, steplike actions, and springlike actions, and many of the elements under the position and timing categories will result in many fun activities for the children in your classes.

Often, tasks in educational gymnastics focus on weight transference, rocking, rolling, jumping and landing, and balancing. The lessons presented in this chapter combine these skills. Like the lessons in chapter 11, each lesson is progressive, both within and between lessons, and presents typical developmental stages. These stages were presented in chapter 3 and a review of table 3.1 might be helpful. The developmental stages presented are only a general guide; a better way to match a lesson topic to a group of children would be to use a developmental analysis to determine their actual stages. Review the lessons and adapt them as needed according to the developmental stage of your students.

## LESSON 1

# Body Part Balance
## Initial and Elementary Stages; Grade K

### Cognitive and Motor Objectives
- Body parts
- Balancing
- Low
- Medium
- High
- Sagittal
- Frontal
- Transverse

### Affective and Social Objectives
- Respecting self-space
- Respecting general space
- Following directions
- Respecting skill differences and skill levels of peers

### Equipment
- Hula hoops (one for each child)
- Music, if desired
- Pedometers (one for each child, if desired)

### Warm-Up
1. Students travel all around the general space using locomotor movements without collisions. (Use music.)
2. Students start and stop on your signal, making balanced shapes when they stop. Focus students' attention on being balanced, or on balance.
3. Students travel all around the general space, making balanced shapes when they stop. Students stay inside the general space designated.
4. Students make balanced shapes demonstrating wide and narrow shapes.
5. Students travel at different speeds while they move around the general space.
6. As students stop and make balanced shapes, encourage them to move smoothly from one shape to the next.

## Body Part Base (of Support)

You want to see if students can demonstrate their understanding of balancing on different bases of support. You may choose the number of body parts students can use, or have them choose. This can be both a teacher- and student-directed activity.

1. As you stand or sit inside your hoop [self-space], I am going to see if you can show me these different movement combinations:
   - One body part inside your hoop and one body part outside your hoop
   - Two body parts inside your hoop and one body part outside your hoop
   - One body part inside your hoop and two body parts outside your hoop
   - Three body parts inside your hoop and one body part outside your hoop
2. As you make these balances inside and outside of your hoop, sometimes your feet and hands will be close together. This is a narrow base of support. Sometimes your feet and hands will be farther apart. This is a wide base of support. Which one makes it easier to hold your balanced shape? Why?
3. Now, see if you can create your own examples. Show me some body parts inside your hoop and some body parts outside your hoop. Think of two examples and practice these examples.
4. Can you use both a wide base of support and a narrow base of support? We are working on having you solve the movement problem of using different bases of support to create balances.

Give the students two minutes to practice their examples, and then ask them to sit inside their hoops and show you they are ready to listen. Ask some students to show their examples. You may choose to have half the class show their examples and the other half to watch, and then switch places.

### Variation

You can create a list of different numbers of body parts, in addition to those listed above, for students to place both inside and outside of the hula hoop. You might use large and small body parts or have the students create their own movement combinations. You may ask students to make number shapes out of their bodies. Can they hold the number very still? They can then move to making letters with their bodies. For children at a lower developmental stage, choose numbers and letters that are easy to make. For example, you may ask two children to work together to create letters and numbers with their bodies. Ask children if they can show you how they can create the number 4. What type of shape are they making? What about the number 6? The same process may be done with letters. See if children can show you the letter I. What about the letter V? This wonderful activity combines both the literacy focus (number and letter awareness and recognition) and movement elements.

## Body Shapes and Base of Support Balancing

This activity helps children distinguish between being balanced and being unbalanced. Ask children to identify which plane their movements are in and then ask them if their movements match the plane in which the equipment is positioned. Does this help to increase or decrease balance? Have them count "one-thousand-one planes, one-thousand-two planes" and so on to help be objective about their discovery. See if they can describe this prior to demonstrating.

1. In your own self-space, show me how you can make a shape and hold it very still. Right now you are on balance. What is your base of support? [Students might answer feet, knees, hands.] Can you relate the planes to body shapes? [Make sure that they do all body shapes facing the same direction.] Compare a narrow and a wide shape. Which plane does each move in? [Typical answer is that narrow is in sagittal and wide is in frontal.] Relate these shapes and planes to whether they help you balance or make you more unbalanced. Make a body shape which places different parts of your body in the sagital plane. Find a different base of support for each plane.
2. See how many different body shapes, or balanced shapes, you can make using the number of body parts I call out.
   - Four parts
   - Three parts
   - Five parts
   - Two parts

3. Show me how you can change your balanced shape and make a new shape. Find a different base of support for your balanced shape. Decide how many body parts you will use as your base of support.

4. Show me your three best shapes after you have practiced them for a few minutes. Work on making smooth transitions between balanced shapes.

## Balanced Shapes at Various Levels

Combining balancing with other elements such as levels brings together movement content for children.

1. Do you remember what we learned about different levels? [Review for children high, medium, and low levels.] We are going to practice making balanced shapes (staying on balance) at different levels. Can you show me a balanced shape at a low level? Hold it very still for a count of three bananas (or cherries). Now, change your balanced shape at a low level. Make a new one.

2. OK, let's try at a medium level. This is easier. Make a different balanced shape at a medium level.

3. Now, I want you to try a high-level balanced shape. I am looking for really still, balanced shapes. Can you make your shape very distinct and still?

4. I would like you to try to make three shapes in a row and make each very still and distinct. See if you can hold each shape for three cherries (seconds) and then change to the new shape. Let's try together first. Everyone make a balanced shape, in your own space, at a low level. Go. [Count for the children one cherry, two cherries, three cherries.]

5. Now, change to a medium-level balanced shape. Go. [Again, count for the children to help them hold for a count of 3.]

6. Finally, show me your balanced shape at a high level. [Once again, provide the count cue.]

7. I want to see now if you can make your three shapes on your own. When I say "Go," show me your low level, hold it still for a count of 3, change to your medium level, again, holding it still, and then to your high level, keeping that shape still for a count of 3. Ready, go.

## Balancing Activities Combined With Traveling

A nice progression is to include traveling once students have worked on and solved movement problems in a static environment.

1. I am going to put on some music now. When you hear the music, begin traveling all around the general space. Remember, when you travel, stay on your feet and in your own self-space.

2. When the music stops, I want you to stop and make a shape with your body. This time, see if you can become still very quickly as soon as the music stops. I want to see a really clear body shape.

3. After you have held your shape for three counts, change your shape. So, each time you stop, you should make two really clear and different body shapes. I am looking to see if you can stop quickly when the music stops and then make a really clear shape and hold that shape.

Repeat this activity, encouraging children to change their body shapes each time. Ask them to think about different levels as they stop and make their shapes. Reinforce those who are holding their shapes very still.

## LESSON 2

# Rockin' Body Part Balance
### Initial and Elementary Stages; Grade 1

This lesson may be divided into 2A and 2B.

## Cognitive and Motor Objectives

- Body parts
- Balance
- Low
- Medium
- High
- Free
- Partner

## Affective and Social Objectives

- Respecting self-space
- Respecting general space
- Following directions
- Respecting skill differences and skill levels of peers
- Working with a partner

## Equipment

- Hula hoops (one for each child)
- Music, if desired
- Pedometers (one for each child, if desired)

## Warm-Up

1. Students travel all around the general space using locomotor movements without collisions. (Use music.)
2. Students start and stop on your signal, making balanced shapes when they stop. Focus their attention on being balanced.
3. Students travel all around the general space, making balanced shapes when they stop. Students must stay inside the big line around the gym. (You can use cones and ask students to focus on the general space you have said is their working space.)
4. Students make balanced shapes showing you wide and narrow shapes.
5. Students travel at various speeds while they move around the general space.
6. As students stop and make balanced shapes, encourage them to move smoothly from one shape to the next.

## Body Part Balancing

In this activity, students create balanced shapes and hold them. Remember to use a problem-solving perspective.

1. In your own self-space, show me how you can make a shape and hold it very still.
2. Right now you are on balance. What is your base of support? [Students might answer feet, knees, hands.]
3. See how many different body shapes, or balanced shapes, you can make using the number of body parts I call out.
   - Four parts
   - Three parts
   - Five parts
   - Two parts
4. Show me how you can change your balanced shape and make a new shape.
5. Find a different base of support for your balanced shape. How many body parts can you use as your base of support?

6. Show me your three best shapes after you have practiced them for a few minutes. See if you can make your transitions very smooth.

## Variation

You may choose to have children work in hula hoops to denote their self-space.

## Balanced Shapes at Different Levels

You are looking for students who can show you both balancing and levels. See if they can combine the various movement elements they have learned.

1. Do you remember what we learned about various levels? [Review for the children high, medium, and low levels.] We are going to practice making balanced shapes (staying on balance) at different levels.
2. Can you show me a balanced shape at a low level? Hold it very still for a count of three bananas.
3. Now, make a new balanced shape at a low level.
4. OK, let's try at a medium level. This is easier.
5. Make a different balanced shape at a medium level.
6. Now, I want you to try a high-level balanced shape. I am looking for really still balanced shapes. Can you make your shape very clear and still?
7. Try to make three shapes in a row and make each one very still and clear. See if you can hold each shape for three cherries [seconds] and then change to the new shape.
8. Let's try together first. Make a balanced shape in your own space at a low level. Go. [Count for the children one cherry, two cherries, three cherries.]
9. Now, change to a medium-level balanced shape. Go. [Again, count for the children to help them hold for a count of 3.]

10. Finally, show me your balanced shape at a high level. [Once again, provide the count cue.]

11. Now I want to see if you can make three shapes on your own. When I say "Go," show me your low level, hold it still for a count of 3, change to your medium level, again, holding it still, and then to your high level, keeping that shape still for a count of 3. Ready, go.

## "Copy That" With Balanced Shapes

As students play Copy That, you want to see if they can create balanced shapes that include the use of levels. Encourage them to hold the shapes for a count of 3.

1. When I say "Go," I want you to find a partner and stand beside that partner. Choose someone with whom you can really work well. Go.

2. Now that you have found your partner, we are going to play Copy That. The partner who is taller will go first. That partner makes a balanced shape at either a medium, low, or high level. Make sure to hold that balanced shape for a count of three cherries.

3. The other partner will then copy that shape. Each partner has three turns to choose the shape first, and then you switch places.

4. I am looking for good balances, holding each for a count of 3, and for good copying of shapes. Go.

If you have already worked on partners as listed in the Critical Element section, on page 28, children should easily be able to find a partner. If not, discuss how to find and work with a partner at this point. Some teachers count to 5 if children are having trouble choosing partners.

MMSD Elementary School Physical Education Curriculum Committee, A Guide to Curriculum Planning in Elementary School Physical Education, 1986, updated 1991 (Madison, WI: Madison Metropolitan School District).

## Weight Transfer

You are looking for students to create various ways to transfer weight to adjacent body parts. See what students can create.

1. You did a great job with Copy That. We will play again in a few minutes with our new skill.

2. I want you to find your own self-space again. Show me how quickly and quietly you can do that. Go.

3. Now, when I say "Go," I want you to stay in your self-space and find different ways to rock your weight back and forth on body parts that are next to each other.

4. See if you can lie on your back and shift your body weight up and down your spine. Can you do a bigger rock if you stretch out your arms and legs or if you are in a curled shape? Why?

5. See how many ways you can rock on your tummy. Can you make your rocking smooth without any stops? What if you hold on to your ankles with your hands? Can you do this? Which is easier—rocking on your front or your back?

6. Make sure every part of your body is touching the floor when you rock.

7. Now, I want you to think of the three best rocks you have done and practice those. Show me your three best rocking motions.

## Movement Sequence: Weight Transfer—Rocking

Have half of the class be the audience and the other half perform their movements or sequences. You are looking for three good rocking motions. Before the demonstrations, tell students what to watch for—for example: "Watch for rocks on body parts that are next to each other. Do you see anyone rocking back and forth on their spine? How about on their belly? Do you see anyone holding a body part while they rock?"

1. Choose your three best rocks. We are going to put these into a movement sequence. You will do these three in a row.

2. Half of the class will watch first, and then they will get to show their rocks.

3. See if you can do your three rocks so we can really see how they are different and distinct.

4. Choose a starting position and then show your three rocks.

## LESSON 3

# Rock and Roll

### Initial, Elementary, and Mature Stages; Grade 2

## Cognitive and Motor Objectives

- Body parts
- Balance
- Rock
- Low
- Medium
- High levels
- Free
- Weight transfer
- Roll
- Fast
- Forward
- Backward
- Sideways
- Slow
- Acceleration
- Strong

## Affective and Social Objectives

- Respecting self-space
- Respecting general space
- Following directions
- Respecting skill differences and skill levels of peers

## Equipment

- Mats (one for every two children)
- Music, if desired
- Pedometers (one for each child, if desired)

## Warm-Up

1. Students travel all around the general space using locomotor movements without collisions. (Use music.)
2. Students start and stop on your signal, making balanced shapes when they stop. Focus their attention on being balanced, or on balance.
3. Students travel all around the general space, making balanced shapes when they stop. Students must stay inside the big line around the gym.
4. Students make balanced shapes, demonstrating wide and narrow shapes.
5. Students travel at various speeds while they move around the general space.
6. As students stop and make balanced shapes, encourage them to move smoothly from one shape to the next.

## Weight Transfer

Students are working on demonstrating weight transference along adjacent body parts.

1. I want you to find your own self-space on one of the mats you see around the gym. You will share a mat with one other person, so you each have your own space on the mat. Show me how quickly and quietly you can do that. Go.
2. Now, when I say "Go," I want you to stay in your self-space and find different ways to rock your weight back and forth on body parts that are next to each other. Remember, rocking is moving back and forth along body parts that are adjacent, or next to each other.

Remind children about self-space. Give them a few minutes to explore various ways to transfer weight. They might transfer weight from one foot to the other and back to two feet; shift weight from different positions (lying faceup, lying facedown). They may also use both hands and feet.

3. See if you can lie on your back and shift your body weight up and down your spine. Can you do a bigger rock if you stretch out your arms and legs or if you curl your body?
4. See how many ways you can rock on your tummy. Can you make your rocking smooth without any stops? What if you hold on to your ankles with your hands? Can you do this?
5. Which is easier—rocking on your front or rocking on your back? Make sure every part of your body is touching the floor when you rock.
6. Now, I want you to think of the three best rocks you have done and practice those. Show me your three best rocking motions.

## Weight Transfer: Changing Direction and Speed

As students work on weight transfer with rocking, encourage them to add changes in direction and speed. Can they rock slowly as well as more quickly?

1. While you are still in your own self-space, can you change direction while you rock on your back? Can you go from side to side? How about forward and backward?
2. Now, see if you can change speed—moving slowly and then more quickly.

3. I have a challenge for you. See if you can rock hard enough while on your back to shift your weight onto your feet.

## Weight Transfer: Changing a Rock Into a Roll

A logical progression is changing the rock into a roll. Students are still working on weight transference; however, with greater momentum, they are now changing this rock into a roll.

1. When we change a rock into a roll, we have to keep the momentum going in the same direction. We are going to do log rolls, turtle rolls, shoulder rolls, and forward and backward rolls. You may choose the ones you feel most comfortable doing. First, let's practice changing a rock into a roll.

As you introduce each roll, provide appropriate movement learning cues. You may choose to have a child demonstrate each roll, to do it yourself, or to show pictures. Keep in mind that children demonstrate rolls differently. Provide feedback that encourages safety and success. Children should only try the rolls they feel most comfortable doing.

2. Charles is going to demonstrate for us. He is going to rock from side to side on his front in a stretched-out position. We turn this into a roll by keeping the movement going in one direction. This is a log roll.

3. When you practice the log roll, think about really keeping a long, stretched shape. Is Charles' body really loose or tight? We need to use muscle tension to keep our bodies nice and long.

4. Now, when you are ready, find a place on your mat and try a log roll. Each person takes half of the mat. Right now, we will be rolling slowly so we stay on our mats. Go.

5. Now, see if you can show me three really good, stretched log rolls on your mat. If you do not want to try three, show me one log roll.

As children are working on the log rolls, walk around and provide positive feedback. Comment on their long, stretched shapes and strong muscle tension.

6. The next roll we are going to learn is a turtle roll. How do you think turtles might roll? They would get into their shells and curl up in a tight ball, right?

7. What type of directions might we see? Turtles might roll in a variety of directions, sideways, sort of forward, and sort of backward.

8. Find your own space on your end of the mat and see if you can show me a tight turtle shape.

9. Now, remember, when we change a rock into a roll, we have to keep our momentum going in one direction. Decide how your turtle is going to roll.

10. Let's try it. Show me two turtle rolls. Go.

Make sure students are keeping tight, curled shapes as they roll. They should not be doing forward rolls, but rolling sideways left, sideways right, and at angles in a sideways direction. Walk around and give positive feedback on their tight turtle rolls.

11. Find your own working space on your mat again. Now, we are going to think about rolling in a forward direction. When you do this, we need to think about keeping a tight, curled shape.

12. We will start by squatting down on the mat in a round shape and really keeping our chins tucked to our chests.

13. Put your hands on the floor just in front of your feet with your chin tucked to your chest. Lift your hips up and look between your legs. Keep looking, but remember to keep your chin tucked as you look.

14. We will transfer our weight from our feet to hands to one shoulder and roll out on that shoulder. This is a shoulder roll.

15. What are the important parts of the shoulder roll?

   a. Tight, round shape, really tucking in your chin

   b. Squatting down in a curled position with your hands on the floor

   c. Lifting your hips and looking between your legs (using your hands to help you lift up)

   d. Transferring your weight from your feet to your hands to your shoulder

You may choose to have a child demonstrate the shoulder roll.

16. Now, this time you have some choices. You may practice your log roll, turtle roll, or

shoulder roll. See if you can do three rolls really well. I will come around and see how you are doing. I want to see three of your very best rolls. Go.

## Movement Sequence: Rolling

In this activity students develop a movement sequence using the element of rolling. You want to ensure that they are comfortable with the type of roll they choose. Whatever roll they choose, they should be able to complete it using appropriate and safe form, and without assistance. Allow children to choose how they wish to roll. You are looking for three smooth rolls.

1. In your self-space, see if you can create a movement sequence that has three rolls. You can choose any of the rolls we have worked on so far. I want to see smooth transitions between rolls.

2. Once you have practiced for a couple of minutes, you will show your movement sequence to the class. A movement sequence has a definite beginning, a definite middle, and a definite ending.

3. Can you create a movement sequence with three rolls in it? What kind of transition can you do between rolls? Can you walk, skip, or hop? Can you travel slowly?

Once the children have practiced their movement sequence rolls, have half of the class demonstrate their sequences. Because some children may not be comfortable demonstrating their movement sequences, have those who want to demonstrate move to the front of their mats. Those who stay near the back of the mats are not required to demonstrate their movement sequences.

## LESSON 4A

# Just Plane Rolling
### Elementary and Mature Stages; Grade 3

## Cognitive and Motor Objectives

- Rock
- Roll
- Weight transfer
- Sagittal
- Frontal
- Transverse
- Strong
- Stretch
- Narrow
- Round
- Curl
- Forward

## Affective and Social Objectives

- Respecting self-space
- Respecting general space
- Following directions
- Respecting skill differences and skill levels of peers

## Equipment

- Mats (one for every two children)
- Music, if desired

## Warm-Ups

1. Students travel around the gym looking for open mats. As they come to open mats, they stop and make balanced shapes on the mats (holding the shape for a count of 3) and continue on. You can use music for this warm-up.

2. As students practice making shapes on mats, ask them to think about using strong muscle tension so their shapes are really strong.

3. Traveling actions should include the steplike actions of walking, bear walking, and crab walking, and a variety of springlike actions.

4. Students travel around the gym using a variety of steplike and springlike actions. As they travel, have them vary their speed and range (sometimes traveling slowly, sometimes more quickly). Have them vary the size of their steps. Can they take small steps as well as larger ones?

5. As students travel around the gym using a combination of steplike actions and springlike actions, on your signal, have them find partners and make shapes that show counterbalance and countertension. You may also have them make symmetrical and asymmetrical balanced shapes.

6. As students travel around the gym using a combination of steplike actions and springlike actions, see if they can stop on your signal and make three different balanced shapes. Use the term *smooth transition* so they will become familiar with making smooth transitions between balanced shapes.

## Weight Transfer: Rolling

Introduce each station and provide appropriate movement learning cues. You may choose to have a child demonstrate each roll, to do it yourself, or to show pictures. Keep in mind that children demonstrate rolls differently. Relate the transfer of weight for three different types of rolls to planes. Provide feedback that encourages safety and success. Also, encourage children to try the rolls they feel most comfortable doing and to choose stations as they are ready. The number of children at each station should be limited. You may choose to assign children to stations, if needed.

For stations 2 and 3, give the children choices so they all feel comfortable transferring weight using rolling. Children should be allowed to choose the type of rolling they practice. Encourage them to create different types of rolls in a forward direction, if they choose to do so. Some may want to try the shoulder or forward roll as presented, whereas others may not feel comfortable doing so. Children who are ready may try both. It is important to stress safety because children who are not ready may roll on their heads and not on the shoulders.

## Station 1: Rolling Around—Log (Pencil) Rolls

As children are working on log rolls, walk around and provide positive feedback. Comment on their long, stretched shapes and strong muscle tension. Encourage those whose muscle tension is not tight to think about using strong muscle tension.

1. At this station, you will work on log rolls, or pencil rolls. Roll slowly so you can stay in control. Maria is going to demonstrate a log, or pencil, roll for us.

2. When you practice this roll, think about really keeping a long, stretched shape. What plane are you moving in if you do a log roll? [Transverse] Is Maria's body really loose or tight? We need to use muscle tension to keep our bodies nice and stretched.

3. See if you can show three good stretched log, or pencil, rolls.

## Station 2: Rolling Sideways—Shoulder Roll

1. At this station, you will work on rolling in a forward direction. When you do this, you need to think about keeping a tight, curled shape. What plane are you moving in if you do a shoulder roll? [Frontal] If you are ready to try this, you may.

2. If you prefer, you may continue to practice log or pencil rolls.

3. You may also choose to create a different roll in a forward direction. See what types of rolls in a forward direction you can create.

4. Start by squatting down on the mat in a curled shape and really keeping your chin tucked to your chest. Put your hands on the floor just in front of your feet (with your chin tucked to your chest). Lift your hips up and look between your legs. Keep looking (but remember to keep your chin tucked as you look).

5. Now transfer your weight from your feet to your hands to one shoulder, and roll out on that shoulder. This is a shoulder roll.

6. Try the shoulder roll three times. See if on the last time you can come back to your feet.

7. What were the important parts of the shoulder roll?
   a. Tight, round shape, really tucking your chin
   b. Squatting down in a curled position with your hands on the floor
   c. Lifting your hips and looking between your legs (using your hands to help you lift up)
   d. Transferring your weight from your feet to your hands to your shoulder

## Station 3: Rolling Forward—Forward Roll

You may choose to have a child demonstrate rolling in a forward direction. As you walk around, make certain that students are rolling on the backs of their shoulders and not on their heads. Look for tight, curled rolls with tucked chins.

1. At station 3, you will work on rolling forward by transferring your weight from your feet to your hands to the back of your shoulders and then rolling. It is just like the shoulder roll we just worked on, but instead of rolling on one shoulder, you will roll onto the back of your shoulders (not your head) as you roll forward. What plane are you moving in if you

do a forward roll? [Sagittal] If you are ready to try this, you may.

2. If you prefer, you may continue to work on creating rolls of your choice in a forward direction.

3. If you choose to try this roll, here are the important cues:
   a. Tight, curled shape, really tucking your chin
   b. Squatting down in a curled position with your hands on the floor
   c. Lifting up your hips and looking between your legs (using your hands to help lift you up)
   d. Transferring your weight from your feet to your hands to the back of your shoulders as you roll over

## LESSON 4B

# Weight Transfer: Creating a Movement Sequence
## Elementary and Mature Stages; Grade 3

### Cognitive and Motor Objectives
- Weight transfer
- Roll
- Low
- Medium
- High
- Small
- Large
- Fast
- Slow
- Movement sequence

### Affective and Social Objectives
- Respecting skill differences and skill levels of peers

### Equipment
- Mats (one for every two children)
- Music, if desired
- Pedometers (one for each child, if desired)

### Warm-Ups
1. Students travel around the gym looking for open mats. As they come to open mats, they stop and make balanced shapes on the mats (holding the shapes for a count of 3) and continue on. You can use music for this warm-up.

2. As students practice making shapes on the mats, ask them to think about using strong muscle tension so the shapes are really strong.

3. Traveling actions should include the steplike actions of walking, bear walking, and crab walking, and a variety of springlike actions.

4. Students travel around the gym using a variety of steplike and springlike actions. As they travel, have them vary their speed and range or extension (sometimes traveling slowly, sometimes more quickly). Have them vary the size of their steps. Can they take small steps as well as larger ones?

5. As students travel around the gym using a combination of steplike actions and springlike actions, on your signal, have them find partners and make shapes that show counterbalance and countertension. You may also have them make symmetrical and asymmetrical balanced shapes.

6. As students travel around the gym using a combination of steplike actions and springlike actions, see if they can stop on signal and make three different balanced shapes. Use the term *smooth transition* so they will become familiar with making smooth transitions between balanced shapes.

### Weight Transfer (Rolling) With a Movement Sequence

It is important that students make smooth transitions from one movement to another as they work on their sequences. You are looking for students to solve this movement problem in a variety of ways. Have them show you their best movement sequences. Watch for children who are able to put a movement sequence together. Children should choose the difficulty level of roll with which they are comfortable.

1. We have worked on a variety of rolls so far—log, or pencil, roll; shoulder roll; turtle roll; and forward roll. Now we are going to work on making a movement sequence with our rolls. You can choose any rolls you wish. You can even repeat a type of roll. That is OK.

2. I want you to think about doing three rolls with traveling in between. So, you will do a roll, travel with steplike or springlike actions, do a second roll, do additional traveling, and then do a third roll.

3. Your steplike action would be walking, bear walking, or crab walking. You may choose your springlike action.

4. You can use all the space for traveling. If you come to an open mat, that is where you do your roll. If someone is on the mat, keep going and look for an open mat. You will travel and do all your rolls on an open mat.

## Weight Transfer: Steplike Actions

Allow children to choose the level (low, medium, or high) at which to demonstrate their weight transfer.

1. We are going to work on transferring our weight from two feet, to two hands, and back to two feet.

2. First, let's do this in a stationary position. In your self-space on the mat, see if you can transfer your weight from feet to hands and back to feet. You can decide how to transfer your weight.

3. When I say "Go," I want you to move into all the general space by shifting your weight from two feet to two hands as you move. Can you feel your weight shift from your feet to your hands and back again?

4. Remember, as you take weight on your hands, arch your head slightly backward. This will help you keep your balance.

5. Also, think about staying in your self-space. You will use all the general space as you practice. Go.

Allow students to try this for a couple of minutes, and then add the following:

6. As you travel now, see if you can move at different speeds, sometimes faster and sometimes slower.

7. Think about changing the range, or size, of your steps. Sometimes, I want you to make big steps and sometimes small ones. Which are easier to do? [They should say that small steps are easier because they do not have to shift their weight so far to stay balanced.] It should be easiest to balance on your hands when they are about shoulder-width apart.

8. Now, everyone stop and freeze in your own working space and show me you are listening.

9. I want to see if you can transfer your weight from one foot to two hands. We are going to do this without traveling. Put all your weight

on that one foot before you put your hands down again.

10. After you have practiced this for a couple of minutes, think what you can do with the leg that is not taking the weight. Is this leg at a low, medium, or high level? Can you stretch this leg out? Can you curl it? Can you kick this leg into the air? Can you kick it so that the balancing foot comes off the floor?

11. Now transfer your weight to the other leg.

Allow students to practice this for a couple of minutes, and then add the following.

12. Let's practice all the weight transfers using steplike actions we have learned so far. I am looking for the following:
    • Weight shifting from feet to hands and back to feet
    • Small extensions (ranges) of your hands and feet (with hands about shoulder-width apart so you have a more stable balance)
    • Transferring weight from one foot to two hands
    • Transferring weight using two hands and one foot with the free foot (leg) moving at different levels and coming off the mat or floor

13. Practice for a couple of minutes and then show me three of your best weight transfers using steplike actions. You may choose how you want to transfer your weight. Go.

As you walk around, make sure students are transferring weight using both two feet and one hand and one foot and two hands. You are also looking for students lifting their free legs at various levels.

## LESSON 5A

# Inverted Balances
### Elementary, Mature, and Transitional Stages; Grade 4

## Cognitive and Motor Objectives
- Balance
- Low
- Medium
- High
- Fast
- Slow
- Above
- Below
- Inverted

## Affective and Social Objectives

- Respecting skill differences and skill levels of peers

## Equipment

- Mats (one for every two children)
- Music, if desired
- Pedometers (one for each child, if desired)

## Warm-Ups

1. Students travel around the gym looking for open mats. As they come to open mats, they stop and make balanced shapes on the mats (holding the shapes for a count of 3) and continue on. You can use music for this warm-up.

2. As students practice making shapes on mats, ask them to think about using strong muscle tension so the shapes are really strong.

3. Traveling actions should include steplike actions of walking, bear walking, and crab walking, and a variety of springlike actions.

4. Students travel around the gym using a variety of steplike and springlike actions. As they travel, have them vary their speed and range (sometimes traveling slowly, sometimes more quickly). Have them vary the size of their steps. Can they take small steps as well as larger ones?

5. As students travel around the gym using a combination of steplike actions and springlike actions, on your signal, have them find partners and make shapes that show counterbalance and countertension. You may also have them make symmetrical and asymmetrical balanced shapes.

6. As students travel around the gym using a combination of steplike actions and springlike actions, see if they can stop on your signal and make three different balanced shapes. Use the term *smooth transition* so they will become familiar with making smooth transitions between balanced shapes.

## Weight Transfer (Steplike Actions): Inverted Agility

This activity is an additional step in weight transference. Students work on steplike actions as well as inverted agility.

1. We have been working on transferring weight from feet, to hands, and back to feet. Today, I have some new challenges for you.

2. When I say "Go," I want you to find your working space on the floor. You are going to put your hands down about shoulder-width apart and keep them there.

3. See if you can find different things to do with your feet. For example, can you take them for a walk around your body? Can you jump them together so they land in a new place each time?

4. Now, find your balanced position with two hands and one leg. Lift your free leg off the floor [or mat]. Can you kick the free leg to a high level and quickly switch legs so that the other leg is up and the first leg is down?

5. As you practice this for a couple of minutes, think about changing legs slowly, then more quickly. You can decide what level you are going to kick your free leg. Can you kick your legs from side to side?

## Weight Transfer: Inverted Balances I

Inverted balances are a step beyond inverted agility. Allow your students to participate at the difficulty level with which they are most comfortable. Some may choose a low level (easier) over a medium level (more difficult). Student participation and activity is the key.

1. We are going to try something really fun. I want you to start in a standing position. You are going to transfer weight onto your hands and one foot from a standing position.

2. Put one foot in front of the other and bend your knee to lean out over your lead foot. See if you can stretch your arms out and reach down to the mat.

3. Transfer your weight onto your hands and one foot and kick the other leg up to a medium level. See if you can come back to the same starting position.

4. How high can you kick your back leg? Practice this for a couple of minutes on your part of the mat.

5. We are going to let our legs switch places. Everyone stand on your mat. All our skills start with standing.

6. Step forward on one foot and lean down so you are taking weight onto your hands. Keep your arms straight and strong, with good muscle tension, as you take the weight onto your hands.

7. As you lean down and take the weight, kick your rear leg up into the air behind you so that the other leg comes off the mat. Quickly bring the high leg down to the mat for support with your hands as the other leg switches places with it. Your legs are switching places! As you try this, think about the following:

   a. Leaning down onto your arms (strong tension)

   b. Kicking your rear leg up behind you

   c. Your trailing leg coming off the mat

   d. Your high leg coming down

   e. Your legs switching places

8. After you have tried this, see if you can do this with bent knees. You decide at what level you want to kick—low, medium, or high. Practice the leg switch for a few minutes.

As you walk around, make sure children are using strong muscle tension and switching legs. Allow children to decide at what level they are comfortable kicking. You may ask them to switch legs and come down at different places. Can they bring their legs down to one side? As you walk around, look for strong arms (muscle tension) and their bodies turning into the lean.

## Weight Transfer: Inverted Balances II

The following balances can be done in a station format, if desired. Students can rotate from one station to the next or choose the station with which they feel most comfortable.

1. We are going to use our mats and try some inverted balances.

2. By the way, what does *inverted* mean? Right, it means upside down with some body parts above and some below. Those words were on our chart today.

3. You have four tasks to choose from. It is OK to try all four or only one or two. You decide when you are ready to try each one.

You may have a child demonstrate each of the four options as you provide learning cues. Allow children to choose the one(s) with which they feel most comfortable. After each one, review the cues and add the options that follow. You are looking for strong balanced shapes. Allow children to practice each after you have introduced them. They may choose to practice only the first one or may choose to practice all four.

## Station 1: Head Balance

The first task is called a head balance. It is a five-part balance.

1. Place your head on the mat (with your hairline touching first).

2. Raise your hips and make your legs straight.

3. Balance on your head, toes, and hands.

4. If you want, try to raise one arm off the mat.

5. If you want, you can make this a three-part balance by raising both arms and making them straight too.

## Station 2: Hip and Hand Balance

1. This is called a hip and hand balance. I want to see if you can find a variety of ways to keep both hands on the floor and to get one or two feet above, or higher than, your head.

2. What do you need to do to keep your weight on your hands, even for a second? [Transfer body weight onto your hands.] What are some ways to take weight onto your hands while getting your hips high? Where do you need to place your hands? Can you move smoothly from one balance to another?

3. Think of three ways to take weight onto your hands while lifting your hips high. Show me smooth, strong balances.

## Station 3: Knee and Elbow Balance

The next task is called a knee and elbow balance. This is a four-part balance. Think about tight elbows next to your body.

1. Sit on your heels with your hands beside your knees.

2. Keep your hands beside your knees.

3. Bend forward placing the hairline of your head on the mat.

4. Raise your hips up so your legs are straight.

5. Put one knee on top of your elbow. Make a four-part balance.

6. Keep your elbows in and tight.

7. Think about making a triangle with your head and hands.

See if you can let your knees take turns with each elbow.

## Station 4: Tripod

1. The next task is called a tripod. How many body parts are you using to balance now? Right, *tri* means "three." Think about the following when you do the tripod:

   a. Start with your knee on one elbow (just as you did in our knee and elbow balance).

   b. Hold your first knee on your elbow and raise the other knee to meet the other elbow.

   c. Keep your elbows in toward your body and tight.

   d. Keep that triangle with your hands and head.

   e. Hold a tight three-part balance.

2. If you want to challenge yourself, try to raise one leg off the tripod. You may choose to try to raise one knee off and then straighten that leg up to a medium or high level.

3. I want you to practice these strong inverted balances. I am looking for good, tight muscles and still balanced shapes, even though we are inverted and have some body parts above and some below.

## LESSON 5B

# Individual and Partner Balancing
### Elementary, Mature, and Transitional Stages; Grade 4

## Cognitive and Motor Objectives

- Balance
- Strong
- Free
- Partner
- Inverted
- Movement sequence
- Match

## Affective and Social Objectives

- Respecting skill differences and skill levels of peers
- Working with a partner

## Equipment

- Mats (one for every two children)
- Music, if desired
- Pedometers (one for each child, if desired)

## Warm-Ups

Spend a few minutes reviewing the balances in lesson 5A.

1. Students travel around the gym looking for open mats. As they come to open mats, they stop and make balanced shapes on the mats (holding the shapes for a count of 3) and continue on. You can use music for this warm-up.

2. As students practice making shapes on mats, ask them to think about using strong muscle tension so the shapes are really strong.

3. Traveling actions should include steplike actions of walking, bear walking, and crab walking, and a variety of springlike actions.

4. Students travel around the gym using a variety of steplike and springlike actions. As they travel, have them vary their speed and range (sometimes traveling slowly, sometimes more quickly). Have them vary the size of their steps. Can they take small steps as well as larger ones?

5. As students travel around the gym using a combination of steplike actions and springlike actions, on your signal, have them find partners and make shapes that show counterbalance and countertension. You may also have them make symmetrical and asymmetrical balanced shapes.

6. As students travel around the gym using a combination of steplike actions and springlike actions, see if they can stop on your signal and make three different balanced shapes. Use the term *smooth transition* so they will become familiar with making smooth transitions between balanced shapes.

## Smooth Transition Balance Sequence: Individual

You are looking for students to create a movement sequence using a variety of balances. See if they can include inverted balances. However, allow them to use only those balances with which they are most comfortable.

1. Now that we have learned several inverted balances, let's see if you can create a movement balance sequence. Remember, a movement sequence has a definite beginning and a definite ending.

2. I want you to create a sequence of three balances. I am looking for tight balanced shapes and smooth transitions. Choose your balances from the ones we have worked on so far.

3. Move into and out of each balance distinctly before doing the next one.

4. Practice for a few minutes, and when you are ready, sit down on your part of the mat and be ready to show everyone your sequence. Go.

Give students a few minutes to practice their sequences. As you walk around, look for strong balanced shapes and smooth transitions. Children should be able to demonstrate a movement sequence. You may choose to have half the class show their sequences to the other half and then reverse roles. Encourage the children to be supportive of all types of movement balance sequence choices.

### Smooth Transition Balance Sequence: Partner Matching

Prior to having children demonstrate balanced sequences, give them a focus. For example, while you are watching your friends show their movement sequences, see if you can find those whose transitions are smooth. Ask students to tell you what balances they saw. Have half of the class show their balance sequences to the other half. Encourage students to be supportive of all movement sequence choices.

1. Now that we have worked on smooth transitions in your individual balance sequence, let's see if you and a partner can create a matching balance sequence.

2. You and your partner will create a three-balance sequence that matches. [Review what *matching* means.] Your sequence should have tight balanced shapes and smooth transitions.

3. Choose your balances from the ones we have worked on so far. When you and your partner are ready to show your balance sequence, sit down on your mat.

## LESSON 6A

## Partner Activities

### Elementary, Mature, and Transitional Stages; Grade 5

### Cognitive and Motor Objectives

| | |
|---|---|
| • Balance | • Inverted |
| • Low | • Movement sequence |
| • Medium | • Symmetrical |
| • High | • Asymmetrical |
| • Strong | • Counterbalance |
| • Partner | • Countertension |

### Equipment

- Mats (one for every two children)
- Music, if desired
- Pedometers (one for each child, if desired)

### Warm-Ups

1. Students travel around the gym looking for open mats. As they come to open mats, they stop and make balanced shapes on the mats (holding the shapes for a count of 3) and continue on. You can use music for this warm-up.

2. As students practice making shapes on mats, ask them to think about using strong muscle tension so the shapes are really strong.

3. Traveling actions should include steplike actions of walking, bear walking, and crab walking, and a variety of springlike actions.

4. Students travel around the gym using a variety of steplike and springlike actions. As they travel, have them vary their speed and range (sometimes traveling slowly, sometimes more quickly). Have them vary the size of their steps. Can they take small steps as well as larger ones?

5. As students travel around the gym using a combination of steplike actions and springlike actions, on your signal, have them find partners and make shapes that show counterbalance and countertension. You may also have them make symmetrical and asymmetrical balanced shapes.

6. As students travel around the gym using a combination of steplike actions and springlike actions, see if they can stop on your signal and make three different balanced shapes.

Use the term *smooth transition* so they will become familiar with making smooth transitions between balanced shapes.

## Inverted Balances: Options

Children should have other options available if they are not comfortable with the tripod. They may continue to work on body part balances, seeing if they can do five-, four-, or three-part balances.

1. When I say "Go," find a space on a mat. You will have one end of the mat as your working space. When you get to your end, sit in your self-space. Go.

2. We have worked on a variety of inverted balances so far. You will see stations set up around the general space where you can do various inverted balances. You may choose the ones that you want to do.

3. Now try creating your own three-, four-, or five-part balances. Think about using body parts above and below (such as your head below your hips). Can you bring one knee to an elbow?

   a. Raise one knee off your elbow. Remember our triangle shape with head and hands. Keep your elbows in close to your body. When you raise your knee off your elbow, you can keep it at a low or medium level. You decide the level.

   b. Make that one knee straight so your leg is straight. Can you raise this knee? You may choose to keep your knee on your elbow.

   c. Can you have both knees free? Your hips need to rise up and be very balanced and still. You choose if you want to raise both knees, keep one knee on an elbow, keep both knees on your elbows, or have one knee on the floor.

   d. Can you raise one knee up and then, if you are able, slowly bring the other knee up next to the first one?

   e. If you are ready, see if you can raise one leg up to a high level and then slowly raise the other leg up to a high level. Can you make other shapes with your legs? Think about different types of shapes you can make.

   f. Create your own three-, four-, or five-part balances. See how many different balances you can create. Can you create balances at different levels? Can you show me above and below in your balances?

Allow students to practice this for a few minutes. Then suggest that they change stations when they are ready. If this does not work, you may have them rotate stations. Again, respect skill differences by allowing students to modify their balances. After students have practiced at the stations, you may add the following:

4. We have worked on a variety of inverted balances. I want you to choose your best three inverted balances and practice those.

5. When you have practiced these three, show them to me. Then make them into a smooth movement sequence. Go.

Once children have practiced their sequences, you may have them show them to their mat partners. Then add the following:

6. Now, I want you to find a partner and play Copy That. You need to have a partner with whom you feel comfortable working. Go.

7. When we play Copy That, one partner chooses an inverted body part balance and the other partner copies it. Each of you takes two turns and then you switch places.

As you walk around, look for strong balanced shapes with body parts above and below.

8. That was awesome! I saw some strong balanced shapes with body parts below and above.

## Balanced Shapes: Counterbalance and Countertension, and Symmetrical and Asymmetrical

If you have not covered the definitions of *counterbalance* and *countertension* and *symmetrical* and *asymmetrical,* you should make sure children understand their definitions. Ask students if they have used the elements symmetrical and asymmetrical in math class. You can gather students in front of the chart again or have them look at a word wall. You are looking for the use of counterbalance and firm muscle tension. Students who are uncomfortable completing any of the partner balances in this section should be encouraged to create their own counterbalance and countertension balances.

1. We are going to work on partner balances now. Stay with the same partner you have and sit down on your mat together.
2. Our partner balances will work on counterbalance and countertension and making symmetrical and asymmetrical shapes. These balances also work on receiving the weight of your partner.
3. Here are three balances you may try, or you may choose to create your own partner counterbalance and countertension balances.

## Double Knee Bend and Walk

1. Stand back to back with your partner and lock elbows. Bend your knees and come to a medium level. You are using counterbalance.
2. See if you and your partner can walk a short distance in one direction. Decide which direction you want to go first.
3. Can you move at different speeds?

Before going on, have students review the concepts of symmetrical and asymmetrical. You may also review countertension.

## Symmetrical Shapes

You and your partner will be working on making symmetrical shapes. See if you and your partner can think of three symmetrical shapes. Make them really clear.

## Asymmetrical Shapes

Now, we will make asymmetrical shapes. I want you and your partner to think of three asymmetrical shapes. Make each one very clear and hold the shape for at least three seconds.

## Symmetrical and Asymmetrical Sequence

1. You and your partner will make a movement sequence that consists of both symmetrical and asymmetrical shapes.
2. You decide what your combination will be. You might choose one symmetrical and two asymmetrical shapes.
3. I want to see clear distinct shapes, and I want you to move smoothly between shapes.
4. Practice for a few minutes and be ready to show your sequence.

Students should practice symmetrical and asymmetrical shapes and the movement sequence. As they work, you are looking for clear symmetrical and asymmetrical shapes. Once they have worked for a few minutes, they can demonstrate their sequences.

Students who are watching the demonstrations should be able to point out which balances are symmetrical and which are asymmetrical and why.

## Countertension

Now that you and your partner have made awesome movement sequences with symmetrical and asymmetrical shapes, I want you to add shapes that show countertension. See if you can add one balanced shape to your sequence that shows countertension.

Students should be able to show you a movement sequence that includes a combination of symmetrical, asymmetrical, and countertension.

## LESSON 6B

# Balancing on Beam and Benches
### Elementary, Mature, and Transitional Stages; Grade 5

## Cognitive and Motor Objectives

- Balance
- Round
- Wide
- Narrow
- Twisted
- Symmetrical
- Asymmetrical
- Weight transfer
- Counterbalance
- Countertension
- Low
- Medium
- High
- Forward
- Backward
- Sideways
- Free
- Movement sequence
- Turn
- Mount
- Dismount

## Affective and Social Objectives

- Respecting skill differences and skill levels of peers

## Equipment

- Floor beams, low balance beams, or low benches
- Mats (one for every two children)
- Music, if desired
- Pedometers (one for each child, if desired)

## Warm-Ups

1. Students travel around the gym looking for open mats. As they come to open mats, they stop and make balanced shapes on the mats (holding the shapes for a count of 3) and continue on. You can use music for this warm-up.

2. As students practice making shapes on mats, ask them to think about using strong muscle tension so the shapes are really strong.

3. Traveling actions should include steplike actions of walking, bear walking, crab walking, and a variety of springlike actions.

4. Students travel around the gym using a variety of steplike and springlike actions. As they travel, have them vary their speed and range (sometimes traveling slowly, sometimes more quickly). Have them vary the size of their steps. Can they take small steps as well as larger ones?

5. As students travel around the gym using a combination of steplike actions and springlike actions, on your signal, have them find partners and make shapes that show counterbalance and countertension. You may also have them make symmetrical and asymmetrical balanced shapes.

6. As students travel around the gym using a combination of steplike actions and springlike actions, see if they can stop on your signal and make three different balanced shapes. Use the term *smooth transition* so they will become familiar with making smooth transitions between balanced shapes.

## Balances Using Steplike Actions on the Floor

Students may work on this for a few minutes. As they work, you are looking for different ways they are traveling across the floor beams, and that they are showing strong balanced movement with no wobbles.

1. We have some floor beams all around the gym. We don't have enough for all of you to have your own floor beam, so you will have to work in small groups.

2. I want you to find a group of four. Show me you can find a group with whom you can work.

3. We have been working on balances, and we know that to balance means to hold very still for a count of 3. We are going to take the ele-

ment of balancing now and use our floor and low beams.

4. When it is your turn, see how many ways you can move across the beam using steplike actions or springlike actions such as walking, crawling, sliding, hopping, and leaping.

5. Now that you have worked on this for a few minutes, see if you can move forward, sideways, and backward.

6. When we move across the beam in a forward direction, we think of our feet moving in a heel-toe pattern. Going backward, we think of a toe-heel pattern.

7. Once you have worked on this, see if you can stop on the beam and make a balanced shape and hold that shape for a count of 3.

Allow the children to practice these tasks and challenges for a few minutes. As you walk around, look for the use of steplike actions and springlike actions, different directions, and balanced shapes.

## Low Balance Beam and Benches

Begin using the low beams (or benches). Divide the class into small groups depending on the number of low balance beams you have. You may also choose to put the children into a station format and have some continue to create movement sequences on the floor beams, while others move to the low balance beams to work. If benches are available, some groups may work on benches and not on floor beams so they can also practice different ways to mount the apparatus. Have students trade stations so all get a chance to work on the low balance beam(s).

1. We are going to take our balanced work now to the low balance beams and benches. You may practice the same elements on either the beam or the bench. You will have a turn on each piece of equipment.

2. With your group of four, I want you to find a low beam or a bench and stand at one end. Go.

3. As you start working now, see if you can think of a different way to mount the beam besides stepping on it. Can you jump (using two feet) onto the beam? Maybe you will choose to mount the beam by hopping (using one foot). You may also still step or walk onto the beam.

4. Think about really maintaining good balance before you begin moving across the beam. See

if you can move across the equipment using steplike actions by walking only.

5. Walk about halfway across the beam, and then see if you can balance on one foot. How about the other foot? Can you turn around and return to your starting place? Can you think of a different way to move across the beam? Can you move across the beam, stop, and change levels? You might choose to slide across sideways.

6. Show me the following:
   - Mounting the beam in a different way
   - Moving across the beam in a different way
   - Starting in one direction and turning around
   - Changing levels on the beam
   - Remembering our heel-toe or toe-heel pattern
   - Traveling across the beam, stopping and making a balanced shape, and then continuing to the end and dismounting

Students should be working on direction changes, level changes, and balanced shapes. Encourage smooth movements. Once children have practiced these tasks for a few minutes, you may choose to do one of the activities in this lesson.

## Balance Beam Movement Sequence

Students enjoy creating movement sequences on the balance beam. See if they can show you smooth (free-flowing) sequences. Remind them of level changes, direction changes, and steplike and springlike actions.

1. Sit in your groups beside your piece of equipment. The last task we will work on today is making three-part movement sequences on the balance beam. Remember, movement sequences have a definite beginning, middle, and ending.

2. See if you can work on the following:
   a. Mounting the beam or bench
   b. Creating three different tasks on the beam or bench
   c. Dismounting the beam or bench

3. I will be looking for smooth transitions and three distinct movements. You will need to take turns on the low beam or bench. While you are waiting your turn, practice your sequence on the floor beam or on a line that is near your group. Remember to stay in your own working space. Go.

# Teaching Educational Dance

Educational dance has long been a part of the movement curriculum and should be considered an integral part of any physical education curriculum. Educational dance, like educational games and gymnastics, is based on movement elements with which students are already familiar. For this reason, it is easy to integrate into a physical education curriculum. Some teachers believe that they are not qualified to teach dance; others fear that students will be bored with dance units. The intent of including dance in a movement curriculum is to heighten children's ability to express themselves and to communicate feelings and create a mood (Barrett, 1984).

The movement inherent in games and gymnastics has a functional quality to it; that is, a functional goal is attached to the performance. Typically, that goal is to win. Children, however, also need to learn how to express themselves appropriately and to have ample opportunity to practice demonstrating a wide range of emotion. Dance provides an opportunity not only to reinforce the cognitive and motor aspects of movement, but also, more important, to help children share their feelings. Simple folk or line dances may also be included in an elementary curriculum and the movement elements quite easily applied. In addition to using the dance lessons in this chapter, you can address movement elements with simple folk or line dances. Be wary, though, of teaching students traditional dances such as the Hokey Pokey, Chicken Dance, and Looby Loo and calling that educational dance.

One creative dance, the Umbrella Dance, is used throughout this chapter. The design of these lessons takes the part practice approach (see table 13.1). Each individual lesson provides the opportunity to practice each part of the dance separately (fractionalization). Finally, in the last lesson, each of these pieces is put together (segmentation) for a presentation of the entire dance.

**Table 13.1** Motor Learning Application to the Teaching of Educational Dance

| Practice Method | Progression | | | | | | | | |
|---|---|---|---|---|---|---|---|---|---|
| Fractionalization | 1—Body Shapes Dance | + | 2—Weather or Not | + | 3—Sway and Balance | + | 4—Blowing in the Wind | = | 5—Umbrella Dance |

# Educational Dance Lessons

As previously presented in chapter 2, the MEF approach suggests a problem-solving perspective. While you can apply this with more traditional dances (e.g., folk dances, line dances), another option is to focus on using imagery. Using images (e.g., a raindrop on its way to the ocean or a flower closing in the winter and opening in the spring), props (e.g., rubberbands, umbrellas, pasta noodles), words from a story or poem, and words from music can be great ways to enhance children's use of imagery. Bringing in elements of a holiday, such as Thanksgiving, may also enhance imagery in movement.

If you are using a traditional approach (e.g., animals, a folk dance, or a line dance), your focus should be on the movement elements in the lesson. For example, if you are using animals as examples of movement, telling students to move like a cat, duck, elephant, or lion will not emphasize a movement approach. Instead, think about the types of movements these animals exhibit (e.g., quick, low, waddle, strong, light, powerful, hard) and encourage children to exhibit these movements as they demonstrate how a cat, duck, elephant, or lion might move. In other words, the focus is on the movement elements rather than the animals. The emotions of the animal can be brought into the dance through the movement element. For example, you might associate a quick movement with a sly attitude or encourage the children to describe the feeling that might belong to the movement element. Children can have a lot of fun trying to guess what their classmates are portraying (it can be a bit like the game of Charades).

The lessons in this unit reflect an imagery approach. The prop being used in each lesson is an umbrella. These lessons are appropriate for children at the initial, elementary, and mature developmental stages.

Each of the five lessons is progressive both within and between lessons. These stages were presented in chapter 3. The developmental stages presented are only a general guide; a better way to match a lesson topic to a group of children would be to use a developmental analysis to determine their actual stage(s). Review the lessons and adapt as needed according to the developmental stage of your students.

Each lesson includes an introduction, and the wording of the directions and student expectations for each lesson is appropriate to the developmental stage the lesson addresses. At the close of each lesson, you should review the elements emphasized, encouraging students to articulate them. Emphasize creating movement phrases, sentences, and stories, much like in the classroom. You can also include additional activities, as described in chapter 4. For example, students can draw movement pictures of their dance structures. They can also write about how they felt creating the dance structures or use the umbrella as a tool for creating a story in the classroom. Including music in the dance structures allows children to experience rhythm in creating their movement stories.

## LESSON 1

## Body Shapes Dance
### Initial Stage; Grade K

### Cognitive and Motor Objectives

- Narrow
- Wide
- Round
- Twisted
- Stretch
- Curl
- Fast
- Slow
- Low
- Medium
- High
- Strong
- Bound

### Affective and Social Objectives

- Respecting self-space
- Respecting general space
- Following directions
- Respecting skill differences and skill levels of peers

### Equipment

- Umbrella (a large golf umbrella makes a big impression and can be seen more easily)
- Music that is appropriate for the lesson (e.g., rain and wind sounds, nature tunes, "Singing in the Rain")
- Drum (the bottom of a plastic pail)
- Maraca (a water bottle with some dry rice in it)

### Warm-Up

1. Have you ever watched a spider? How do you think a spider controls all of its legs? The spider uses the core, or center, of its body.

Today we are going to use our abdominal muscles to control our movements. We are going to be working on various body shapes and nonlocomotor movements such as stretching, curling, and twisting using small and large space. Our abdominal muscles control all of our movements. We call this the core, or center, of the body.

2. In your self-space, show me how you can sit on your bottom in a very small, tight ball. Be really small.

3. Now I want to see if you can stretch one arm up and out into the space. Can you add the other arm?

4. Can you lift one leg up off the floor and out into the space, followed by the other leg? You should be balanced on your bottom using your abdominal muscles, or core, for control, just like an upside-down spider. Let's see if we can do this several times. I want to see very tight abdominal muscles.

5. Let's reverse your position. This time, start by kneeling down in a very tight, curled shape. Can you open one arm at a time? Can you place your tummy on the floor and open both your arms and your legs? Think about your tummy being very tight and making a strong core.

## Variation

Have the children wave arms and legs around, open slow, or open fast. Your language should reflect a movement approach.

1. Show me how you can curl up in a very tight ball and make your shape as small as possible.

2. Now, just like a spider stretching a leg, can you stretch one arm up and out into space?

3. How about the other arm?

4. Can you stretch slowly and maintain your balance?

5. Can you do this more quickly?

6. Can you wave all of your limbs in the air at one time and still maintain your balance?

7. How about one limb at a time?

An object that we use when it rains that also has a center and opens and closes is an umbrella. When we work on our umbrella dance today, we will use our center like an umbrella. When we do our activities, we will also be using the levels we have learned (low, medium, and high).

## Bound and Free (Rotation) Movements: Body Shapes

In this portion of the dance, you are encouraging students to show you a variety of body shapes. However, the key is to emphasize making the body shapes narrow, wide, round, or twisted. You also want to see children really stretch their bodies.

1. We are going to work on body shapes today. Find your own self-space and show me how you can make a round shape. Can you make it really round?

2. How about a tall, narrow shape? Really stretch tall, as tall as a skyscraper!

3. Now, can you show me a wide shape?

4. What do you have to do when you make a wide shape? When you made your round shape, what did you have to do?

5. Can you hold your body shape for a count of 3? [Remember, we learned about counting one cherry, two cherries, three cherries—saying "cherries" just adds more fun.]

6. Now, let's try a twisted shape. When you twist, you are rotating your whole body. The result is a twisted shape. Now, show me how you can untwist. Can you do this slowly? How about quickly? When you are ready, practice twisting and untwisting slowly and quickly.

7. Can you make a shape at a low level? How about a medium level? Now, show me a high level. Show me how you can change your shape from one level to the next. Think of three different shapes at each level and change when you are ready.

8. This time I want you to think of making strong, tight shapes. When we make strong shapes, we are bound, or tight, and use a lot of muscle tension. Think of three strong, tight shapes and change from one to the next.

9. Now, we will make free, light, airy shapes. Show me a free, light shape. What body parts can you use to make this light shape?

10. Let's put these together to make a shape dance. Think of three different shapes you have made and put them together in a movement sequence. There should be a beginning shape and then two additional shapes. Make all your shapes clear and distinct.

You can add music for the shape dance. Students can also show their shape dances to other groups, or half the class can demonstrate as the other half watches. As students watch their classmates demonstrate, ask them to look for specific movement elements. Can they see shapes at a low level, medium level, and high level? Can they see round, narrow, or twisted shapes? Can they identify bound and free?

## Closure Activity

1. Place the movement elements for the lesson in the pocket chart and have the students gather around.

2. Point to an element and have students demonstrate a movement that identifies that element. Ask them, for example, "What part of the body controls balance? What will control balance when you are in an extended shape balancing on one foot? What helps you spin all the way around?"

3. You can reinforce the activity and encourage continued activity outside of the classroom by saying something like: "You have a great umbrella dance that you can teach a friend or show your parents or caregivers. Make sure you teach them about their core as we discussed in the beginning."

Reprinted, by permission, from Gladys Keeton.

## LESSON 2

# Weather or Not
### Elementary Stage; Grade 1

## Cognitive and Motor Objectives

- Narrow
- Wide
- Curl
- Low
- Medium
- High
- Slow
- Bound
- Free
- Movement sequence

## Affective and Social Objectives

- Respecting self-space
- Respecting general space
- Respecting skill differences and skill levels of peers

## Equipment

- Umbrella (a large golf umbrella makes a big impression and can be seen more easily)
- Music that is appropriate for the lesson (e.g., rain and wind sounds, nature tunes, "Singing in the Rain")
- Drum (the bottom of a plastic pail)
- Maraca (a water bottle with some dry rice in it)

## Introduction

Start this lesson with a discussion of weather and what we need to keep us dry or out of the sun. This provides a theme to encourage students to be more expressive.

## Warm-Up

1. In our last lesson, we talked about a spider that has tight abdominal muscles. Do you remember showing me how you could curl up in small shapes and stretch each limb, just like a spider? Let's try that again. Curl up like a spider and then very slowly open one limb at a time, really working on keeping your balance and a tight core.

2. This time, I want you to stand in your self-space and think about the wind blowing you from side to side. Let's work on maintaining balance while you sway from side to side. Stretch your arms out to help you with balance. Can you move slowly? How about more quickly as the wind picks up?

## Bound and Free (Rotation) Movements: Umbrella Dance Introduction

At the end of this lesson, students become umbrellas and create umbrella dances using the movement elements you have discussed.

1. It is helpful to begin by talking about the weather and asking students about the last time it rained. What does an umbrella look like in the rain? How about when it has stopped raining? A story about the weather, wind, rain, and how the umbrella moves and changes during a soft rain versus a hard rain will help them imagine using all the elements you are discussing.

2. Show the closed umbrella to students. Have students make small shapes like umbrellas at a low level. Identify the umbrella as being wrapped tight around the center rod. Ask students, "Can you show me a tight, bound shape at a low level?"

3. Release the tab to show the umbrella being very free. Have the students mimic the actions of the umbrella as you call out "Bound" and "Free." Continue to do this until you see that students are appropriately demonstrating

bound and free as you open and close the umbrella.

Students must use their core so as not to fall over while their arms are moving freely from side to side. Keep reminding them of the spider core activity.

## Umbrella Dance Structure: Bound and Free

Students perform bound and free rotation movements to the sounds of instruments— bound to a drum beat and free to a maraca sound (short–long rhythm).

Ask students to think of ways to make bound and free movements to the sounds of the instruments. There are no correct responses. Encourage them to start and end when they are ready. You are looking for movements that are bound and free. You are also looking for a beginning shape and an ending shape (movement sequence).

## Opening and Closing at Various Levels

This portion of the dance encourages children to apply the various levels they have learned. Students should think about the umbrella all the way open, midway open, and closed tight.

1. It is now beginning to rain, so we need to open our umbrella. Can you open your body like the umbrella? [Push the button on the umbrella to open it midway; then close it again. Repeat this action several times while students mimic the umbrella with their bodies (open/close).]
2. Now I'm going to open the umbrella completely. See if you can completely open and stretch with your arms extended in a round shape like the umbrella.
3. As I open and close the umbrella, follow the actions with your body, sometimes opening a little, sometimes midway, and sometimes completely. Can you feel the difference of opening at different levels?
4. See if you can move slowly and smoothly as you open and close. How is your core controlling your balance movement at the various levels?

## Dance Structure at Various Levels

In this activity, students put the three levels together in any order (e.g., medium, low, high).

1. Think of the umbrella opening and closing at various levels. Do you remember how I was opening and closing the umbrella?

2. Put together three levels in any order. Practice these for a few minutes and be ready to show them.

For students in grades K through 2 (elementary developmental stage), you can emphasize breathing: inhale when expanding and exhale when closing. For students at the mature or transitional developmental stages (typically in grades 3 through 5), consider emphasizing dynamics (e.g., expanding with a sharp movement). Encourage children to close softly.

## Combining the Dance Structure of Bound and Free With Levels

Close the umbrella again and reopen it. Remind students about the elements of bound and free. Then open it at various levels.

1. Let's combine our bound and free movements with levels. First, find a starting position. Every movement sequence has a beginning shape, just as a story you might read in the classroom has a beginning sentence.
2. When you are ready, combine the shapes you created for our bound and free dance with the shapes you made at different levels.

Let students practice this for a few minutes. You can then add music. Again, you may choose to have students demonstrate their dance structures. All students should be able to identify MEF elements. Ask older students to tell you what their beginning and ending shapes were and why.

## Closure Activity for Each Lesson

1. Place the movement elements for the lesson in the pocket chart and have the students gather around.
2. Point to an element and have students demonstrate a movement that identifies that element. Ask them, for example, "What part of the body controls balance? What will control balance when you are in an extended shape balancing on one foot? What helps you spin all the way around?"

3. You can reinforce the activity and encourage continued activity outside of the classroom by saying something like: "You have a great umbrella dance that you can teach a friend or show your parents or caregivers. Make sure you teach them about their core as we discussed in the beginning."

Reprinted, by permission, from Gladys Keeton.

## LESSON 3

# Sway and Balance

### Elementary Stage; Grade 2

### Cognitive and Motor Objectives

- Fast
- Slow
- Strong
- Movement sequence
- Balance
- Forward
- Backward
- Sideways
- Small
- Large

### Affective and Social Objectives

- Respecting skill differences and skill levels of peers

### Equipment

- Umbrella (a large golf umbrella makes a big impression and can be seen more easily)
- Music that is appropriate for the lesson (e.g., rain and wind sounds, nature tunes, "Singing in the Rain")
- Drum (the bottom of a plastic pail)
- Maraca (a water bottle with some dry rice in it)

### Introduction and Warm-Up

Remind students about their spider core activity. That activity would be a great warm-up for this and other portions of the Umbrella Dance. With this lesson, you are moving into the rainy portion of the dance.

When it is raining hard and the wind is blowing, would the umbrella be blown around hard and fast or softly and lightly? Is it hard to keep control of our umbrella when the wind and rain are very strong?

You can review directions (forward, backward, sideways) with children, if needed. You can also review what it means to balance, if needed.

### Swaying in a Variety of Directions With Balance

Students make an open umbrella shape and sway slowly from side to side keeping both feet on the ground. As the wind gets harder, the students sway farther to the side with one foot coming off the floor. They repeat this to both sides as you emphasize the function of the core as a control for balance.

1. The wind is beginning to blow our umbrella now. It is very soft but makes the umbrella move from side to side.
2. Oh, no, the wind is getting harder and blowing the umbrella way over to the side, back and forth.

Use the umbrella to demonstrate it moving from side to side and back and forth.

- For students at an elementary developmental stage or in grade 1: Repeat the activity with tempo changes.
- For students at an elementary developmental stage or grade 2: Repeat the activity with the wind moving the umbrella forward and backward.
- For students at a mature or transitional developmental stage or grades 3, 4, or 5: At some point, when the students are moving from side to side, cue them to freeze to find out how long they can balance in a tilted, open T position on one foot. Ask what is keeping them from falling over. Encourage them to think about what keeps them balanced. Explain that they should be extending from the center as if someone were pulling their head and someone else were pulling their leg away from the center, or that they are making a large T that will take up a lot of space. Discuss the body shapes they are making and how they are moving in different directions, slowly, and then more quickly.

### Swaying in a Variety of Directions With Balance: Dance Structure

With music playing, students sway from side to side beginning small and gradually increasing the size of the sways in their own time or at their own tempo. Once they have made the sways large, they then go back to small and repeat. This continues until you have them freeze when you stop the music. Students should be able to demonstrate a starting and ending position, or shape, for the entire structure.

1. I want you to think about a beginning shape. Show me ways you can sway from side to side and back and forth as the umbrella.
2. Can you create large sways and small sways? Can you make the range of your movements big and small?

You may also choose to combine the elements from lesson 2 with this one and ask students to demonstrate both movement sequences. This will add variety to your lesson.

## Closure Activity for Each Lesson

1. Place the movement elements for the lesson in the pocket chart and have the students gather around.
2. Point to an element and have students demonstrate a movement that identifies that element. Ask them, for example, "What part of the body controls balance? What will control balance when you are in an extended shape balancing on one foot? What helps you spin all the way around?"
3. You can reinforce the activity and encourage continued activity outside of the classroom by saying something like: "You have a great umbrella dance that you can teach a friend or show your parents or caregivers. Make sure you teach them about their core as we discussed in the beginning."

Reprinted, by permission, from Gladys Keeton.

## LESSON 4

# Blowing in the Wind
## Elementary and Mature Stages; Grade 3

### Cognitive and Motor Objectives

- Balance
- Forward
- Backward
- Sideways
- Low
- Medium
- High
- Bound

- Free
- Spin
- Clockwise
- Counterclockwise
- Sagittal
- Frontal
- Transverse

### Affective and Social Objectives

- Respecting skill differences and skill levels of peers

### Equipment

- Umbrella (a large golf umbrella makes a big impression and can be seen more easily)
- Music that is appropriate for the lesson (e.g., rain and wind sounds, nature tunes, "Singing in the Rain")
- Drum (the bottom of a plastic pail)
- Maraca (a water bottle with some dry rice in it)

### Introduction and Warm-Up

1. We have talked about a spider having tight abdominal muscles. Show me how you can curl up in a small shape and stretch each limb, just like a spider. Curl up like a spider and then very slowly open one limb at a time, really working on keeping your balance and a tight core.
2. Can you think of another animal or bug that would open slowly and have to focus on staying balanced?

### Rotation, or Spinning, With Momentum for Balance

Students rotate their umbrella shapes to the left and then to the right. They repeat this several times until they have enough momentum to spin on one foot. Remind them to extend their bodies out from the core to engage the abdominal muscles for balance when spinning. Refer to the tilted T position. Ask students in what plane(s) rotation or spinning occurs. [Transverse] Students should practice spinning in both directions.

1. The wind is getting very strong and is coming from all directions! What do you think will happen to our umbrella? [Guide students in their responses.]
2. Can you think of other body parts you can spin on—your knees or your seat? [This develops problem-solving skills.]

### Rotation, or Spinning, Dance Structure

1. You are going to make a spinning dance. The wind has really been blowing our umbrella. It is moving all around in both a clockwise and counterclockwise direction, very fast.
2. Can you create two different ways to spin?

Begin with the first, perform the second, and then repeat the first.

This demonstrates a relationship to sequencing. Students need to perform a sequence from memory. Encourage them to practice this a few times so they can remember the sequence. Students at the mature developmental stage can think of more than one pattern.

### Closing an Umbrella With Vibratory Movement

Tell students it looks like the rain and wind are stopping.

1. Can you make your umbrella close by moving to a low level and creating a small, loose shape?
2. Since it has been raining so hard, you are still very wet. Can you shake off the rain? Would you move slowly to shake off the rain?
3. Show me you are finished shaking off the rain by making your body into a small, tight, bound shape just like a closed umbrella.

Allow students to complete this portion of the dance when they are ready. Ask students in what plane(s) the vibratory movement occurs. [Any of the three planes depending upon how the vibratory movement is performed] This demonstrates problem solving.

### Closure Activity for Each Lesson

1. Place the movement elements for the lesson in the pocket chart and have the students gather around.
2. Point to an element and have students demonstrate a movement that identifies that element. Ask them, for example, "What part of the body controls balance? What will control balance when you are in an extended shape balancing on one foot? What helps you spin all the way around?"

3. You can reinforce the activity and encourage continued activity outside of the classroom by saying something like: "You have a great umbrella dance that you can teach a friend or show your parents or caregivers. Make sure you teach them about their core as we discussed in the beginning."

Reprinted, by permission, from Gladys Keeton.

## LESSON 5

# Umbrella Dance
### Elementary, Mature, and Transitional Stages; Grades 4 and 5

### Cognitive and Motor Objectives

- Balance
- Spin
- Forward
- Backward
- Sideways
- Clockwise
- Counterclockwise
- Low
- Medium
- High
- Sagittal
- Frontal
- Transverse
- Large
- Fast
- Slow
- Strong
- Light
- Bound
- Free
- Movement sequence

### Affective and Social Objectives

- Respecting skill differences and skill levels of peers

### Equipment

- Umbrella (a large golf umbrella makes a big impression and can be seen more easily)
- Music that is appropriate for the lesson (e.g., rain and wind sounds, nature tunes, "Singing in the Rain")
- Drum (the bottom of a plastic pail)
- Maraca (a water bottle with some dry rice in it)

### Introduction and Warm-Up

1. Let's try our spider core activity. Show me how tight you can make your abdominal muscles. Really focus on a tight core.
2. Can you turn and keep your core tight?
3. How about a spin? Can you spin on different body parts?

In this activity, children begin to put the Umbrella Dance together (i.e., work on sequencing). Children at different developmental stages will need different amounts of guidance. However, in this problem-solving activity, children create their own movements to each of the portions of the overall movement dance. You are looking for the application of movement elements in this imagery setting. Explain that their Umbrella Dance may not look like their friends' dances, and that is great. Help them problem solve and create their own movements.

## Umbrella Dance: Applying Movement Concepts From Previous Lessons

Guide students in sequencing movements for the dance by adding the previous dance structures (movement elements) together.

1. Umbrella begins small with bound and free movements.
2. Umbrella opens to small, medium, and high levels (little, midway, and completely open).
3. Umbrella sways with changes in direction, time, and force.
4. Umbrella moves in sagittal, frontal, and transverse planes.
5. Umbrella spins using different body parts.
6. Umbrella changes levels to low, quick, or slow movements to shake off rain and finally bound. Add music.

You can structure the dance by having all students use a specific count, or allow students to decide how long to perform their movement sequences. Each sequence must have a definite beginning shape and ending shape, especially if the sequences end at different times. Students may choose to end their dance when they are ready. The ending shape will help you know when each student has completed his or her dance sequence.

## Closure Activity for Each Lesson

1. Place the movement elements for the lesson in the pocket chart and have the students gather around.
2. Point to an element and have students demonstrate a movement that identifies that element. Ask them, for example, "What part of the body controls balance? What will control balance when you are in an extended shape balancing on one foot? What helps you spin all the way around?"
3. You can reinforce the activity and encourage continued activity outside of the classroom

by saying something like: "You have a great umbrella dance that you can teach a friend or show your parents or caregivers. Make sure you teach them about their core as we discussed in the beginning."

Reprinted, by permission, from Gladys Keeton.

# Lesson Review Activities for Chapters 11-13

In each of the preceding chapters, we present complete lessons across developmental levels. In this section, we will provide a few review activities which may be used with any of the core content lessons. It is also a fun way to identify what children have learned as well as to apply integrated curricular teaching.

## REVIEW ACTIVITY 1

## Show What You Know: Gaming

Review the elements learned in one or more of the lessons by asking children to give you the definitions of each element. This can be done in a matching activity, as outlined in chapter 10 on page 191, or you may choose to have children write the definitions on their own movement cards. Ask children, particularly those who are at the upper elementary or mature levels to create their own movement game. This should be done in small working groups. Provide them with choices of movement elements as well as equipment. You may provide additional parameters such as how many children should be in their game or the length of time their game may last. Give them a brief period of time to create the game and practice it and then allow all other children to play the game. You may choose to ask children to write down their game and turn it in as well.

Reprinted, by permission, from Gladys Keeton.

## REVIEW ACTIVITY 2

## Dance Response: Doodle or Noodle

As presented in chapter 5 on page 92, have children write about how they felt during one of the lessons in the core content chapters. For example, after children have created their umbrella dance, ask them to draw their feelings about this lesson. You may also choose to have them write about how they felt during the umbrella dance lesson. Younger children may use only a few words, while older children may write a full paragraph.

Reprinted, by permission, from Gladys Keeton.

## Say It in Movements

Ask students to not only create a movement sequence but to write it down as well. You may choose to give students a specific number of elements to include in the sequence. Students at a lower developmental level may create a two- or three-element sequence, while older students may create a five-element sequence. This can be done individually, in partners, or in small groups. Provide paper and pencils for the appropriate number of children.

Once children have created their sequence, ask them to practice it and show it to another group or to the whole class. Younger children may choose  to draw pictures of the movement elements, while older children can create their sequence in words. Students can relate the sequence to creating a sentence, paragraph, or story for any of the three core content areas. In educational dance, students might create a dance movement sequence that shows strong, light, and bound actions. For an educational games movement sequence, students might create three movement elements (e.g., run, leap, jump or strike, pass, shoot). For an educational gymnastics movement sequence, students might create movements that show direct, indirect, and free.

Reprinted, by permission, from Gladys Keeton.

# APPENDIX A: FLIP 'N' FOLD

## EFFORT
Concept: How?

THE MOVEMENT FLIP 'N FOLD
Movement Education Framework: CONCEPTS, CATEGORIES, ELEMENTS

1. **Time** *(rate)* **E1-E3**
   Fast (sudden)
   Slow (sustained)
   Acceleration (Change)

2. **Force** *(tension)* **E4-E5**
   Hard (strong)
   Soft (light)

3. **Flow** *(fluidity)* **E6-E7**
   Bound (stoppable)
   Free (ongoing)

4. **Focus** *(effort in space)* **E8-E9**
   Direct (pointed or in a line)
   Indirect (expanded or flexible)

Teach Effort Concepts with **Sportime Pocket Chart Cards E1-E9**

*Fold here first*
*Fold here second*

## SPACE
Concept: WHERE?

THE MOVEMENT FLIP 'N FOLD
Movement Education Framework: CONCEPTS, CATEGORIES, ELEMENTS

1. **Location** **S1-S2**
   Self-space, General space

2. **Direction** **S3-S9**
   Forward, Backward
   Sideward (right, left)
   Up, Down
   Clockwise, Counterclockwise

3. **Level** **S10-S12**
   Low, Medium, High

4. **Pathway** **S13-S15**
   Straight, Curved, Zigzag

5. **Plane** **S16-S18**
   Sagittal (divides into sides; wheel)
   Frontal (divides front/back; door)
   Transverse (divides top/bottom; table)

6. **Extension** **S19-S20**
   Small (near), Large (far)

Teach Space Concepts with **Sportime Pocket Chart Cards S1-S20**

---

# THE MOVEMENT FLIP 'N FOLD
Movement Education Framework: CONCEPTS, CATEGORIES, ELEMENTS

## RELATIONSHIPS
Concept: Connections with WHO? or WHAT?*

1. **People** *(organization of)* **R1-R13**
   Solo, Alone in a mass, Partners, Even group(s),
   Uneven group(s)
   Individual to group, Group to group
   Triangle, Circle, Square, Scattered, Spokes of a wheel, "X"

2. **Position** *(spatial relationship)* **R14-R27**
   Above/below (still), Over/under (moving), Inverted,
   Mount/dismount, In front of/behind, Beside, Alongside,
   Through, Surround, Around, Support/supported (still),
   Lift/lifted (moving), Meet/part, Near to/far from

3. **Timing** **R28-R37**
   **Simultaneous:** Mirror, Match, Contrast, Unison
   **Alternate:** Taking turns
   **Successive:** Movement sequence, Canon, Question/answer,
   Act/react, Lead/follow

4. **Goal** *(of the activity)* **R38-R40**
   Cooperative (help), Collaborative (outwit), Competitive (win)

5. **Environment** *(nature of the)* **R41-R42**
   Static, Dynamic

   \* The Who or What can be…
   Body parts, Individuals, Groups
   Rules, Objects, Boundaries, Equipment
   Writing, Music, Pictures, Lighting, Nature (Arts)

Teach Relationship Concepts with **Sportime Pocket Chart Cards R1-R42**

---

# THE MOVEMENT FLIP 'N FOLD
Movement Education Framework: CONCEPTS, CATEGORIES, ELEMENTS

## BODY
Concept: WHO?

1. **Body Parts** **B1**
   Head, Neck, Ears, Eyes, Nose, Mouth, Shoulders,
   Elbows, Wrists, Hands, Fingers, Belly, Chest, Spine, Back,
   Bottom, Hips, Knees, Ankles, Feet, Toes

2. **Body Shapes** **B2-B7**
   Narrow, Wide, Round, Twisted, Symmetrical, Asymmetrical

3. **Actions of Body Parts** **B8-B12**
   Weight bearing, Receiving force or weight, Apply force,
   Lead the action, Weight transfer

4. **Actions of the Whole Body**
   **Nonlocomotor** **B13-B27**
   Stretch, Curl, Twist, Turn, Spin, Swing, Push, Pull, Rise, Sink, Gesture,
   Dodge, Balance, Counterbalance, Counter-tension
   **Locomotor** **B28-B41**
   Step-like actions: Walk, Cartwheel, Crawl (climb),
   Bear walk, Crab walk
   Spring-like actions: Run, Leap, Hop, Skip, Jump, Gallop, Slide
   Roll-like actions: Rock, (Body) roll
   **Manipulative** **B42-B50**
   Send away: Throw, Roll, Strike, Kick, Volley
   Gain control: Catch, Trap
   Propel: Dribble, Carry

Teach Body Concepts with **Sportime Pocket Chart Cards B1-B50**

---

From K. Weiller Abels and J.M. Bridges, 2010, *Teaching Movement Education: Foundations for Active Lifestyles* (Champaign, IL: Human Kinetics). © Karen Weiller Abels and Jennifer Bridges.

# APPENDIX B: RESOURCES FOR TEACHING THE MOVEMENT EDUCATION FRAMEWORK

More detail on the resources that were introduced in chapter 5, Innovative Teaching Methods, are presented here. This list is neither exhaustive nor exclusive. It simply represents resources with which we are familiar. Any list like this will eventually become dated so we hope that the information here will inspire you to search for items which are relevant, current, and which enhance your teaching. Provided below is a brief product description, product number, and Web site address for each resource to assist you in finding these or other products that might facilitate your implementation of a movement education curriculum.

**Animal cone caps.** Item 01-180. Seventeen animal cone caps and twelve blank caps with dry erase markers to label (6 inches W × 4 inches H × 1/16 inch). Available from Gopher Sport (www.gophersport.com).

**Blank Clever Catch beach ball.** Item SR-1468. Available from American Educational Products (www.amep.com).

**Bonnie's Fitware, Inc.** (Materials available in both English and Spanish). www.pesoftware.com.

- BF652 Elementary Quality of Movements, 55 cards, 8.5 × 11 inches, PDF on CD, grades K-6
- BF21 Elementary Basic Skills Task Cards, 20 cards, 8.5 × 11 inches, PDF on CD, grades K-3
- BF24 Elementary Tumbling Task Cards, 10 cards, 8.5 × 11 inches, PDF on CD, grades 3-6
- BF650 Elementary Manipulatives, 19 cards, 8.5 × 11 inches, PDF on CD, grades 1-3
- BF654 Elementary Locomotor/Nonlocomotor Task Cards, 20 cards, 8.5 × 11 inches, PDF on CD, grades K-3
- BF2664 Elementary Physical Education Dictionary, available as software, trial version available, grades 2-6

**Directions cone caps.** Item 01-183. Ten locomotor movements and twelve blank caps with markers to label (6 inches W × 4 inches H × 1/16 inch). Available from Gopher Sport (www.gophersport.com).

**Four Elements of Dance instructional posters; body, movements, space, time, and energy with suggested activities pamphlet.** Available from Dance Ware: Tools for Teaching Dance (www.danceware.us).

**It's Your Move.** Item 02-130. Six 12-sided locomotor game dice with mesh bag and five activities. Available from Gopher Sport (www.gophersport.com).

**Jellyfish floor discs, inserts, and print-your-own pattern for inserts by Gonge.** Item #s G-2150, G-2154, and G-2156. Available from American Educational Products (www.amep.com).

**Locomotor cone caps.** Item 01-181. Twelve locomotor movements and twelve blank caps with markers to label (6 inches W × 4 inches H × 1/16 inch). Available from Gopher Sport (www.gophersport.com).

**McCall, R. & Craft, D. (2000).** *Moving with a purpose: Developing programs for preschoolers of all abilities.* Available from Human Kinetics (www.HumanKinetics.com).

**McCall, R. & Craft, D. (2004).** *Purposeful play: Early childhood movement activities on a budget.* Available from Human Kinetics (www.HumanKinetics.com).

McGreevy-Nichols, S., Scheff, H., & Sprague, M. (2005). *Building dances: A guide to putting movements together* (2nd ed.). Available from Human Kinetics (www.HumanKinetics.com).

McGreevy-Nichols, S., Scheff, H., & Sprague, M. (2001). *Building more dances: Blueprints for putting movements together.* Available from Human Kinetics (www.Human Kinetics.com).

**Movement Education Framework Pocket Chart Card Deck.** (2010). 121 two-sided alphanumerically labeled cards; term on one side, definition on the other side, handy reference card (the Flip 'n' Fold) with the MEF, teacher's activity guide, travel case. This item is currently under development and will be available from Sportime in 2010. For more information, visit the Sportime Web site (www.sportime.com).

**Movement Education Framework Word Wall poster set.** 18 posters total or in parts. This item is currently under development and will be available from Sportime in 2010. For more information, visit the Sportime Web site (www.sportime.com).

Overby, L., Post, B., & Newman, D. *Interdisciplinary learning through dance: 101 MOVEntures.* Available from Human Kinetics (www.HumanKinetics.com).

**Plane Jane Complete Learning Package.** Item PJ99. Includes 3D table model and instructional CD. Available from Denoyer-Geppert (www.denoyer.com).

**Pocket Chart and chart stand designed for physical education/movement education framework pocket chart card deck.** (2010). This item is currently under development and will be available from Sportime in 2010. For more information, visit the Sportime Web site (www.sportime.com).

**Station to Station timed interval music CDs.** Items 3401 to 3413. Thirteen unique music CDs with six timed intervals that automatically provide cues to students to move during the timed music and to rotate to the next station during the timed silence. Available from Station PE, Inc. (www.s2smusic.com/s2s.htm; click on "Get S2S Resources Here" CD icon to review the user guide).

**Teaching the Elements of Dance workbook.** Available from Dance Ware: Tools for Teaching Dance (www.danceware.us).

# GLOSSARY OF MOVEMENT EDUCATION TERMS

This glossary is based upon the movement education framework which is summarized in the Flip 'n' Fold document in chapter 2 (which provides a more detailed description and slightly different wordings of many of these terms) and appendix A. It was created to provide a single source for all of the movement education terms in this text. We hope that it is a simple yet accurate, very practical set of terms that support National Association of Sport and Physical Education (NASPE, 2004a) standard 2 which asks that children understand movement concepts as they relate to the learning and performance of physical activities. These definitions, with abbreviated wording to fit in a smaller format, are also presented in the movement education pocket chart cards, available from Sportime (www.sportime.com). The glossary in this text is also available in Spanish.

# B. Body

The parts of or the entire person which serves as the instrument of the action.

## Body Parts

**B1. Body parts**—Head, neck, ears, eyes, nose, mouth, shoulders, elbows, wrists, hands, fingers, belly, chest, spine, back, bottom, hips, knees, ankles, feet, toes.

## Body Shapes

**B2. Narrow**—A thin or arrow-like shape. Example: Log roll, stretching in a handstand or basketball layup shot.

**B3. Wide**—Making a stretched or broad action or expanding out to the sides. Examples: Cartwheel, defensive stance.

**B4. Round**—Like a ball or tucked shape. Example: Forward roll.

**B5. Twisted**—Wound around each other. Example: Playing a game of Twister.

**B6. Symmetrical**—Same, matched, or balanced positions on both sides of the body.

**B7. Asymmetrical**—Unique or different positions on both sides of the body.

## Actions of Body Parts

**B8. Weight bearing**—Base of support; holding up the body or body part. Example: Hands in a handstand.

**B9. Receive force or weight**—"Stop." Outside force is absorbed. Example: Getting kicked in karate.

**B10. Apply force**—"Go." Giving a push or pull to object or self. Example: Lifting a dumbbell.

**B11. Lead the action**—The body part that starts a movement. Example: Hands in a dive into a pool.

**B12. Weight transfer**—Shifting the base of support; a new body part holds up the body. Example: Changing from the right to the left foot in a walk.

## Actions of the Whole Body

### Nonlocomotor

**B13. Stretch**—A primary body movement where body parts are made longer. Examples: Sit and reach, side bends.

**B14. Curl**—A primary body movement where body parts pull toward the center. Example: Arm curl (elbow flexion).

**B15. Twist**—A primary body movement where body parts wind around each other as one part of the body remains fixed and the other part(s) continue to move. The amount of torsion increases with increasing twist. Example: Head looks to the right with the body facing forward.

**B16. Turn**—Faces a new direction; temporary loss of orientation in space; base of support may move. Examples: While in a stride stance, lifting the heels and keeping the balls of the feet on the floor and pivoting to face the opposite direction; or standing facing one wall and then lifting the feet to step and face a new wall.

**B17. Spin**—The entire body rotates on a central axis. The base of support is not lifted from the supporting surface. Examples: A basketball player rotating on the ball of the foot while pivoting to pass the ball to another player; a figure skater rotating on one skate.

**B18. Swing**—Axis at fixed end to allow the rotation of a body or body part.

**B19. Push**—Directing force away from the body.

**B20. Pull**—Directing force toward the base of support.

**B21. Rise**—Moving or stretching upward; lifting oneself.

**B22. Sink**—Giving into gravity; falling gently.

**B23. Gesture**—Non-weight-bearing movement shaped in the air; to counterbalance or express mood.

**B24. Dodge**—Changing direction to avoid being caught or hit.

**B25. Balance**—Holding a still position.

**B26. Counterbalance**—Pushing equally against another.

**B27. Countertension**—Pulling equally against another.

## Locomotor

### Steplike Action

**B28. Walk**—An alternate stepping action with an arm–leg opposition in the sagittal plane.

**B29. Cartwheel**—In an extended body position; hand-hand and foot-foot.

**B30. Crawl (climb)**—Traveling on hands and knees.

**B31. Bear walk**—Traveling on hands and feet; alternately in opposition; abdomen facing floor.

**B32. Crab walk**—Traveling on hands and feet; alternately in opposition: abdomen facing ceiling.

### Springlike Action

**B33. Run**—Alternating steps (right, left, right, left, and so on) with flight and arm–leg opposition at a fast pace.

**B34. Leap**—Running with longer flight.

**B35. Hop**—Taking off and landing on the same foot.

**B36. Skip**—Alternating: step, hop, step, hop.

**B37. Jump**—Two-foot takeoff and two-foot landing; one-foot takeoff and two-foot landing, or two-foot takeoff and one-foot landing.

**B38. Gallop**—A forward step followed by a closing of the rear foot.

**B39. Slide**—A side step followed by a closing of the rear foot.

### Roll-Like Action

**B40. Rock**—Body weight transferred back and forth on a rounded body surface.

**B41. Roll (body)**—Continual transfer of weight onto the next closest body part.

## Manipulative

### Send Away

**B42. Throw**—Hand releases object, sending it through the air.

**B43. Roll (ball)**—Sending an object (e.g., ball) across a surface.

**B44. Strike**—Making contact with another object.

**B45. Kick**—Using the foot to send an object through the air.

**B46. Volley**—Receiving an airborne object and immediately directing it away through the air before it hits the ground.

### Gain Control

**B47. Catch**—Grasping a moving object with the hand(s).

**B48. Trap**—Usually using chest, legs, or feet to keep an object still.

### Propel

**B49. Dribble**—Traveling with an object that is repeatedly contacted by hands or feet.

**B50. Carry**—Traveling with an object held in the hands.

# S. Space

Where the body moves.

## Location

**S1. Self-space**—The space directly around a person; kinesphere. Example: The body moving as if in a soap bubble.

**S2. General space**—All the area available for movement. Example: Where the soap bubble can move.

## Direction

**S3. Forward**—The front of the body leads the action.

**S4. Backward**—The back of the body leads the action.

**S5. Sideways (right or left)**—The side of the body leads the action.

**S6. Up**—Toward the sky.

**S7. Down**—Toward the floor.

**S8. Clockwise**—To the right, or the same direction as clock hands move.

**S9. Counterclockwise**—To the left, or opposite, the direction that clock hands move.

## Level

**S10. Low**—Near the floor; between the knees and the floor.

**S11. Medium**—Between low and high or knees and shoulders.

**S12. High**—Near the ceiling or sky; above the shoulders.

## Pathway

**S13. Straight**—Moving in a direct line.

**S14. Curved**—Moving in an arch or semicircle.

**S15. Zigzag**—Moving in a crisscross manner.

## Plane

**S16. Sagittal plane**—A left-right body division in which forward and backward movements occur. Examples: Arm swing in running; forward roll.

**S17. Frontal plane**—A front-back body division in which sideways movements occur. Examples: Sliding, jumping jack.

**S18. Transverse plane**—A top-bottom body division in which twisting movements occur. Examples: Trunk twisting, flipping pancakes (pronation).

### Extension

**S19. Small (near)**—Little body movements; movements close to the body. Examples: Holding a tennis racket close to the body; holding the hands close to the face in boxing defense.

**S20. Large (far)**—Big body movements; movements away from the body. Examples: Holding a tennis racket away from the body; holding the hands far from the face in boxing defense.

# E. Effort

The quality with which the movement is executed.

### Time

**E1. Fast (sudden)**—Quick, explosive. Example: Sprinting.

**E2. Slow (sustained)**—Unhurried, long duration. Examples: Tai chi, playing Statues.

**E3. Acceleration (change)**—Change of pace, faster or slower.

### Force

**E4. Hard (strong)**—Strong, energetic movement.

**E5. Soft (light)**—Delicate, gentle movement.

### Flow

**E6. Bound (stoppable)**—Carefully controlled; stoppable.

**E7. Free (ongoing)**—Fluid and streaming; ongoing.

### Focus

**E8. Direct (stabbing)**—Piercing; closing of energy.

**E9. Indirect (expanding)**—Wavy; spreading of energy.

# R. Relationship

The types of connections that occur as the body moves—with objects, people, and the environment.

### People

**R1. Solo**—Performing by oneself.

**R2. Alone in a mass**—In a group, but all work individually.

**R3. Partners**—Two people; a pair.

**R4. Even groups**—Equal numbers of people together.

**R5. Uneven groups**—Unequal numbers of people together.

**R6. Individual to group**—One person relating to two or more people.

**R7. Group to group**—Two or more people relating to two or more people.

**R8. Triangle**—People making a three-sided, three-pointed shape.

**R9. Circle**—People making the shape of a perfect hollow ring.

**R10. Square**—People making a box shape with four equal sides.

**R11. Scattered**—People randomly spaced.

**R12. Spokes of a wheel**—People forming lines moving out from a center point.

**R13. X**—People forming two lines that cross in the middle.

### Position

**R14. Above/below (still)**—On top of; lower than something; beneath (still).

**R15. Over/under (moving)**—On top of; lower than something; beneath (moving).

**R16. Inverted**—Upside down; head side down.

**R17. Mount/dismount**—Action of getting on or off something.

**R18. In front of/behind**—Positioned before another; positioned after another, or on the backside.

**R19. Beside**—Generally near the side.

**R20. Alongside**—Immediately next to the side.

**R21. Through**—Moving to one side or the other side of a plane (or a barrier with an open space, like a hoop).

**R22. Surround**—Covering all the sides or borders of something or someone.

**R23. Around**—Moving in a circular motion; orbiting.

**R24. Support/supported**—Holding up a person or object; being held up (still).

**R25. Lift/lifted**—Raising something up; having been moved up (moving).

**R26. Meet/part**—Coming together; moving away.

**R27. Near to/far from**—A small or large distance between people or objects.

### Timing

#### Simultaneous

**R28. Mirror**—Facing; the illusion of being the same; right side movements are reflected by left side movements of a partner.

**R29. Match (shadow)**—Identical movements; right side movements appear exactly the same as the right side movements of a partner.

**R30. Contrast**—Movers try to be opposite or very different from one another.

**R31. Unison**—All moving at the same time; moving together as one.

## Alternate

**R32. Take turns**—One person moves, then there is a pause, then the next person moves.

## Successive

**R33. Movement sequence**—Movements that are combined one after the other; a routine.

**R34. Canon**—Repeating exactly the movement or sequence of another person or of other people (same dynamics).

**R35. Question/answer**—A movement response to a movement invitation.

**R36. Act/react**—The first movement is the cause; the second movement is the effect. Examples: Shooting and rebounding, or bringing arms in while spinning (to spin faster).

**R37. Lead/follow**—One person starts a movement and another person copies it.

## Goal

**R38. Cooperative**—Working to help another perform better; sharing.

**R39. Collaborative**—Working to create a better strategy; outwitting.

**R40. Competitive**—Working to win or be better (solo or in group[s]); winning.

## Environment

**R41. Static**—Fixed; the mover adapts to a nonmoving object.

**R42. Dynamic**—The person and the object are moving; the person tries to control both.

# Comments

- Twist(ed) appears correctly twice: first as a body shape (B5) and again as a nonlocomotor primary body movement (B15).
- Roll appears correctly twice: first as a locomotor roll-like action (B41) and again as an action for sending an object away (B43).

# GLOSARIO EN ESPAÑOL DE TERMINOLOGÍA EDUCATIVA DE MOVIMIENTO

Este glosario está basado en el currículo educativo del movimiento, siendo resumido en el folleto/panfleto mostrado en el capítulo 2 y en los apéndices A. En el capítulo 2 hay descripciones más detalladas con algunas variaciones en las expresiones de los términos descritos, estas definiciones están en forma abreviada en un formato más compacto, las cuales también se encuentran en las tarjetas de bolsillo de Educación sobre Movimiento, disponibles en *Sportime* (www.sportime.com); este sitio electrónico fue creado para proveer una referencia total y completa, en forma sencilla pero precisa, un juego de términos prácticos que coinciden con los establecidos por la Asociación Nacional del Deporte y Educación Física (*NASPE* por sus siglas en inglés, 2004a), estándar 2, el cual requiere que los niños comprendan los conceptos de movimiento y del cómo se relacionan con el aprendizaje y práctica de actividades físicas. El glosario presentado en este sitio de la red electrónica está también disponible en castellano.

## B. Cuerpo

Parte Enter de la persona que sirven como instrumento en la acción.

### Partes del Cuerpo

**B1. Partes del cuerpo**—Cabeza, cuello, orejas, ojos, nariz, boca, hombros, codos, muñecas, manos, dedos, abdominales, pecho, columna vertebral, espalda, glúteos, caderas, rodillas, tobillos, pies, dedos del pie.

### Formas del Cuerpo

**B2. Estrecho**—Delgado como una flecha. Ejemplo: Estirarse con los brazos levantados, o como para hace un pase alaro en basquetbol.

**B3. Estirándose**—Acción de extenderse hacia los lados. Ejemplos: rueda de carreta, postura defensiva.

**B4. Redondo**—Como una pelota o forma oval. Ejemplo: Rodando hacia adelante.

**B5. Torcido**—Enrollándose uno al otro. Ejemplo: Cuando se juega al "twist", en que se ponen las extremidades en forma selectiva en una plantilla con patrón de colores al suelo.

**B6. Simétrico**—Iguales, emparejadas o balanceadas posiciones en ambos lados del cuerpo.

**B7. Asimétrico**—Posiciones únicas o diferentes en ambos lados del cuerpo.

### Acciones de las Partes del Cuerpo

**B8. Soporte de peso**—Base de soporte; sosteniendo el cuerpo o parte de él. Ejemplo: Las manos al estar parado en ellas.

**B9. Aguantar fuerza o peso**—"Detenerse." Fuerza exterior es absorbida. Ejemplo: Recibir una patada de karate.

**B10. Aplicar fuerza**—"Darle." Dar un empujón o jalar un objeto. Ejemplo: Levantar pesas.

**B11. Dirigir la acción**—Parte del cuerpo que inicia un movimiento. Ejemplo: Manos al echarse un clavado en una alberca.

**B12. Transferencia de peso**—Desplazar la base de soporte. Diferentes partes del cuerpo soportan el peso del cuerpo. Ejemplo: Cambiar de pie derecho a izquierdo al caminar.

### No Motor

**B13. Estirar**—Movimiento primario del cuerpo al hacer estiramientos de las partes del cuerpo mas largas. Ejemplo: Sentarse y extenderse en movimientos de lado a lado.

**B14. Encorvar**—Movimiento primario del cuerpo al encoger las partes del cuerpo hacia el centro. Ejemplo: Doblar el brazo (flexión del codo).

**B15. Torcer**—Movimiento primario del cuerpo en que las partes del cuerpo se contraen mientras una parte del permanece fija y las otras partes continúan moviéndose. La intensidad de torcer aumenta entre más se flexiona. Ejemplo: La cabeza girada a la derecha con el cuerpo viendo hacia el frente.

**B16. Voltear**—Dar la cara hacia una nueva dirección; perdida temporal de orientación en espacio; la base de soporte puede cambiar. Ejemplos: Mientras en posición de caminar, levantar los talones y mantenerse de puntas, voltear hacia la dirección opuesta o pararse viendo hacia una pared y luego levantar los pies para dar la cara a otra pared.

**B17. Girar**—Dar la cara a una nueva dirección; el cuerpo entero gira sobre un eje central. La base de soporte no se levanta de la superficie de soporte. Ejemplos: El giro del jugador de baloncesto sobre la planta de un pie mientras da un giro para pasar el balón a otro jugador o la acción de un patinador artístico en hielo rotando sobre un patín.

**B18. Mecerse**—Eje fijo que permite la rotación de una parte del cuerpo.

**B19. Empujar**—Dirigir el esfuerzo hacia fuera del cuerpo.

**B20. Jalar**—Dirigir el esfuerzo hacia la base del soporte.

**B21. Levantarse**—Moverse o estirarse hacia arriba; levantándose a si mismo.

**B22. Hundirse**—Cederse a la gravedad; caerse ligeramente.

**B23. Gesto**—Movimiento en el aire sin peso; para contrarrestar o expresar el estado de ánimo.

**B24. Esquivar**—Cambiar de dirección para evitar ser atrapado o golpeado.

**B25. Balancearse**—Mantenerse en posición.

**B26. Contrapeso**—Empujar igualmente en contra de otro.

**B27. Contra-tensión**—Jalar igualmente en contra de otro.

## Locomotor

Acción de Dar Pasos

**B28. Caminar**—Mover los pies y los brazos en oposición del uno al otro alternándose en el plano sagital con concordancia y coordinación.

**B29. Rueda de carreta**—El cuerpo en posición extendida; mano-mano y pie-pie.

**B30. Gatear (trepar)**—Desplazarse en manos y rodillas.

**B31. Caminar como oso**—Desplazarse en manos y pies alternando en oposición; boca abajo (decúbito-ventral).

**B32. Caminar como cangrejo**—Desplazarse en manos y pies alternando en oposición, boca arriba (decúbito-dorsal).

Acción de Dar Saltos

**B33. Correr**—Caminar aceleradamente alternando manos y pies, tocando el suelo lo menos posible.

**B34. Saltar**—Correr con despegues más largos.

**B35. Salto en un pie**—Despegar y aterrizar en el mismo pie.

**B36. Brincos pequeños**—Alternando: paso, brinquito, paso y brinquito.

**B37. Brincar**—Proyectar el cuerpo al aire.

**B38. Caminata**—Paso hacia adelante seguido de cerca por el pie trasero.

**B39. Deslizarse**—Paso de lado abierto, seguido de cerca por el pie trasero en moción similar.

Acción de Enrollar

**B40. Piedra**—Peso del cuerpo transferido de atrás para adelante en una superficie redondeada del cuerpo.

**B41. Cuerpo enrollado**—Transferencia continua de peso a la siguiente y más cercana parte del cuerpo.

## Manipulado

Echar

**B42. Lanzar**—Uso de manos para aventar algo por el aire.

**B43. Rodar (la pelota)**—Deslizar un objeto (pelota) sobre una superficie.

**B44. Golpear**—Hacer contacto con otro objeto.

**B45. Patear**—Uso del pie para hacer que algo se mueva por el aire.

**B46. Rebotar**—Recibir un objeto en el aire con las manos y enviarlo de inmediato en otra dirección.

Tomar Control

**B47. Agarrar**—Tomar un objeto en movimiento con las manos.

**B48. Atrapar**—Usando usualmente el pecho, piernas o pies para mantener un objeto inmóvil.

Propulsar

**B49. Driblear**—Desplazarse con un objeto que está en continuo contacto con manos o pies.

**B50. Cargar**—Desplazarse con un objeto sostenido en las manos.

# S. Espacio

Donde el cuerpo se mueve.

## Ubicación

**S1. Espacio propio**—Espacio directamente alrededor de una persona; kinesphere. Ejemplo: Cuerpo moviéndose como en una burbuja de jabón.

**S2. Espacio general**—Toda el área disponible para movimiento. Ejemplo: Donde la burbuja de jabón puede moverse.

## Dirección

**S3. Hacia adelante**—La acción se dirige de frente.

**S4. Hacia atrás**—La acción se dirige de espaldas.

**S5. Hacia un lado (derecha o izquierda)**—La acción se dirige de lado.

**S6. Para arriba**—Hacia el cielo.

**S7. Para abajo**—Hacia el suelo.

**S8. En sentido de las manecillas del reloj**—A la derecha, en sentido de las manecillas de un reloj.

**S9. En contra de las manecillas del reloj**—A la izquierda u opuesto a las manecillas del reloj.

## Nivel

**S10. Bajo**—Cerca del suelo; entre rodillas y suelo.

**S11. Mediano**—Entre bajo y alto y rodillas y hombros.

**S12. Alto**—Cerca del techo o cielo; arriba de los hombros.

## Ruta

**S13. Derecha**—Moviéndose en línea directa.

**S14. Curveada**—Moviéndose en arco o semicírculo.

**S15. Zigzag**—Moviéndose cruzando los pasos.

## Plano

**S16. Plano sagital**—La división de cuerpo hecha de izquierda a derecha en la cual suceden movimientos de avance y retroceso. Ejemplos: La oscilación de los brazas al correr o contrayéndose hacia adelante.

**S17. Plano frontal**—División de frente-revés del cuerpo en la que se ubican movimientos laterales. Ejemplos: Deslizarse; salto de mariposa.

**S18. Plano transversal**—División corporal de arriba hacia abajo en la cual movimientos de flexión abdominal lateral ocurren. Ejemplos: Girar el tronco sobre la cintura, voltear tortillas (pronación).

## Extensión

**S19. Mínima (cerca)**—Movimientos pequeños; movimientos cerca del cuerpo. Ejemplos: Acercar una raqueta de tenis al cuerpo, manos cerca de la cara en posición de defensa en el boxeo.

**S20. Grande (lejos)**—Movimientos grandes. Movimientos lejos del cuerpo. Ejemplos: Alejar una raqueta de tenis del cuerpo, manos lejos de la cara en posición de defensa en el boxeo.

# E. Esfuerzo

Donde se mueve el cuerpo.

## Tiempo

**E1. Rápido (repentino)**—Rápido, explosivo. Ejemplo: Esprintar o echarse a correr.

**E2. Lento (sostenido)**—Sin prisa, de larga duración. Ejemplo: Tai chi; jugar a estatuas.

**E3. Aceleración (cambio)**—Cambio de velocidad en el paso.

## Fuerza

**E4. Duro (fuerte)**—Fuerte, movimiento enérgico.

**E5. Suave (liviano)**—Delicado, movimiento suave.

## Fluidez

**E6. Controlado (se puede detener)**—Con mucho control. Se puede detener.

**E7. Libre (continuo)**—Fluido continuo.

## Enfoque

**E8. Directo (punzante)**—Penetrante; contener la energía.

**E9. Indirecta (extendiéndose)**—Ondulante; displacer la energía.

# R. Relación

Calidad en que el movimiento ocurre.

## Gente

**R1. Solo**—Completar la acción solo.

**R2. Solo en grupo**—En un grupo, pero todos trabajan individualmente.

**R3. Parejas**—Dos personas, en pareja.

**R4. Grupos iguales**—En grupos iguales en número.

**R5. Grupos irregulares**—En grupos desiguales en número.

**R6. Individuo a grupo**—Una persona relacionándose con dos o más personas.

**R7. Grupo a grupo**—Dos o más personas relacionándose con dos o más personas.

**R8. Triángulo**—Gente formándose en figura de tres puntos o trilateral.

**R9. Círculo**—Gente formándose en hueco perfecto o aro.

**R10. Cuadrado**—Gente haciendo una formándose en cuadrado o cuatro lados iguales.

**R11. Dispersos**—Gente dispersa al azar.

**R12. Rayo de una rueda**—Gente formando líneas saliendo de un punto central.

**R13. X**—Gente formando dos líneas que se cruzan en el centro.

## Posición

**R14. Por encima/por debajo (inmóvil)**—Arriba de; más abajo de algo; por debajo (inmóvil).

**R15. Sobre/debajo (en movimiento)**—Arriba de; más abajo de algo; por debajo (en movimiento).

**R16. Invertido**—Al revés; cabeza hacia abajo.

**R17. Montar/desmontar**—Acción de subirse o bajarse de algo.

**R18. Delante de/detrás de**—Posicionarse frente a otro; posicionado después de o detrás de otro.

**R19. Al lado**—Generalmente cerca del lado.

**R20. Junto a**—Inmediato.

**R21. A través de**—Moviéndose a uno u otro lado de un plano (o una barrera con un espacio abierto en forma de gancho).

**R22. Rodear**—Cubrir todos los lados o bordes de algo o alguien.

**R23. Alrededor**—Moviéndose en forma circular; orbitando.

**R24. Sostener/sostenido**—Sostener a una persona u objeto; ser sostenido (inmóvil).

**R25. Levantar/levantado**—Alzar algo; haber sido levantado (moviendo).

**R26. Pegarse/despegarse**—Juntarse. Alejarse.

**R27. Cerca de/lejos de**—Poca o mucha distancia entre gente u objetos.

## Coordinación

### Simultáneamente

**R28. Espejo (de frente)**—Ilusión de ser igual en movimiento estando de frente (derecha = izquierda).

**R29. Igualar (o sombra)**—Movimientos idénticos (derecha = derecha).

**R30. Contraste**—Los participantes tratan de ser opuestos o muy diferentes.

**R31. Unísono**—Todos se mueven al mismo tiempo; se desplazan juntos como si fueran uno.

### Alternar

**R32. Tomar turnos**—Una persona se mueve, entonces hay una pausa, luego la siguiente persona se mueve.

### Sucesivamente

**R33. Secuencia de Movimiento**—Los movimientos que son combinados una después del otro; una rutina.

**R34. Canon**—Gente repite un movimiento o secuencia exactamente como lo ha hecho la primera persona (misma dinámica).

**R35. Pregunta/respuesta**—Un movimiento de respuesta a un movimiento de invitación.

**R36. Actuar/reaccionar**—Primer movimiento es la causa. Segundo movimiento es el efecto. Ejemplos: Bote y rebote; encoger los brazos mientras se gira velozmente.

**R37. Dirigir/seguir**—Una persona comienza el movimiento y alguien más le copia.

### Objetivo

**R38. Cooperativo**—Trabajando para ayudar a otros a esforzarse mejor; compartir.

**R39. Colaborativo**—Trabajando para crear una mejor estratégia; sobresalir.

**R40. Competitivo**—Esforzarse para ganar o mejorar (solo o en grupo[s]); ganar.

### Medio Ambiente

**R41. Estático**—Fijo; el participante se adapta a un objeto fijo.

**R42. Dinámico**—Uno mismo y el objeto están móviles; el participante intenta controlar ambos.

# Comentarios

- Torcer (torcido): Como forma corporal aparece dos veces (B5) y de nueva cuenta como movimiento non-locomotor primario del cuerpo (B15).

- Enrollar aparece dos veces: como acción locomotora de enrollar (B41) y como acción de lanzar algo (B43).

# REFERENCES

Brown, M., & Sommer, B. (1969). Movement education: Its evolution and a modern approach (p. 34). Reading, MA: Addison-Wesley.

California Department of Education. (2005). The California Physical Fitness Test: A study of the relationship between physical fitness and academic achievement in California using 2004 test results. Sacramento, CA: Standards and Assessment Division of the California Department of Education. Retrieved from www.cde.ca.gov/ta/tg/pf/documents/2004pftresults.doc.

Canadian Fitness and Lifestyle Research Institute. (2005-2006). Objective measures of physical activity levels of Canadian children and youth. Canadian Physical Activity Levels Among Youth (CANPLAY) Study. Retrieved from www.cflri.ca.

Gallahue, D. & Cleland Donnelly, F. (2003). Developmental physical education for all children (4th ed.). Champaign, IL: Human Kinetics.

Gallahue, D. & Ozmun, J. (2006). Understanding motor development. Infants, children, adolescents, adults (6th ed., pp. 49-51). Boston, MA: McGraw-Hill. (The phases of motor development, p. 46, Figure 3.1).

Gilliom, B. (1970). Basic movement education for children: Rationale and teaching units. Reading, MA: Addison-Wesley.

Guinhouya, C.B., Hubert, H., Soubrier, S., Vilhelm, C., Lemdani, M., & Durocher, A. (2006). Moderate-to-vigorous physical activity among children: Discrepancies in accelerometry-based cut-off points. Obesity, 114, 774-777.

Hansen-Smith, B. (2008). How to fold circles: 4. Make a tetrahedron, and 6. Make an icosahedron. Wholemovement Publications. Retrieved from www.wholemovement.com/

Haywood, K.M., & Getchell, N. (2009). Life span motor development (5th ed.). Champaign, IL: Human Kinetics.

Himberg, C., Hutchinson, G., & Roussell, J.M. (2003). Teaching secondary physical education: Preparing adolescents to be active for life (p. 19). Champaign, IL: Human Kinetics.

Hodgeson, J. (2001). Mastering movement. The life and work of Rudolph Laban. New York: Routledge. Online preview at http://books.google.com, p. 191-192.

Ignico, A. (1992). Assessment of fundamental motor skills (3 DVDs). New York: Insight Media.

Kirchner, D. (1977). Introduction to movement education. Burr Ridge, IL: McGraw-Hill College.

Laban, R. and revised by Ullmann, L. (1963). Modern educational dance (2nd ed.). London: MacDonald & Evans.

Laban, R., & Ullmann, L. (1971). The mastery of movement (3rd ed.). London: MacDonald & Evans.

Logsdon, B., Barrett, K., Broer, M., McGee, R., Ammons, M., Halverson, L., & Roberton, M. (1984). Physical education for children: A focus on the teaching process. Philadelphia: Lea & Febiger.

Madison Metropolitan School District, Physical Education teachers: Jane Koval, M. Lynn Vande Sande, and Karen Myers. Madison, WI

Maulden, E. & Layson, J. (1965). Teaching gymnastics and body control. Boston, MA: Plays Inc.

Mauldon, E., & Layson, J. (1979). Teaching gymnastics. 2nd ed. London: MacDonald & Evans.

Maulden, E., & Redfern, H. (1969). Games teaching: A new approach for the primary school. London: MacDonald & Evans.

Meredith, M., & Welk, G., with The Cooper Institute. (2007). FitnessGram/ActivityGram test administration manual, Updated 3rd edition. Champaign, IL: Human Kinetics.

Mosston, M. & Ashworth, S. (1986). Teaching physical education. Columbus, OH: Merrill.

National Asociation for Sport and Physical Education (NASPE). (1995). Moving into the future. National standards for physical education: A guide to content and assessment (1st ed.). Reston, VA: Author.

National Association for Sport and Physical Education (NASPE). (2004a). Moving into the future: National standards for physical education (2nd ed.). Reston, VA: Author.

National Association for Sport and Physical Education (NASPE). (2004b). Physical acitvity for children: A statement of guidelines for children ages 5-12 years (2nd ed.). Reston, VA: Author. From www.aahperd.org/naspe/standards/nationalguidelines/PA-children-5-12.cfm.

National Association for Sport and Physical Education (NASPE). (2005). Physical education for lifelong fitness. The physical best teacher's guide (2nd ed., p. 3). Champaign, IL: Human Kinetics.

National Association for Sport and Physical Education (NASPE). (2006). Shape of the nation report: Status of physical education in the USA. Reston, VA: Author.

National Association for Sport and Physical Education (NASPE). (2007, August 24). Press release. New FIT Kids Act introduced in Congress. Retrieved from www.aahperd.org/naspe/template.cfm?template=pr07_0824.htm

National Association for Sport and Physical Education (NASPE). (2008). PE Metrics: Assessing the national standards. Standard 1: Elementary. Reston, VA: Author.

National Association for Sport and Physical Education (NASPE). (2009). Appropriate maximum class length for elementary physical education [Position statement]. Reston, VA: Author.

Payne, G. & Isaacs, L. (2002). Human motor development: A lifespan approach (7th ed.). Boston, MA: McGraw-Hill.

Rink, J. (2006). Teaching physical education for learning. Boston, MA: McGraw Hill.

Russell, J. (1975). Creative movement and dance for children. 2nd ed. London: MacDonald & Evans.

Scruggs, P., Beneridge, S., Watson, D., & Clocksin, B. (2005). Quantifying physical activity in first-through fourth-grade physical education via pedometry. Research Quarterly for Exercise and Sport,76(2), 166-175.

Stanley, S. (1977). *Physical education: A movement orientation* (2nd ed.). New York: McGraw-Hill.

Stodden, D., Langendorfer, D., & Robertson, M. (2008). The association between motor skill competence and physical fitness in young adults. *Quarterly for Exercise and Sport (80)*2, 223-229.

Tudor-Lock, C., Lee, S., Morgan, C., Beighle, A., & Pangrazi, R. (2006, October). Children's pedometer-determined physical activity during the segmented school day. *Medicine & Science in Sports & Exercise, 38* (10), 1732-1738.

Ulrich, D. (2000). *Test of gross motor development—2* (2nd ed.). Austin, TX: Pro-Ed.

Welk, G. (1999). The youth physical activity promotion model: A conceptual bridge between theory and practice, *Quest, 51*(1), 5-23.

Wrisberg, C. (2007). *Sport skill instruction for coaches* (p. 104). Champaign, IL: Human Kinetics.

# INDEX

Note: Page numbers followed by an italicized *f* or *t* refer to the figure or table on that page, respectively.

# ABOUT THE AUTHORS

**Karen Weiller Abels, PhD,** is an associate professor in the department of kinesiology at the University of North Texas in Denton. She has more than 25 years of teaching experience, including teaching elementary physical education. She has developed and taught many courses at the collegiate level that focus on teacher preparation, particularly in movement education.

Dr. Abels coauthored selections of the *Children Moving* ancillary materials and helped shoot, edit, and design 20 live-action video analysis activities covering all four developmental levels. She also codeveloped the flip 'n' fold movement education document that serves as a quick reference for teachers and children.

She has coauthored many articles related to teaching elementary physical education and served as the Southern District representative for the Council on Physical Education for Children.

Dr. Abels enjoys running, weightlifting, spending time with her family, and taking her two dachshunds for walks.

**Jennifer M. Bridges, PhD,** is a professor of kinesiology in the College of Health and Human Services at Saginaw Valley State University in University Center, Michigan. For more than 20 years she has taught motor development, motor learning, movement fundamentals, and dance to preservice majors in physical education teacher education. She also held the ACSM health fitness specialist certification for 15 years.

Dr. Bridges has coauthored portions of the well-known *Children Moving* ancillary materials, which involved shooting, editing, and designing 20 live-action movement analysis activities covering all four motor development levels for the online interactive ancillary video set. In addition, she developed the electronic, animated Movement Analysis E-Wheel based on the handheld manipulative wheel she adapted from the early work of Dr. Graham. This work led her to codevelop the manipulative document, presented in this text, called the flip 'n' fold, which presents the movement education framework as a practical reference for teachers and children.

In her leisure time, Dr. Bridges enjoys being active with her family in a variety of outdoor pursuits, playing competitive badminton, and developing innovations.

You'll find other outstanding
physical education resources at
**www.HumanKinetics.com**

In the U.S. call . . . . .1.800.747.4457
Australia . . . . . . . . . 08 8372 0999
Canada. . . . . . . . . 1.800.465.7301
Europe . . . . .+44 (0) 113 255 5665
New Zealand . . . . . . 0800 222 062

**HUMAN KINETICS**
*The Information Leader in Physical Activity & Health*
P.O. Box 5076 • Champaign, IL 61825-5076